"[Birgit Gurr] writes for the busy clinician and bridges the gap between medical and psychosocial understandings of chronic headaches following mild brain injury. Indeed, anyone working with survivors of mild brain injury who are suffering from headaches will find this volume a valuable therapeutic tool."

—**Barbara A. Wilson** OBE, PhD, DSc, CPsychol, FBPsS, FmedSC, AcSS, Founder of the Oliver Zangwill Centre for Neuropsychological Rehabilitation at the Princess of Wales Hospital in Ely, Founder and editor of the journal *Neuropsychological Rehabilitation*, Fellow of the Academy of Medical Sciences, the Academy of Social Sciences and the British Psychological Society, Past president of the British Neuropsychological Society and the International Neuropsychological Society

"The second edition of this very helpful handbook provides an updated and expanded overview of posttraumatic headache management, focusing on psychotherapeutic interventions after a mild traumatic brain injury/concussion. There is really no other resource like this for practitioners and, due to its scope, it should be an invaluable resource for those dealing with this often-perplexing disorder."

—**Nathan D. Zasler**, MD, DABPM&R, FAAPM&R, FACRM, BIM-C, CBIST, Founder, CEO & CMO, Concussion Care Centre of Virginia, Ltd., Founder, CEO & CMO, Tree of Life Services, Inc., Professor, affiliate, Department of Physical Medicine and Rehabilitation, Virginia Commonwealth University, Richmond, Virginia, Associate Professor, adjunct, Department of Physical Medicine and Rehabilitation, University of Virginia, Charlottesville, Virginia, Chairperson, Emeritus, IBIA, Vice-Chairperson, IBIA

"The second edition is an invaluable guide to psychological treatment for patients with persistent headaches after a concussion. It incorporates evidence-based practices, and where the evidence trail ends, it offers practical recommendations based on the author's deep clinical expertise. Chapter 1 provides a comprehensive review of theories underlying persist posttraumatic headache and relevant biopsychosocial predisposing, precipitating and perpetuating factors. Chapter 2 explores the experiences, desires, concerns, questions and motivations that posttraumatic headache sufferers often bring to their initial clinic a nice overview of various psychological trea

GW00777334

to posttraumatic headaches, with case examples for each, enough to give a flavor for how therapy 'looks.' Chapter 3 provides more detailed guidance on assessment and the specific 'how to's' of delivering CBT, complete with homework sheets, session outlines, suggested scripts and other useful tools. The book is filled with clinical pearls, such as how to use the CBT model to guide interviewing and case formulation. Readers with a background in CBT will be able to use this manual right off the shelf."

—**Noah D. Silverberg** PhD, RPsych, ABPP-CN,
Assistant Professor, Department of Psychology,
University of British Columbia, Vancouver Campus &
GF Strong Rehabilitation Centre, Musqueam,
Squamish & Tsleil-Waututh Traditional Territory

Headaches and Mild Brain Trauma

This important book describes the biopsychosocial nature of persisting and complex headache presentations following a mild brain trauma and offers a predominantly cognitive behavioural therapy programme to guide patients toward better health and less pain.

The book provides both a robust theoretical underpinning and practical therapeutic guidance for helping those who suffer from posttraumatic headaches. Placing physical symptoms of trauma in context with personal and social issues, it discusses the broader psychological implications at work after brain injury, including the idea that headaches play a functional role for the patient. Updated with the latest research findings, the book features clinical guidelines, practitioner worksheets and relaxation scripts, offering an all-inclusive manual for therapists setting up their own programmes.

Written with the busy clinician in mind, it is essential reading for anyone working with brain trauma survivors.

Birgit Gurr is a consultant clinical neuropsychologist and works as the clinical lead for the Acquired Brain Injury and Adult Neuropsychology Services in Dorset HealthCare University NHS Foundation Trust, UK. She is also a visiting lecturer at Bournemouth University, where she teaches neuropsychology, and a clinical supervisor for the clinical psychology doctorate courses at Southampton and Exeter Universities. She is a full member of the Division of Neuropsychology and Associate Fellow of the British Psychological Society, UK.

The Brain Injuries Series

Series Editors: Dr Giles N. Yeates and Dr Fergus Gracey

This series is dedicated to psychological therapies, social interventions and psychosocial issues following acquired brain injury, emphasising both theoretical exploration and the 'how-to' of therapeutic work. These titles stand in contrast with previous clinical titles in the brain injury literature that have been assessment-focused and offered little in the way of intervention. Every jobbing clinician and therapist working with survivors of brain injury and their significant others should have this series on their shelves.

Previous titles in the series:

A Relational Approach to Rehabilitation
Thinking about Relationships after Brain Injury
Ceri Bowen, Giles N. Yeates and Siobhan Palmer

Practical Neuropsychological Rehabilitation in Acquired Brain Injury
A Guide for Working Clinicians
Edited by Gavin Newby, Rudi Coetzer, Audrey Daisley and Stephen Weatherhead

Narrative Approaches to Brain Injury
Edited by Stephen Weatherhead and David Todd

Psychological Therapy for Paediatric Acquired Brain Injury
Innovations for Children, Young People and Families
Edited by Jenny Jim and Esther Cole

Headaches and Mild Brain Trauma
A Practical Therapy Guide
Birgit Gurr

For further information about this series please visit: https://www.routledge.com/The-Brain-Injuries-Series/book-series/KARNACBI

Headaches and Mild Brain Trauma

A Practical Therapy Guide

2ND EDITION

Birgit Gurr

Routledge
Taylor & Francis Group

LONDON AND NEW YORK

Second edition published 2021
by Routledge
2 Park Square, Milton Park, Abingdon, Oxon, OX14 4RN

and by Routledge
605 Third Avenue, New York, NY 10158

Routledge is an imprint of the Taylor & Francis Group, an informa business

Front cover, illustrations and graphic designs: Sofia Angus

[First edition published by Karnac Books Ltd. 2015]
[Second edition published by Routledge 2021]

British Library Cataloguing-in-Publication Data
A catalogue record for this book is available from the British Library

Library of Congress Cataloging-in-Publication Data
Names: Gurr, Birgit, author.
Title: Headaches and mild brain trauma: a practical therapy
guide / Birgit Gurr.
Other titles: Headaches and brain injury from a biopsychosocial
perspective Description: 2nd edition. | Milton Park,
Abingdon, Oxon; New York, NY: Routledge, 2021. |
Series: The brain injuries series | Headaches and brain injury
from a biopsychosocial perspective. 2015. |
Includes bibliographical references and index.
Identifiers: LCCN 2020044664 (print) | LCCN 2020044665 (ebook) |
ISBN 9780367403676 (paperback) | ISBN 9780367726089 (hardback) |
ISBN 9781003155546 (ebook)
Subjects: LCSH: Brain damage—Treatment. | Brain—
Wounds and injuries—Treatment. | Headache—Treatment. |
Psychotherapy.
Classification: LCC RC387.5 .G87 2021 (print) | LCC RC387.5 (ebook) |
DDC 617.4/81044—dc23
LC record available at https://lccn.loc.gov/2020044664
LC ebook record available at https://lccn.loc.gov/2020044665

ISBN: 978-0-367-72608-9 (hbk)
ISBN: 978-0-367-40367-6 (pbk)
ISBN: 978-1-003-15554-6 (ebk)

Typeset in Times New Roman
by codeMantra

Contents

Figures

Therapy worksheets

Relaxation scripts

Acknowledgements

I would not have been able to produce such a wide-ranging book as this without the inspiration, guidance and encouragement of many people. It has been shaped by many years of experience in the fields of clinical and neuropsychology at the Acquired Brain Injury Rehabilitation and Neuropsychology Services of Dorset HealthCare University NHS Foundation Trust, UK.

The initial sparks of inspiration for this book were ignited by John Burn, consultant in rehabilitation medicine in Poole, who suggested that much help was needed for patients with headaches after brain injury. Over the years, he has continued to nurture our shared interest in the medical, neurophysiological and psychosocial understanding of mild brain trauma, which has encouraged me to advance our successful therapeutic approach within our brain injury rehabilitation team. I am very proud of this team, especially my clinical and neuropsychology colleagues, who offer effective headache clinics, as well as group and individual therapy programmes. As far as the writing of this book is concerned, I am particularly grateful for the contributions offered by Tina Vaughan, who provided her reflections and outcomes from Emotional Resilience Therapy. Tina, along with Shanti Shanker and Hayley Cheshire, also supplied her experience and evaluation of our Mild Head Trauma Clinics. Irma Konovalova offered valuable feedback on the manuscript, particularly on the section about headaches as a functional condition. A warm thank you to Dorset HealthCare NHS University Foundation Trust for providing me with the opportunity to develop this headache and mild brain trauma service, which is continuing to help reduce our patients' long-term suffering.

Rudi Coetzer, consultant clinical neuropsychologist and lead at the North Wales Brain Injury Service, guided me through my initial research project on this subject, which provided the basis for the biopsychosocial headache therapy model that eventually evolved. Alongside Nathan Zasler and Barbara Wilson, many high-ranking researchers and clinicians in the field of the mind-body interface and advanced stress theories have helped clarify for me the nature and mechanisms of complex symptoms such as headaches after mild brain trauma.

The book has also been greatly influenced by the experiences of those patients of mine who have worked so diligently to implement the recommended strategies and exercises in order to overcome their headaches and reshape their lives. I am very grateful for their trust in my approach.

Regarding my literature research for this book, I could not have wished for more efficient, reliable and friendly support than that which I received from Barbara Peirce and the team of librarians at Poole Hospital, UK.

I need to give a very special thank you to Sofia Angus, my graphic designer and illustrator, for the immense amount of work she has put into redesigning the front cover and the many figures and worksheets throughout this second edition.

The book would not have been possible without the encouragement and support of my husband, Julian, who, as an English language specialist, fine-tuned the text's clarity and style.

Finally, I would like to thank my publisher, Routledge, for offering me the opportunity to write a second edition, and my editors for their invaluable support throughout the writing process.

Forewords

From her wide experience as a clinical neuropsychologist both in Germany and the United Kingdom, Birgit Gurr now gives us the second edition of her successful book about headaches and mild brain injury. She writes for the busy clinician and bridges the gap between medical and psychosocial understandings of chronic headaches following mild brain injury. She introduces a health-psychological approach to the assessment and treatment of such headaches, using predominantly cognitive behavioural therapy methods.

The reader is given the health-physiological background and practical implementation of a biopsychosocial programme for patients with persisting headaches following mild brain injury. An inclusive manual with a large range of worksheets, relaxation scripts and other resources, it provides rehabilitation workers with the necessary materials to set up a therapy programme, thus reducing the amount of time required to organise and run an agenda.

This latest edition updates theoretical influences and therapeutic techniques for dealing with headaches that are a common consequence of mild brain injury. Psychologists, psychotherapists, counsellors, rehabilitation assistants, occupational therapists, physiotherapists, neuropsychologists, doctors, specialist nurses and students of all related health disciplines will benefit from this comprehensive book helping them re-evaluate their lives. Another improvement on the first edition is the inclusion of a section about single-session headache clinics offered early after trauma to help in the prevention of secondary problems. We are provided with models of stress and with an information sheet for people with mild brain trauma. These are just a few of the improvements on the first edition of this book. The worksheets, information sheets and advice should prove a boon to professionals working in the field. Indeed, anyone working with survivors of mild brain injury who are suffering from headaches will find this volume a valuable therapeutic tool.

Barbara A. Wilson OBE, PhD, DSc,
CPsychol, FBPsS, FmedSC, AcSS
Founder of the Oliver Zangwill Centre for Neuropsychological
Rehabilitation at the Princess of Wales Hospital in Ely
Founder and editor of the journal *Neuropsychological Rehabilitation*
Fellow of the Academy of Medical Sciences, the Academy of Social
Sciences and the British Psychological Society
Past president of the British Neuropsychological Society and the
International Neuropsychological Society

This second edition of this book is extremely practical and provides clinicians treating posttraumatic headache sufferers with a large and diverse armamentarium to better facilitate assessment and management of this challenging patient group, emphasising a biopsychosocial approach. There is really no other resource like this for practitioners and, due to its scope, it should be an invaluable resource for those dealing with this often perplexing disorder.

The causes and treatment options for posttraumatic headaches remain hotly debated and come with a number of controversies. There are still concerns regarding the nature of current classification systems and their lack of value in guiding treatment, as well as debates regarding the underlying pathophysiology of posttraumatic headaches. The medical community and, in particular, physicians do not always fully appreciate the role of psychological and behavioural interventions in pain management, especially outside the field of pain medicine. There is often also a stigma attached to any psychological referral, including for pain management on the part of clinicians, patients and healthcare funders. Such treatments, however – particularly when approached from an interdisciplinary, biopsychosocial perspective – have clearly been shown to produce the best outcomes when dealing with these types of pain disorders.

The first part of this book focuses on some primary concepts regarding concussions and resultant headaches, as well as the classification and subtypes of the same. This is followed by a section on biopsychosocial approaches, which emphasises the role of the Diathesis-Stress and Allostasis models in the context of posttraumatic headaches. Appropriately, Dr. Gurr also discusses the influence of personality style and the role of psychotherapeutic models for headache management. Chapter 2 gets into the meat of the assessment process, utilising a biopsychosocial model and includes discussion of general as well as specific approaches to the clinical interview, psychometric testing and the role of observation. A detailed discussion of different cognitive behavioural therapy techniques for headache management follows. Chapter 3 expounds further on cognitive behavioural therapeutic programmes for the management of headaches following concussions. It furthermore includes discussions of various types of assessments, the role of specialised headache clinics, health management strategies and individual headache therapy protocols for the modulation of headache-related impairment. There are several very helpful appendices at the end of the book focusing on a wide array of therapy worksheets as well as relaxation scripts. There is also a brief guide on mild traumatic brain injury/concussion for use as a practical handout for patients and a listing of supplementary materials. The book is further complemented by a number of excellent figures and illustrations and is well indexed. The second edition of this very helpful handbook provides an updated and expanded overview of posttraumatic headache management focusing on psychotherapeutic interventions after a mild traumatic brain injury/concussion. The second edition provides unique information, not just in terms of understanding the complex biopsychosocial variables involved in the disorder but also by providing clinicians with practical information on assessment and management, including four appendices, self-help resources and the Headache Needs Assessment. The organisation of the book also lends itself well to understanding the scientific evidence that serves to support the ideas posited in the text. I particularly liked that each chapter was followed by the references pertinent to that chapter rather than having all the references at the end of the book.

There are several sections that are worth mentioning which will likely be of particular interest to readers, including the section on the role of Allostasis on neurobiological systems and post-concussive impairments, including persistent headache and affective symptoms. Dr. Gurr provides some unique insights into how such a model explains psychophysiological resilience and autonomic as well as neuroendocrine functions in the context of a Diathesis-Stress type model. Another section I found particularly interesting and relevant to the general theme of posttraumatic headaches following concussions was the discussion of consequences including cognitive, emotional, behavioural and social spheres; these factors should always be considered by clinicians when assessing and treating such patients. The assessment section is highly informative and the case examples further add to the justification of the approaches being espoused by Dr. Gurr.

In the third chapter, Dr. Gurr does an excellent job in outlining the critical aspects to focus on in a specialised headache clinic, emphasising engagement, reassurance and normalisation, i.e., medical education, reformulation and motivation for ongoing self and health management. In addition, there is an abundance of great resource information in this book, which will be of great value to clinicians, patients and concerned significant others.

Nathan D. Zasler, MD, DABPM&R, FAAPM&R, FACRM, BIM-C, CBIST
Founder, CEO & CMO, Concussion Care Centre of Virginia, Ltd.
Founder, CEO & CMO, Tree of Life Services, Inc.
Professor, affiliate, Department of Physical Medicine and Rehabilitation, Virginia Commonwealth University, Richmond, Virginia
Associate Professor, adjunct, Department of Physical Medicine and Rehabilitation, University of Virginia, Charlottesville, Virginia
Chairperson, Emeritus, IBIA
Vice-Chairperson, IBIA

Series editors' foreword
to the first edition

This latest addition to the Brain Injuries Series is a comprehensive therapy manual. Firmly rooted in the cognitive behavioural tradition, this single-authored work extends and synthesises cutting-edge treatment for post-traumatic headaches in a clear and compelling way. The area of headaches after a brain injury is particularly germane to this approach. The ideas presented here allow the reader to replicate evidence-based treatment using expert verbatim comments and frames of reference, complete with handouts and assessment tools to follow up on progress made.

Building on the previous contributions to the series, the author outlines a biopsychosocial approach, with a strong emphasis on careful assessment and co-constructing a formulation of interlocking components in an empowering way for both therapist and patient. By relearning the degree of response that has become habitual in terms of thoughts, feelings and behaviour, not to mention bodily response, the management of pain shifts from an intransient and protracted subjective experience to an area of posttraumatic evolution. A sensitised system of arousal and monitoring of threats – in short, a system on constant "high alert" – that is unable to deregulate is the take-home message.

Articulating a therapy that will appeal to those who work with a broad spectrum of pain conditions, Birgit Gurr offers practical instruction about how to navigate therapeutically the area between pain and neuropsychology, motivation and mood. This book will be of interest to clinicians across the spectrum in terms of professional background and work settings. This is a very practical and clinically useful book – a gold mine!

Ceri Bowen and Giles Yeates

Introduction

This book describes the biopsychosocial nature of persisting and complex headache presentations following mild brain trauma and offers a programme that is predominantly based on cognitive behavioural therapy to guide patients to achieve better health and less pain.

This second edition is a fully revised and updated version of its forerunner, providing the same robust theoretical underpinning and practical therapeutic guidance, yet further emphasising the biopsychological nature of stress factors and how they shape the life and health history of a person, both before and after their brain trauma.

This comprehensive therapy guide is intended for rehabilitation professionals who have taken it upon themselves to ease the pain of brain trauma survivors and to show them a better way to cope and re-evaluate their lives. Such professionals include psychologists, psychotherapists, counsellors, psychology and therapy assistants, occupational therapists, physiotherapists, neuropsychologists, doctors, specialist nurses and students of all related health disciplines.

This book illustrates that great advances continue to be made within research and clinical practice in shifting from a predominantly medical approach towards a greater integration of patients' life-long experiences. It is these past health and personal histories combined with acute accident factors that are vital for our understanding of complex and chronic conditions such as headaches. The way a person adapts to the aftermath of a traumatic event that has affected their head and has resulted in chronic pain depends on many factors in regards to their health, well-being and lifestyle, both before and after the onset event. This book explains how such a life-story approach enables health professionals to be open-minded about the wide range of their patients' personal experiences.

Detailed guidance is offered here about how to engage patients in exploring and manipulating the many contributing facets of their condition, stemming from their past experiences, their health behaviours and their beliefs about how to overcome the trauma and headaches associated with an accident.

Ultimately, connecting a person's past with the accident and the resulting head pain must lead towards substantial changes in how they care for their body and approach their own health management. This book provides headache therapists with practical resources to help them support their patients in facing such challenging changes.

Along the way, the reader will be provided with several research-based explanations about the neurophysiological and biopsychological mechanisms that are active within the body as a result of acute and persistent accident-related problems. These explanations can then be used to establish a shared understanding of the condition between the clinician and the patient, which will become the starting point for therapeutic and proactive lifestyle changes.

By working through the therapeutic programme presented in this book, patients and clinicians alike will realise that even when the initial injury has settled, the underlying interconnected mechanisms and the efforts to adapt can maintain symptoms such as posttraumatic headaches.

In short, this book emphasises:

– The understanding of headache symptoms following a critical event as being the result of a complex trauma rather than a lasting injury to the brain
– The neurophysiological context of stress, pain and trauma
– A life and health history approach
– A multifaceted understanding of chronic conditions where "everything is connected"
– The importance of guiding each patient towards a shared understanding of the connections, first between their past and their present suffering, and second, between their bodily mechanisms, psychological processing and lifestyle.

The therapy guide follows the biopsychosocial conceptualisation presented throughout the book and aims to support the patient with numerous creative strategies and exercises. Busy clinicians will find suggestions regarding how to engage patients and help shift them away from a passive medical- to an active health management perspective. Numerous case examples and therapy templates are provided and are easy to follow.

Many of the therapeutic techniques mentioned in this guidebook can also be used with patients who experience headaches due to primary injuries to the head only, idiopathic headache conditions or more generic post-concussion symptoms. Furthermore, the therapy plans and therapeutic methods provided here (e.g., the health management module or relaxation therapies), as well as the practical worksheets, have the potential to be adapted for patients presenting other complex, functional/medically unexplained or psychosomatic complaints (e.g., chronic fatigue). Consequently, the therapy manual will also prove valuable for work with patients presenting a wide range of conditions beyond posttraumatic headaches.

This book is structured in three parts to highlight insights and an understanding of chronic posttraumatic headaches and to introduce a predominantly cognitive behavioural therapeutic approach to optimising them.

- Chapter 1 summarises those theoretical understandings of the mechanisms of headaches after mild brain trauma that seem to be most useful in enabling their clinical and practical implementation.
- Chapter 2 provides applied clinical and therapeutic guidance on the preparation of the specialist headache therapy programme.
- Chapter 3 outlines a practical, step-by-step guide to the modules of the proposed headache intervention. This particular chapter has been expanded in this second edition to describe the usefulness and implementation of single-session headache clinics. These clinics offer early education and re-conceptualisation for patients, with the intention of preventing secondary problems.
- The Appendix includes a huge range of worksheets, relaxation scripts, and an information brochure about mild head trauma for patients, as part of an all-inclusive manual for therapists. All this should greatly reduce the amount of time required to set up a structured and individualised therapy programme.

To summarise, the integrated biopsychosocial approach will optimise interactions between clinicians and headache patients in mild brain injury rehabilitation or pain management centres. The success of such headache programmes can be further enhanced if they are linked within medical and interdisciplinary services that aim to encourage a shift from a medical repair perspective to a motivated and proactive self-care methodology.

Chapter 1

Theory

Introduction

Clinicians and researchers have long been puzzled by patients presenting enduring problems following a mild traumatic brain injury. Despite advances in clinical practice, the literature on mild brain injury, post-concussion symptoms and posttraumatic headaches continues to report the lack of symptom specificity, the controversies and complexities surrounding the existence of such problems and the rarity of good studies that help identify their causes and consequences. Consequently, doctors and therapists have often felt paralysed in their attempts to help patients with posttraumatic headache.

The aim of this book is to provide the headache clinician with an understanding of this complicated and multifaceted condition in such a way that it optimises skill and confidence. Sharing this biopsychosocial formulation with patients who experience posttraumatic headaches has been shown to lead to genuine trust in this approach. This has resulted in their engagement with effective and lasting modifications in their pain-related behaviours.

In combination, headaches and mild brain trauma are examples of the mind-body conundrum. Attempts have been made to define the condition and its subtypes. Research has investigated details of the neurophysiological processes down to cell level on the one hand and explored personality, social behaviours and pre-morbid experiences on the other.

Much progress has been made in recent years to move beyond simplistic or causal descriptions of posttraumatic headaches. Medical and applied health professionals have begun to integrate the multiple and highly dynamic facets of symptomology with patients' past personal histories. Nevertheless, the awareness of the complexity that surfaces often overwhelms clinicians. So where do we start?

This first chapter attempts to present the theoretical information needed in order to engage the headache patient in a constructive dialogue about their condition.

By showing that an understanding of the condition is possible, despite weaknesses in medical or scientific descriptions, scaffolding for later sections of the book will be provided.

A silent epidemic

Acquired brain injuries are a huge problem for individuals and society, almost epidemic in scale, and demand more clinical and public awareness. Apparently, around 1.7 million Americans experience a brain injury each year. In Europe, we find an annual incidence of 250 to 300 brain injuries per 100,000 in the general population as seen in Accident and Emergency Departments. Over 100,000 adults are discharged from UK hospitals with a diagnosis of traumatic brain injury each year. Up to 90% of these people actually present with a mild traumatic brain injury and each of them may be at risk of developing long-term difficulties, maintained by secondary problems.

Motor traffic accidents are the most frequent causes of brain injuries, affecting drivers and pedestrians, followed by physical assaults and sports injuries. Young males are most at risk, especially if there are co-existing factors such as alcohol or drug abuse, psychiatric history or low socioeconomic status. Older adults are also vulnerable to brain injury, aggravated by physical comorbidities, due to the increased risk of falling. Recent years have seen an increase of attention given to mild brain injury due to blast injuries in military personnel and veterans.

The severity of an acquired brain injury is typically described as mild, moderate or severe. It is common for brain injury services to use the Glasgow Coma Scale (GCS) to describe the severity of an injury. A mild brain injury is classified as a traumatically induced loss or alteration of consciousness lasting less than 30 minutes or a period of posttraumatic amnesia lasting less than 24 hours or resulting in a GCS score of 13–15. Some patients with a mild brain injury may show abnormalities on MRI scans, which can be related to poor neuropsychological and neuropsychiatric outcomes. The American Congress of Rehabilitation Medicine and the World Health Organisation task force include the notion of an "altered mental state" as a key symptom for mild brain injury.

A moderate traumatic brain injury involves loss of consciousness for between 30 minutes and 24 hours, a GCS score of 9 to 12, or a length of posttraumatic amnesia between one and seven days. Severe traumatic brain injury involves periods of coma and posttraumatic amnesia beyond the timeframe for a moderate injury.

Concussion, mild brain injury and trauma

This book focuses on patients who have sustained a concussion and, therefore, possibly transient mild injuries to the brain.

"Concussion" describes the immediate temporary symptoms that may occur following the impact of a force that causes the head and the brain inside to shake rapidly and intensively. Depending on the severity of the force, an external trauma to the structures of the head, neck or shoulders is likely. Hippocrates described concussion in 2400AD and medically it was first defined by a Persian doctor as an abnormal physiological state rather than a brain injury. The terms "mild brain injury" and "concussion" seem to be used interchangeably because many of the symptoms overlap.

The core clusters of the post-concussion syndrome are:

- physical: **headache**, vertigo and dizziness, malaise and fatigue, sensitivity to light and noise, sleep problems;
- emotional: **trauma**, stress, irritability, emotional lability, anxiety, PTSD, depression, anger;
- cognitive: concentration and memory problems, reduced mental processing ability;
- other: tinnitus, lower tolerance of alcohol, preoccupation with the injury including irrational fear of brain damage, secondary illness behaviours including avoidance.

The symptoms may develop within a two-week period following the event and are normally expected to resolve within three to six months. This affects about 30–80% of people, but a substantial proportion of cases develop difficulties that can even last years.

Some symptoms, such as cognitive disturbances, may resolve early on, whereas others, such as headaches or vertigo, may persist beyond the onset event. The number of repeated concussions (e.g., in contact sports) is an important factor that influences the severity and timeline of these problems.

Pre-injury and comorbid genetic, psychological and psychiatric presentations – especially depression, anxiety and PTSD, poor motivation and inappropriate coping strategies – play a most significant role in the maintenance of the condition. Further risk factors include illness behaviours, alcohol or substance misuse and the pursuit of compensation claims. Such added vulnerabilities and complexities affect the resilience or hardiness of individuals facing and recovering from such symptoms.

Prolonged post-concussion symptoms may therefore have multiple aetiologies. The spectrum spans from the purely organic to the purely psychological over the course of time following the trauma event (Figure 1.1). As outlined throughout this book, the clinician must be aware of predispositions, onset and setting factors as well as secondary and reinforcing variables.

More severe cases of concussion can lead to mechanical injury or deformation of the neural tissue caused by the rotation or deceleration forces acting on the head and neck. Diffuse axonal injury, associated with the tearing, stretching, compressing or shearing of axons, and the swelling of brain tissue are common organic changes in concussion. Metabolic and molecular neurophysiological changes ultimately contribute to the physiological vulnerability generated by this condition. It is, thus, not surprising that people

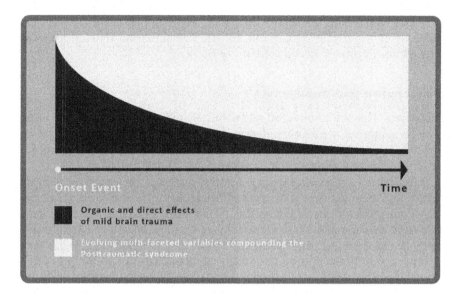

Figure 1.1 Evolving multifaceted post-concussion syndrome.

with enduring concussion symptoms experience information-processing difficulties, which are essentially caused by disturbances of neurotransmitter flow, the processing of chemical messages and their conversion into electrical potentials. The traumatised person may become aware of these abnormalities in the form of cognitive under-performance, particularly in the areas of attention, short-term memory, mental speed and flexibility. Even though such neurocognitive problems may be sub-clinical on testing, they can heighten emotional problems nevertheless. At this point, the syndrome goes "full circle," as hypervigilance and hyperarousal exacerbate the organic strain as well as subjective and psychogenic sensitivity. It may not be surprising, therefore, that headaches can be a consequence as well as a trigger within this whole conundrum.

Headaches are the key symptom of concussion. Persistent posttraumatic headaches are also associated with a multifaceted expression of experiences that were perceived to have developed after a traumatic onset.

The term "mild brain *trauma*" has emerged in clinical practice to aid the paradigm shift from the concept of an organic brain lesion that requires medical interventions towards an understanding of its biopsychosocial nature requiring proactive life-management. The term "mild brain *trauma*" is used throughout this book in favour of "mild brain *injury*" in order to emphasise the complex and multifaceted nature of the condition. Furthermore, the use of *trauma* crucially highlights the significance of experiences, which may have deeply shattered the identity of an individual, either pre- and/or post-injury. Whilst the scientific literature about mild traumatic brain injury and concussion underpins this work, the focus on brain *trauma* here emphasises the psychological and holistic reformulation that informs the therapeutic approach introduced in this book.

Posttraumatic headaches

Headache is almost a universal and definitely the most common mild brain trauma symptom, with an incidence as high as 90%. This suggests that the rehabilitation of headaches after mild brain injury can facilitate the recovery from concussion overall.

Research has shown an inverse relation between the extent of a brain injury and the occurrence of chronic headaches. Up to two-thirds of patients with mild brain injury suffer chronic daily headache, whereas only one-third of patients with moderate/severe brain injury experience chronic daily headache. How can this be explained? It is assumed that people who survive severe brain injury are initially immobilised due to the injury and are efficiently medicated. This optimal rest period means that the body has an opportunity to rebalance its mechanisms as part of its natural healing. Coma and posttraumatic amnesia interfere with the patient's ability to remember and reflect on the psychologically traumatic impact of the accident. Such reduced awareness further limits the development of secondary psycho-neuropathology.

It has been suggested that it may not be so much *what* happens to the head, but to *whose* head it happens to. This implies that posttraumatic headache is an individual affair depending on a range of factors such as premorbid headaches, previous concussion, gender, age, socioeconomic status, educational attainment, etc. In addition, a history of psychiatric disorder and psychological trauma triggered by the onset event is also considered to be of great significance.

Patients complain of posttraumatic headaches either immediately after the incident or emerging in the days following it. A brief neurological examination at an Accident & Emergency department or primary care practice often confirms the diagnosis of headaches in association with concussion. The treatment advice typically includes information about steps to take in order to reduce symptoms and to facilitate a sensibly paced return to activity.

Patients with persistent problems, especially those who fear underlying and undetected brain damage, often re-present at their doctor's practice. It appears that this clinical group, which is pre-occupied with residual headache symptoms, has the aforementioned psychosocial predispositions and psychiatric comorbidities. The patient may not have disclosed such symptoms or any aspects of contextual distress in the past as this may not have been relevant. However, the combination of an injury to the head, the fear provoked by the potentially dangerous onset event and the anxiety about having perhaps caused substantial damage makes it necessary for the clinician to be informed about all contributing variables.

Patients' narratives often indicate that the psychological impact was the direct result of the event itself. They may report that their insufficient coping ability with ongoing head pain symptoms is associated with the distress related to the aftermath of the event. The clinician might meet a person who may be catastrophizing their headache, demand a medical solution and present with a vicious cycle of self-perpetuating pain. At the same time, they may downplay or disconnect from the relevance of premorbid experiences (the so-called "good old days bias").

Hence, it appears that patients require an information-based, educative and therapeutic interpretation of their posttraumatic headaches that integrates their complex past history with the experiences linked with the critical event. The term "mild brain trauma" supports the understanding of this dynamic. It refers here to the actual impact to the head, in addition to the distressing and traumatising disruption of a person's life. This may include posttraumatic psychological distress, which may reinforce secondary symptoms and behaviours.

A comprehensive biopsychosocial perspective on these matters opens patients' minds for a re-formulation approach, which is followed by a proactive journey towards improvements of their symptoms.

Classification of posttraumatic headaches

Headaches are classified by the International Classification of Headache Disorders as either "primary" or "secondary." Primary headaches are not associated with any particular underlying disease and are also called "idiopathic" headaches. Headache after brain injury is a secondary type and is defined as acute or chronic posttraumatic headache. The criteria for acute posttraumatic headache require that the headache begins within seven days after the injury and disappears three months following the injury. However, according to clinical studies, the onset might be anywhere between one week and a month after mild brain trauma. A high percentage of new headaches were even reported after 6 and even 12 months post injury.

Posttraumatic headaches persisting beyond three months are classified as chronic and are differentiated according to injury severity, whiplash, surgical craniotomy, traumatic intracranial haematoma, other head or neck trauma and pre-existing headaches. The criteria of the International Headache Society are more or less descriptive of clinical symptoms. This method of classification has limitations insofar as it lacks attention to the clinical aetiology and nature of the headache onset and temporal development.

Presently, the description of headaches after brain trauma is based on symptom profiles and models explaining pain pathways. The conundrum of posttraumatic headaches continues to be about the underlying cause. If a patient has experienced an injury to the structures of the head and subsequently develops a headache, then the diagnosis of posttraumatic headache seems obvious. Nevertheless, it may be that the mild brain injury has triggered an underlying vulnerability, perhaps also associated with the aforementioned risk factors, and that the headache condition has been dormant.

It appears that the understanding of many medical conditions is changing. Awareness among the public and among medical professionals is shifting towards a multidimensional understanding of conditions. This incorporates biological factors, developmental vulnerabilities and distress, attributions such as illness onset and the secondary impact of symptoms, as well as social responses to the health problem.

Such a paradigm shift requires a step-wise approach to assessments. Medical investigations and classification are essential first steps in identifying and describing any disturbance. This gives structure to the medical investigation. It also gets the doctor and the patient on the same "wavelength," which facilitates rapport-building and trust. This trust is essential if the patient is to engage with successive steps towards a biopsychosocial approach to headache management.

Types of posttraumatic headaches

Individuals who have experienced a brain trauma may develop one or several types of headache. The most common presentations - tension headache, migraine, cervicogenic headache, neuralgias, and mixed/unclassifiable posttraumatic headache – are clinically similar to their non-traumatic counterparts.

The following description of the different types of posttraumatic headache aims to inform the non-medical headache therapist, so that a common understanding between the medical specialist, patient and therapist can be established.

Tension headache and migraine are the most common types of posttraumatic headache. There seems to be a debate amongst clinicians as to which of these is more likely following a concussion. The section below provides greater detail about some mechanisms of tension headache and, in particular, migraine. This is done in order to highlight the crucial interdependence of pain and psychological factors that is so central to the approach taken in this book.

Patients can become preoccupied with their headache if they assume that the pain represents a dysfunction of the brain due to their injury. It is thus very important to inform them that the brain is insensate, i.e., does not "feel" anything.

Medical causes for headaches that can be directly related to an injury include cerebral vein and sinus thrombosis, epidural and subdural haematoma, intracerebral and subarachnoid haemorrhage, altered intracranial pressure, hydrocephalus, carotid and vertebral artery dissection, cavernous–carotid fistula, cerebral aneurysms, skull and cerebral vertebrae fracture, and cervical disc protrusion.

Tension headache

Tension headache is very common following brain trauma. It is regarded as a muscular tension and is associated with musculoskeletal problems in the head, neck and shoulders. A tension headache may be episodic or chronic. With regards to the pain threshold, stress appears to be a highly related factor. Combinations of tension type and migraine headache are possible.

The onset event commonly involves a force that moves the head rapidly, thus stimulating trigger points, which may then relay tension and pain to the head. Prolonged peripheral headache can substantially influence the pain perception, which can then lead to Central Sensitisation and manifestation of the problem. Pre-morbid headache provides a risk factor for the development of headaches after brain trauma on the basis of pre-existing Central Sensitisation, triggered by muscle tenderness and confounded by reduced psychosocial resilience.

To illustrate tension headaches in more detail, we can refer to the scientific literature. This suggests that posttraumatic tension headaches are related to the sensitisation of myofascial tissues and the subsequent involvement of the central nervous system, leading to malfunctioning pain inhibition and enhanced psychological stress responses in people who have experienced a critical health event and have to cope with its consequences.

Increased pain perception from strained muscles, especially in the case of myofascial tenderness, might be the primary cause of at least episodic tension headaches. Central pain control mechanisms have to incorporate processes triggered by lifestyle-related stress, which can lead to the aggravation, rather than the inhibition, of pain sensations.

A well-received model is that prolonged noxious input from pericranial myofascial tissue may cause sensitisation at the spinal/trigeminal horns and supra-spinal features and be related to deficiency in pain modulatory and neuropsychological networks (e.g., attention to pain). Prolonged pain sensation resulting in more frequent headache episodes is said to lead to Central Sensitisation and chronic headache. In addition to that, it has been suggested that persistent triggering of the pain receptors in myofascial tissue may lead to a summation of such input, which increases the mechanisms of sensitisation peripherally and centrally. The resulting malfunctioning of central, i.e., cortical, pain-processing mechanisms, appears to be associated with a deficiency in pain modulation and inhibition. According to current knowledge, these processes are related to the interference of inhibitory pain control, whereby the nociceptive neurons in spinal and trigeminal horns are inhibited by noxious stimulation remote from their receptive regions.

These processes are also known in relation to extreme survival conditions, where pain may be inhibited when survival behaviour (fleeing, fighting, physical strain to keep the body safe, etc.) takes priority. The neurophysiological systems involved are highly complicated and are thought to include areas in the brain called dorsolateral and ventrolateral nerve bundles, supraspinal circuits, which include the reticular formation in the medulla and brain stem (see also Figure 1.5).

From a clinical point of view, this means that tension headache eventually leads to increased sensitivity to potential pain triggers peripherally and to a lowered pain threshold from a psychological point of view.

Psychological factors that possibly increase the headache include hypervigilance and increased attention to bodily sensations, misattribution of stress or arousal as pain, increased headache-related beliefs and thoughts about the meaning of head pain or increased headache behaviours.

People who have experienced emotional trauma due to an injury in relation to an accident or assault are likely to express increased anxiety, posttraumatic stress or other emotions such as anger or depression, all of which influence the headache condition. In clinical practice, it is commonly thought that people with posttraumatic tension headache report increased pain sensitivity due to psychological rather than physiological sensitisation.

Stress and pain share closely interlinked neural, endocrine, autonomic and behavioural pathways. It has not been fully proven that muscle contractions per se cause the pain in tension headache, but stress can aggravate the sensitive myofascial tissue and activate tension headache trigger points. Muscle tone particularly increases at the site of the pain and when the person becomes aware of the headache. Adrenalin and Noradrenalin are released as part of the sympathetic response (sympathetic-adrenomedullary system, SAM), which aggravates the already sensitised pain receptors at the myofascial trigger sites. These peripheral mechanisms involve the cortisol stress mechanism. At mid-brain level, headache signals interact with the hypothalamic-pituitary-adrenocortical (HPA-) axis and sympathetic-adrenomedullary axis and spark off a cascade of processes involving numerous pain pathways in cortical, subcortical and somatosensory systems. The role of cortisol will be revisited in the section about the Allostasis model; however, it may be mentioned here that cortisol released in response to acute emotional trauma and chronic stress has been found to cause tissue tenderness and damage. Acute stress responses include the activation of the immune system, resulting in the release of proinflammatory cytokines, which are important elements of the immune response and also important for the repair of cell tissue after an acute injury. Glucocorticoids (cortisol) are released as part of the HPA-axis activation to regulate the immune response.

In chronic situations due to ongoing stress and pain, however, immune cells become resistant to the modulating effect of cortisol. Cortisol becomes unable to suppress inflammation. Nevertheless, stress continues to promote the production of proinflammatory cytokines indefinitely. This maintains the sensitivity of trigger points and myofascial tissue. The individual continues to feel the pain and tenderness, which results in fatigue, breakdown of coping ability and other secondary psychological illness behaviours.

The gradual accumulation of the effects of the breakdown of adaptive mechanisms, the summation of nociceptive and stress triggers, the gradually decreasing pain threshold, the dysregulation of stress and inflammation responses and so on, might provide an explanation for late onset headaches and their persistence long after an event which has caused a critical injury.

As headaches cause stress and stress causes headaches, the distinction between psychological and physiological processes appears artificial. The self-perpetuating vicious cycles of peripheral and central mechanisms are not specific to tension headache alone, as will be seen in the discussion of posttraumatic migraine below.

Migraine

The clinical features of migraine after brain trauma appear almost identical to those of idiopathic migraine, either with or without aura.

According to the International Classification of Headache Disorders, migraine attacks include unilateral throbbing pain accompanied by nausea, vomiting and photophobia. As a result, individuals typically avoid routine activities, especially physical ones, but also cognitive tasks.

It is now agreed that migraine is a neurological disorder. Former vascular migraine hypotheses have been discarded. The activation of the trigemino-vascular pain pathways that innervate the dural vasculature is thought to be responsible for this type of headache. The disruption in sensory processing within the brain stem is understood to be the core neurophysiological disturbance.

A typical migraine attack consists of three stages: the aura, headache and postdrome phase. Neurological migraine mechanisms are highly complicated and there is an overlap of neurophysiological pattern in each of the migraine stages.

Migraine provides an example of shared mechanisms between mild brain trauma and pain processes. The experience of acute distress, either due to a trauma event or a migraine attack, triggers the subcortical alarm system. A cascade of neurocognitive disturbances is unleashed, which involves subcortical features such as the fear-processing amygdala and the memory-processing hippocampus. Both play crucial roles in pain and trauma pathways. The hippocampus registers and encodes the negative event and the amygdala amplifies this with a powerful fear response. This ensures such efficient communication with higher level cortical evaluations and memory that the individual is programmed to avoid such unpleasant stimuli in future, even though this process takes place outside conscious awareness.

As migraine attacks cannot be consciously self-regulated, they can lead to generalised anxiety, depression and concentration disturbances or short-term memory problems. Such symptoms are also characteristic of mild brain trauma per se.

Persistent posttraumatic migraines are the combination of a perceived association with a trigger – e.g. traumatic injury event, cognitive difficulty – and secondary mood symptoms.

The hypothalamus, along with the brain stem, is not only a key organ for cognitive processing of pain and trauma. It plays a vital role in regulating the experience of eating and sleeping, as well as in the production of nausea and vomiting symptoms linked with migraines.

The brain stem plays a key role in migraine pathophysiology. Brain stem dysfunction can lead to disturbed eating and sleeping patterns due to dys-regulated dopamine pathways. The trigemino-vascular activation and sen-sitisation amplifies this process. Migraineurs report that food factors as well as sleep disturbances can trigger attacks. However, because brain stem dis-turbances are unbeknown to the individual, a mis-association and psycho-logical conditioning may develop. Altered behaviours after a brain trauma might aggravate a migraine predisposition. A mildly traumatised person might feel disorganised, fall behind on tasks and become stressed or skip meals, thus setting off subcortical and brain stem pain mechanisms.

Migraineurs' prefrontal and temporal cortical networks appear to differ slightly from those of healthy people. Genetic neurophysiological and also lifestyle factors play a substantial role in predisposing people to the condi-tion. It appears to be that challenging life events – such as an injury to the head and potential brain trauma – may be processed inefficiently, hence mak-ing it more likely that a genetic predisposition to the condition is triggered.

Stress and negative emotions are commonly reported by migraine pa-tients whether they have experienced mild brain trauma or not. In contrast, some patients in clinical settings may report that they do not experience elevated stress. Even if they do, they may rather encounter a migraine at-tack during rest periods, e.g., at weekends. A straightforward link between heightened cortisol levels and migraine attacks is indeed not proven. In fact, cortisol levels in migraineurs may be quite dysregulated and may not follow the typical circadian rhythm.

From a neurophysiological point of view, stress can be explained using the Allostatic model. It explains how a long-term maladaptive HPA-axis represents physical or bodily distress. This process results in dysregulated cortisol distribution, which can enhance migraine vulnerability.

It is assumed that posttraumatic migraine mechanisms are similar to idio-pathic migraine. Such primary migraine involves activation and sensitisation of the pain matrix: the trigemino-vascular pathways, brain stem, cingulate cortex, prefrontal cortex, thalamus, nuclei within the diencephalon and other brain areas. It has been suggested that migraines are connected with altered cortical excitability and also with changes in energy metabolism of central pain-processing pathways. At the core of the migraine experience – which can begin many hours before an aura or before the attack is felt – lies a dysfunction of neural processing in the brain stem and hypothalamus, which sets off alterations in cellular and vascular processes in almost all parts of the brain. Dysregulation of neural traffic along the associated brain regions leads to altered sensory experiences and impaired function of pain-processing pathways.

The persistent nature of the migraine condition can lead to Central Sensitisation. This means that cortical vigilance during normal activity is heightened and that situations are sooner identified as challenging. This increases the likelihood of episodes occurring. Anxiety symptoms, particularly fear of pain and depression due to helplessness, are simultaneously primary and secondary emotional experiences. Ultimately, a complex phenomenon is created whereby the sufferer responds negatively to the environment, which in turn reinforces neurophysiological maladaptation.

Confusional migraine

Confusional migraine appears to be a rare subtype of migraine. About half these cases are associated with mild brain trauma. The onset of confusional migraine may almost immediately follow an impact to the head and the symptoms can also disappear within 1–12 hours.

The study of confusional migraine is interesting as it points to a common pathophysiology found in migraine and mild brain injury. It is thought that mild brain injury causes a depression or suppression of neural activity, which spreads in a circular pattern from the site of the impact across the hemisphere concerned. This transient wave of neuronal depolarisation – the cortical spreading depression – is believed to be the pathophysiological mechanism underlying the clinical phenomenon of migraine aura. The aura symptoms, such as scotoma, are also associated with blood flow changes or hypoperfusion. Speculation has, thus, arisen as to whether confusional migraine is actually an indication of mild brain injury, which has a similar pathophysiology. Figure 1.2 compares the multitude of neuro-cortical dysfunctions that can be found in both migraine and mild brain injury. Another explanation for the onset of confusional migraine – and probably also posttraumatic migraines – could be the development of localised cerebral oedema, which occur due to increased vascular permeability following a mild brain injury. As described above, neurological migraine attacks affect the functioning of many areas of the cortex as well as the hippocampus and brain stem. This ties in with explanations of mild brain injury and concussion as transient micro-neurological and ischemic pathologies, which affect the integrity of brain systems and result in a concert of posttraumatic pain and concussion symptoms.

MILD BRAIN INJURY	MIGRAINE
• Increased extracellular potassium	• Increased extracellular potassium
• Increased intracellular sodium, calcium and chloride	• Increased intracellular sodium, calcium and chloride
• Excessive release of excitatory amino acids (mainly glutamate)	• Excessive release of excitatory amino acids (glutamate and aspartate, leading to the spreading depolarisation /cortical depression)
• Abnormal distribution of serotonin transmitters in the central nervous system may impact on vasospasm	• Firing of brain stem nuclei results in the disturbance of the distribution of serotonin transmitters
• Noradrenalin may interact with transmitter release (cholinergic and acetylcholinergic systems)	• Elevation of noradrenalin-related enzyme levels
• Endogenous opoids: potentially increased levels	• Endogenous opioids: reduction of certain elements during headache-free periods and abnormally high levels during attacks
• Decline of magnesium levels	• Inappropriate magnesium levels between and during attacks
• Influx of extracellular calcium	• Disturbed magnesium-calcium ratio impaired mobilisation of liver glycogen
• Nitric oxygen potentially converted to free oxygen radicals leading to cell tissue deterioration	• Abnormal nitric oxide distribution
• Dopamine activation neuropeptides may interact with serotonin	• Dopamine transmission disturbed abnormal neuropeptides and other neurotransmitter systems

Figure 1.2 Similarities in pathology: mild brain injury and migraine.

Cervicogenic headache

Cervicogenic headache is very common following brain injury. This is due to the force of the blow to the head also affecting the musculoskeletal regions of the neck and upper spine. In a typical car accident, the head bends rapidly backwards, causing the mouth and jaw to open. This can lead to jaw dislocation and disc injuries, which can be associated with cervical myofascial pain, cervical ligament strain, cervical disc protrusion and upper cervical joint injury (C2, C3). Cervicogenic headache may also be caused by direct injury to a number of nerves, which can result in neuralgic pain.

Neuralgias

Headache after an injury to the features of the head and brain may also occur in the case of lesions to the soft tissues or when there is scar formation. The site of the injury is often sensitive to finger pressure. Neuralgic headaches may develop following local blunt trauma or penetrating scalp injury, resulting in damage to nerve endings. Types of neuralgic headaches include occipital, trigeminal, scalp laceration and supraorbital neuralgias. Allodynia is characterised by hypersensitivity and localised painful sensory disturbances.

There are a number of other reasons for the development of headache disorders following brain injury. It is useful to be observant of painkiller overuse headaches and headaches linked to the side effects of other medications. In addition, somatoform headaches, malingering and pain in association with any somatic or mental health conditions should be taken into account.

Patients may have different types of headaches at different times or a variety of symptoms together that are characteristic of more than one type of headache.

Initially, it is important for a medical professional to conduct an adequate physical examination of each patient in order to identify the specific headache subtype and to prescribe the correct treatment. The headache therapist will also benefit from a clear understanding of the various headache subtypes outlined above in their formulation of a clear description of the symptom profile. This will facilitate the design and implementation of the most appropriate and thus most effective therapy programme, as suggested in the later chapters of this book.

Physiological mechanisms of brain trauma and headache

Primary mechanisms of brain trauma

A number of anatomic structures of the head and neck can be involved in the generation of pain. A headache following injury to the head, jaw, and neck can be explained by the damage to extra-cranial features including bones, arteries, skin and discs. Injuries causing pain can affect intra-cranial features such as the dura at the brain base, the venous sinuses and a number of cranial nerves such as the optic, oculomotor, trigeminal, glossopharyngeal and vagus nerves. The upper cervical spine, as well as neurological pathways in the spinal cord and brain stem, can also trigger pain.

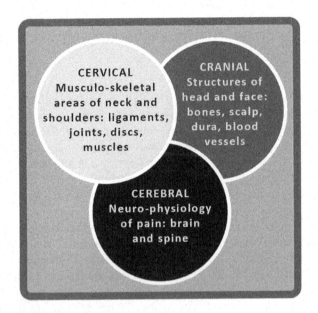

Figure 1.3 Causes of headache following mild brain trauma.

Example: headache generated by activation of the trigemino-cervical complex

An external injury to the head and neck triggers pain sensitive receptors and activates a pain pathway associated with the trigeminal neurovascular system. This can lead to the spreading of the pain sensation known called "referred pain," i.e., pain originating from an injured location that is perceived in a different area.

The trigeminal nerve, as one of the major pain-transmitting pathways, contains afferent nociceptive fibres from the anterior scalp and cranium, face, mouth, teeth, temporomandibular joints, sinuses, cranial blood vessels and meninges. A rich network of nociceptive fibres originates in the trigeminal ganglion and innervates the blood vessels of the meninges and a range of large cerebral arteries.

The occipital nerves, arising from cervical spinal roots (C2, C3), connect pain stimuli from the posterior head and scalp. Trigeminal and cervical nociceptive neurons merge in the upper cervical spinal cord (Figure 1.4). Neurons in this region can perceive afferent pain signals from cervical and trigeminal sources. As a result, the peripheral activation of one area can stimulate the central pain systems of the other and vice versa. It is thought that the trigemino-cervical complex explains how injuries to the neck cause head pain and how the activation of trigeminal pathways is linked to neck and posterior headache.

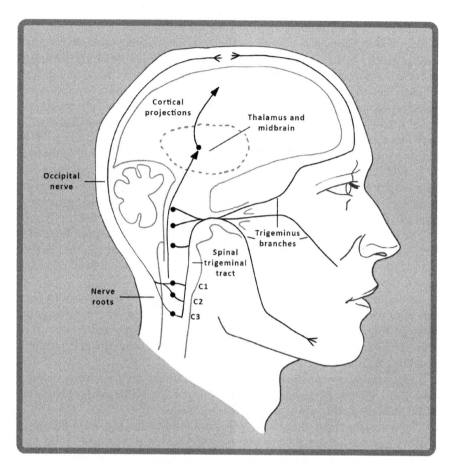

Figure 1.4 Trigemino-cervical complex.

Secondary mechanisms of brain trauma

Mild brain trauma is not associated with major structural injuries affecting the brain.

A focal impact injury represents mechanical damage, which can result in contusions (bruising of brain tissue), lacerations (tears) and intracranial haemorrhage (bleeding). Such clinical findings are more likely to be associated with severe injuries.

Diffuse injuries are characterised by acceleration or deceleration forces, e.g., due to car accidents, which can cause stretching and tearing of fragile brain tissue. Concussion is a milder form of diffuse injury caused by mechanical stresses, but without the presence of overt morphological damage. Nevertheless, the stretching and shearing that originate from the impact can disrupt cell protein functions and lead to the destabilisation of the axons of the neuron almost immediately following the event.

Such tissue damage is related to the rotational acceleration-deceleration forces, which also act on the midbrain and thalamus. The resulting disruption of these systems may cause a dysregulation of the reticular activating system, which is related to a number of symptoms associated with concussion and long-term impairments of neuropsychological pathways, including pain processes.

Even very minor concussions (also called sub-concussive injuries) can – if there are repeated injuries, as in certain sports – lead to subtle changes to the neural axons, disrupt the blood-brain barrier and trigger neuro-inflammation.

Non-traumatic injuries, caused by aneurisms, haemorrhages, tumours or meningitis, may also cause headaches. This is because space-occupying processes and inflammation increase intra-cranial pressure and brain membranes or blood vessels may be subject to related micro-injuries.

The brain itself is not sensitive to pain and, therefore, cannot hurt. It is very useful to inform patients about parts of the head that can and cannot hurt. This is because patients often fear that their persistent headaches signal further injuries to the brain.

Secondary consequences of brain injury begin at the moment of impact, but may present clinically only after a delay. A brain that is undergoing changes following a mild brain injury is in a particularly vulnerable state. Further injuries during this time period exacerbate concussion symptoms, including headaches.

These secondary consequences include metabolic and pathophysiological changes. Understanding such changes is important to determine the extent of the damage and to plan clinical interventions.

The neurochemical alterations following mild traumatic brain injury involve a cascade of destructive events associated with cerebral blood flow changes and the disruption of cell metabolism. Micro-ischaemia leads to anaerobic glycolysis, which is an adaptive process involving the transformation of glucose and very quick production of ATP (adenosine-5'-triphosphate, important for cell energy metabolism and neural signalling) when limited oxygen is available. This process is only efficient as an emergency measure for periods between ten seconds and two minutes. The glycolysis by-products – lactic acids – lead to membrane permeability and micro-oedema. If blood flow and oxygen provision cannot be restored after the very short burst of energy, then ATP resources become depleted. As a result, the ion pumps in axons and nerve cells fail to function, leading to membrane depolarisation and the excessive release of excitatory transmitters. The influx of positively charged ions activates further intracellular reactions. These lead to progressive structural changes of cell membranes and DNA fragmentation and dysfunction. Membrane degeneration of vascular and cellular structures results in the necrotic and programmed death of cells. Such neurochemical disturbances ultimately lead to neurologic deficits.

In a healthy brain, the cerebral blood flow is tightly coupled with the glucose metabolism and neuronal activity. Injuries to the central nervous system cause a deviation from the well-balanced metabolism. The neuron membrane pumps work in overdrive to restore the ionic balance. This causes an energy deficit and a surge of hyperglycolysis to satisfy the demand. This constitutes a period of hypermetabolism and an imbalance between blood flow and metabolism, leading to reduced cerebral blood flow. This increases the energy crisis, which can cause prolonged neuronal dysfunction.

Cerebral blood flow changes following traumatic brain injury can have a detrimental effect in relation to tissue damage, neurophysiological alterations and mechanical vessel distortion. They have been reported months, even years, after an injury and may be associated with chronic headache symptoms.

Immediately following the onset event, stretching and shearing forces act on the neuronal membranes, resulting in a biomechanical injury. This causes a cycle of cell and membrane depolarisation and subsequent excitation of the brain. This is followed by cortical depression. In contrast to the classic cortical depression mentioned in the migraine pathophysiology, the neuronal depression in brain trauma can occur in several diffuse areas of the brain simultaneously. The depletion of energy resources may further intensify this process. It is assumed that these mechanisms cause the cognitive difficulties associated with concussion.

There are a number of additional pathologies associated with concussion including oedema and inflammation. Oedema also develops as a consequence of cell membrane degeneration, leading to intracellular water accumulation associated with an osmotic imbalance. This can further lead to increased intracranial pressure (in more severe injuries) or secondary ischemia (e.g., mini-strokes).

The complex pathophysiological responses associated with brain injury also release cellular regulators that activate inflammatory processes. These are related to immune system activities that aim to eliminate injured neuronal tissue and synthesize scar tissue.

In summary, concussion and mild brain injury can lead to a cascade of alterations in brain tissue related to cerebral blood flow and metabolic disturbances, neuronal hyper-excitability, oedema formation, inflammation and changes to important cell proteins.

It is assumed that such changes are related to the neurological and neuropsychological symptoms reported by people with mild brain trauma. It is important to consider these processes in association with the secondary pain pathways and the complex emotional-cognitive evaluation of the experience.

People with mild brain trauma and posttraumatic headache benefit from the validation from their therapist that that they certainly have hurt themselves. They are keen to receive an appreciation of the fact that their symptoms are real and have a biological substrate, which confirms that they have not made up the whole story. The information about structural muscular-skeletal changes, nerve injuries as well as metabolic and molecular micro-physiological changes can help explain to patients the organic nature of their symptoms. They want reassurance that their condition is well understood, that nothing sinister is going on underneath and that they can make a good recovery.

The headache clinic, with its embedded formulation session, is an ideal setting in which to provide patients with such explanations, prepare them for the shift towards their health management during their recovery and enlist their engagement with a biopsychosocial approach.

Biopsychosocial approaches to posttraumatic headaches

Introduction

Headache patients want to be understood by their clinician. In order to help, it's important for the therapist to fully grasp the facets of this complicated condition and to formulate a mutual understanding of it, together with the patient.

All sensory experiences, and pain most of all, shape the neural processing and organisation of thoughts and emotions, whilst also driving behaviours. In order to modulate a person's headache condition, therapy needs to target all the involved processes, including the vicious cycles that may have been formed.

The challenge for the therapist is to combine science-based recommendations with creative therapy skills to engage the doubtful or worried patient. Quite frequently, one has to think "outside the box."

The following sections introduce ideas concerning the nature of persisting headaches associated with mild brain trauma. Examples of how such ideas can be shared with patients are described one by one. Certain models are more suitable for some patients than for others. As the dialogue with patients and professional colleagues unfolds, these stand-alone models can gradually be woven together into the biopsychosocial approach. The sections that follow set the scene for the holistic assessment and therapy guide presented later in the book.

Pain processing models

The absence of pain is a fundamental need for the well-being of humans and, indeed, for a vast range of species. Understanding pain has been the core theme of healing and medical science since the early days of mankind.

Pain processing models attempt to describe the links between an injury and the perception of pain. The assumption is that pain signals travel along dedicated pathways and reach higher-level structures, where they might be processed. Classical pain theories simplify the illustration of pain. Through the sharing of such theories, headaches can be demystified for patients, thus enabling them to let go of their sense of helplessness, failure to cope or even guilt.

Pain Gate Theory

Acute pain has an important function in signalling tissue damage to bodily systems responsible for the initiation of healing and repair. The injured area becomes hypersensitive, especially when in contact with external stimulation. This has a protective function so that further injury, or the interruption of the healing process, can be avoided.

The Gate Control Theory of Pain was introduced by Melzack and Wall. It can be an ideal starting point for patients who prefer a practical, down-to-earth explanation. The theory proposes neurophysiological mechanisms in the dorsal horns of the spinal cord that act like a gate, which increases or decreases the flow of nerve impulses from the periphery of the body to the central nervous system. If the Pain Gate opens the pathways, then the pain messages can be received by the brain and, following processing, the person perceives pain. In the case of a closed Pain Gate, the brain is less able to receive and interpret the messages and, as a result, the pain experience is modulated (Figure 1.5). The pain receptors in the body, called nociceptors, encode the mechanical, chemical, metabolic or thermal sensations and convert them into pain signals.

Afferent fibres carry the nociceptive message to the corresponding area of the central nervous system. The fast-acting and thinly myelinated $A\delta$ fibres rapidly conduct impulses that are modulated by the slower-acting, unmyelinated C fibres.

The dorsal horn, part of the spinal cord, contains both types of pain fibres. The Pain Gate represents a junction in the pain transmission, which is essentially a neuro-chemical process. The incoming stimuli lead to neuro-transmitter release, which, depending on the type and persistence of the stimulation, results in enhanced synaptic plasticity and, hence, pain signal transmission.

Ascending neurons project from the dorsal horn through the spine to the thalamus, mesencephalic formation and several other midbrain regions. This is the so-called "spino-thalamic tract." The reticular formation is a set of neural networks in the brain stem, which is responsible for core physical systems, body rhythms and cortical arousal. The reticular formation is critical for the development of a pain experience. It integrates motor, autonomic and sensory functions and mediates affective and motivation components of pain via pathways to the thalamus and limbic system.

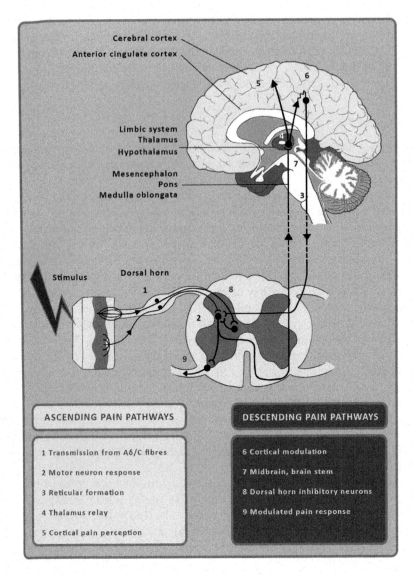

Figure 1.5 Pain pathways.

The thalamus has a central role in relaying sensory information, including pain sensation, to the cortex. The subcortical limbic system – consisting of a number of components and, most importantly, the amygdala and hippocampus – processes motivational elements of the pain and related pain behaviour (avoidance, escape, etc.). The cerebral cortex benefits from the pain information, pre-processed by the anterior cingulate cortex. This part of the brain plays a vital role in detecting and evaluating sensations and stimuli that do not fit with expectations or that pose a cortical dissonance. Somatosensory areas of the anterior insular are also receivers of pain stimulation.

Descending pathways modulate and inhibit all kinds of sensory experiences, including pain. Interactive cortical networks participate in the generation of action patterns, which influence immediate and future pain responses. These are referred to as Action Systems. Descending pain messages can undergo such cortical modulation and inhibition when passing through higher-level cortical areas, the thalamus, the grey matter of the midbrain, the brain stem, the dorsal horns in the medulla and spinal cord. Neurotransmitter activity within these structures can suppress or enhance nociception at the central brain level. The final modulation of descending nociceptive messages takes place in the spinal cord. Concentrated neurotransmitters within the dorsal horn are known for their inhibitory properties in the transmission of nociceptive messages.

Pain matrix

The concept of a "Neuromatrix" was described by Melzack as a widespread collection of neurons whose activity results in the experience of "a whole body processing a sense of self."

This sparked a field of research concerned with brain structures, which would be devoted to the processing of pain only. Similar to the Pain Gate pathway, the pain matrix mechanisms describe how the nociceptive stimuli elicit responses within subcortical and cortical brain structures. These include the primary and secondary somatosensory cortices, the insula and the cingulate cortex. Nociceptive activity in these areas triggers the perception of pain. It is assumed that measuring the activity of the pain matrix would match with the intensity and quality of the pain experience. For instance, mild pain stimuli may elicit low activity in the pain matrix and severe pain sensation would trigger a strong cortical response. In relation to pain management, it was assumed that the inhibition of ascending pain messages would reduce the pain perception at brain level. For instance, distracting a subject's attention away from the nociceptive stimuli would result in decreased pain experience, subjectively in the form of the subject's own rating of their pain and objectively in the form of a weaker brain response. These are, indeed, the findings that support the classical behavioural pain management techniques, introduced in Chapters 2 and 3.

The brain areas involved in pain processing, however, have rather multi-modal functions, i.e., they can be triggered by any kind of stimuli and any kind of sensory modality, not only nociceptive. Sensory stimuli, including pain, need to fulfil some basic requirements in order to activate a neuronal pathway (e.g., the pain transmission to the cortex via Pain Gate).

One is intensity and another is novelty. A novel stimulus always trumps a common one. The cingulate and insular cortices respond specifically to changes in the stream of sensory information. Therefore, if a chronic headache patient experiences a new head pain due to a bump on the head, then the cortical systems prioritise their attention on this new pain rather than a previously perceived headache. Hence, it is the evaluation of incoming stimuli and subjective *importance* allocated to them that determines how the associated brain networks process, encode and respond to these stimuli (see central reorganisation).

There is also no direct link between the magnitude of the pain stimulus and the pain perception. The pain sensation can be measured by event-related potentials in nerve fibres. However, the pain experience is the overall outcome of neural activation and comparison of past experience within the current context. As we will see, motivational and emotional factors play a crucial role in potentially enhancing the involvement of a wide group of cortical systems. This can mean that perhaps mild or harmless pain sensations with a low event-related potential can elicit a powerful pain syndrome, or people with only a mild traumatic injury may present signs of overwhelming suffering.

Pain is a multifaceted experience that is processed by interacting brain networks activated by a multitude of sensory and cognitive stimuli. Therefore, such concerted activity of neurological networks would not unequivocally represent the perception of pain in the brain.

There is no dedicated matrix for pain alone.

Central Sensitisation

The concept and experience of peripheral and Central Sensitisation is associated with a wide variety of chronic and complex pain conditions, posttraumatic headache being just one of them.

Peripheral Sensitisation

The peripheral hyper-sensitisation in acute pain has a protective function. Immediate stimulation of injured areas increases the firing of peripheral nociceptive neurons, leading to avoidance of such stimulation, which enables undisturbed healing to take place.

Chronic pain is the result of either continuing tissue damage, possibly because of inflammation, or altered neurochemical transmission systems that maintain high levels of sensitivity. Initially, such changes can affect peripheral systems. Normally, nociceptive fibres have a substantially high threshold for mechanical, thermal or chemical stimuli. The assumption underlying peripheral sensitisation is that cells have experienced certain types of damage that perpetuate the nociceptive processes, resulting in maintained inflammation and the lowering of the threshold for pain fibre activation. This further alters neurotransmitter behaviours, which lead to extensive and lasting changes of neurophysiological interactions in the dorsal horn, resulting in heightened sensitivity of uninjured neighbouring tissue.

Central Sensitisation

Central Sensitisation has become a well-understood model for explaining persisting somatic symptoms. It is a neuropsychological model that overcomes the restraints of chain-like pain pathways.

"Central" refers to a location that is away from the periphery where the painful tissue damage took place.

The first level of Central Sensitisation is associated with decreased thresholds for the stimulation and excitation of pain-processing neurons in the dorsal horn, which persists after the pain stimulus stops. Often this experience occurs after the injury has healed and plays a part in hyperalgesia and allodynia. People who may have experienced lesions to the features of the skin and skull complain about persisting troubles caused by hyperalgesia, which is caused by micro-damage to nociceptors or peripheral nerves.

Central Sensitisation in posttraumatic tension headache appears to occur at the level of the trigeminal nucleus in the dorsal horn. The firing of the nociceptive neurons is related to ongoing stimulation of the soft tissue around the head. In the case of sensitisation, the triggering of pain sensation is often due to changes of muscle use in the head and neck. People with head pain can develop unnatural postures or movement patterns that maintain nociceptor activity further up the central pain pathway.

The second level of the Central Sensitisation process is based on the aforementioned specialisation of neurophysiological pathways. It is assumed that synaptic and neurotransmitter efficiency in somatic systems is enhanced by a cognitive-emotional focus on the experience.

Central Sensitisation in persisting headache means that pain sensations are processed in such a way that the nervous system becomes more efficient in detecting and responding to pain stimuli as described by the pain matrix.

Nociceptors that were stimulated by lesions resulting from an injury send their signals to corresponding cortical regions for further processing. Evaluated pain sensations represent tissue damage or, potentially, a threat to the survival of the individual. Therefore, emotional, cognitive and autonomic systems are recruited to the pain processing systems. Emotional responses, often related to previous experiences with pain, health problems or, indeed, accidents accelerate and reinforce neurophysiological and neuropsychological processes.

In that sense, Central Sensitisation is understood in the context of skill building and learning. Skill building is the result of fine-tuned interactions between neural networks. This leads to faster processing and eventually to

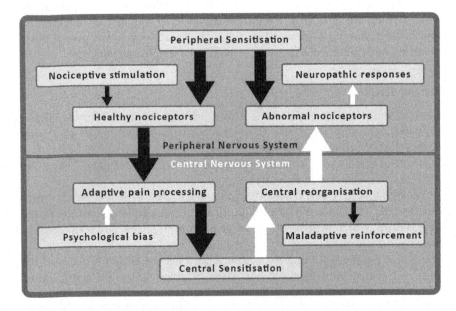

Figure 1.6 Peripheral and Central Sensitisation.

structural changes (e.g., synaptic growth and varied synaptic connections, altered genetic transcriptions, etc.) in those brain regions. These are the elementary processes of brain plasticity.

The body, thus, achieves optimal spontaneous efficiency in reacting to potentially harmful situations. In the case of persisting headache, this leads to an acceleration of a condition that the affected person eventually perceives as stressful and painful.

Attention and pain processing systems prioritise their activity for threat-related information. This is commonly termed "cognitive bias." The protective mechanisms of this bias become maladaptive in chronic pain. The persisting attentional focus inhibits higher-level cognitive processes that could be useful for problem-solving and implementing alternative behaviours, but instead maintain habitual avoidance of behaviours associated with pain triggers, thus preventing desensitisation to the pain experience.

Central reorganisation

Central Sensitisation causes the nervous system to become stuck in a persistent state of reactivity. That is because chronic pain, or in this case chronic headache, is associated with the structural and functional reorganisation of brain networks, which are different from those linked with acute pain and from those of people without pain. The central pain Action

Systems include the cognitive-evaluative, emotional, motivational and sensory networks.

Headache experiences or perceived pain sensations stimulate central Action Systems in order to optimise the perception of imminent or future pain sensations so that all involved brain networks can respond more efficiently and faster.

Central feedback systems evaluate the usefulness of action responses and their effect on peripheral sensations. Motivational components (e.g., directive attention towards sensation) indicate pain relief or intensified suffering.

Sensations coming from the head and neck areas can be part of very normal physical experience. Most sensations do not enter conscious awareness in normal functioning. Following an accident involving these areas, such sensations activate their allocated central networks as usual. Other cortical networks concerned with memory and the processing of accident and injury-related information, as well as networks highlighting the psychological significance of the impact, may be firing at exactly the same time as higher-level sensory networks. The summation of the parallel activity of all these networks creates a level that reaches conscious awareness.

Eventually, due to the conditioning of associated cortical networks, only partial initial activation is required in order to create the full experience – in this case, the headache experience.

The more sensory, emotional and thought processes are involved in streaming the sensations, the better the brain networks become in *creating* the pain.

Cognitive processes play a key role in recognising, monitoring and evaluating the pain. Expectation, future-focused screening and comparing of pain sensations, plus the planning of pain relief activities, all strengthen cognitive pathways. Perhaps we could call this the "neuropsychological pain matrix." The developing complex pain scenario hijacks a number of interacting cerebral networks. This comes at the cost of the efficiency of executive and emotional networks. A bias is created towards headache sensations, headache-related thoughts and feelings, rather than towards alternative internal or external events to which the individual would choose to pay attention if the pain were absent. As a result, the brain reorganises itself to maintain an eventually unhelpful maladaptive experience. Over time, this may lead to the de-skilling of cognitive and action networks that promote a healthy adaptation.

Stress and pain models

Diathesis-Stress model

The Diathesis-Stress model also offers a means of explaining ongoing headaches following brain trauma.

Stress is a phenomenon that arises due to an imbalance between environmental demands and physiological resources and that can result in physical symptoms, particularly if the imbalance persists.

Selye proposed the general adaptation syndrome, which explains how a long-lasting biological stressor can lead to chronic bodily stress. In his three-phase model, he described, first, how stress signals activate the autonomic nervous system via an alarm response; second, how the organism attempts to build resistance on the basis of available resources and third, how continued exposure to the stressor leads to exhaustion of the adaptive mechanisms, resulting in irreversible impairments and death of the organism. Later on, Selye refined his stress response theory by describing the type of stressors that activate the organism and the reaction by the organism to the stressors. Many clinicians and patients have adopted this traditional understanding of the interaction between challenging external demands and physiological resources.

Lazarus and Folkman, basing their work on Selye's definitions, emphasise the subjective evaluation of stressors. The awareness of the exhaustion of bodily resources is subjectively evaluated by the individual as stress. Selye's description of physiological stress was enhanced by adding the concept of motivational appraisal. This concept proposes that the stress reaction takes its course through the following three appraisal levels.

- *Primary appraisal* refers to the emotional meaning of the stressor for the individual, e.g., whether or not a stimulus represents a threat. People with headaches following brain trauma tend to evaluate pain signals, as well as trauma- or accident-related stimuli, as primarily unpleasant and threatening. This is more the case if a Central Sensitisation syndrome has developed.
- *Secondary appraisal* refers to available resources and adaptive strategies. Avoidance behaviours are immediate and spontaneous reactions to painful and distressing stimuli in the case of pain and a perceived threat from within the body. Chronic headache sufferers may suppress their awareness of the pain (e.g., by keeping busy and distracting themselves from thinking about the consequences of their pain) or may reduce activity, hoping to avoid triggering or worsening the pain. Long-term adjustment is really at risk if people lose coping skills and disengage from daily activities due to avoidance behaviours.
- *Cognitive reappraisal* refers to reappraisal of the stress-triggering situation. Cognitive processes negotiate between stimulus and reaction. The headache sufferer evaluates the usefulness of the applied strategy. Failure of a strategy may not result in switching to an alternative method. A person might instead interpret the failure of a particular strategy as being due to its under-use and attempt to intensify the use of that strategy (e.g., taking a double dose of painkillers, increasing social

withdrawal, etc.), resulting in the manifestation of unhelpful coping patterns or depression (see case example Connor).

- *Coping* refers to the potential to operate within the stress situation and, furthermore, the integration of outcomes of coping attempts and physiological adaptation. It refers to behavioural choices, executed on the basis of personality styles, and behavioural preferences, which aim for a balanced interaction between the person and the environment. This can pan out very differently for individuals depending on their particular combination of symptoms and conditions.

The subjectively evaluated level of stress directly influences an individual's vulnerability to a condition. The Diathesis-Stress model examines the relationship between a biological or genetic predisposition (diathesis) with the environment and life events (stressors). This model can be applied to mild brain trauma, helping to describe it as a continuum of biological and psychological vulnerability (Figure 1.1) as formulated from a lifespan perspective (Figures 1.8, and 2.2). The individual's likelihood of developing headaches following a brain injury depends on their degree of resilience versus pre-accident vulnerability, based on biopsychosocial contributors.

Migraine as an example of the Diathesis-Stress model

Applying the Diathesis-Stress model, migraine can be said to develop as a result of the interaction between a physiological and genetic predisposition within a complex or challenging context, i.e., the experience of a brain trauma and its aftermath. The combination of physiological migraine stimuli and subjectively appraised stress levels is said to be responsible for the emergence of this headache condition.

About 75% of migraine patients mention stress and stressful life events as the primary factor related to their migraine condition. Stress is, therefore, seen as a predisposition or vulnerability for the development of migraine as a clinical condition. In line with the above premises, the migraineur's subjective appraisal of the significance of such events and the perceived reduced resilience intensifies the stress experience. The resulting personal tendency to develop such a cognitive bias presents a risk factor for the development of a persisting migraine condition.

It is easy to appreciate that stress symptoms are heightened in the life of a person who has to deal with the additional aftermath of a brain trauma. The injury reduces physiological resilience and, thus, represents a migraine trigger factor. Disturbed cognitive abilities, higher demands on coping resources, increased daily hassles and functional lapses all provide fertile ground for the reduction of the migraine threshold and the onset of the cascade of migraine mechanisms (Figure 1.7, worksheet migraine and mild brain trauma.

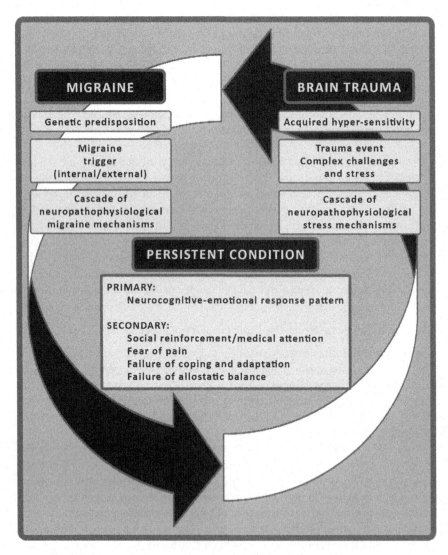

Figure 1.7 Diathesis-Stress model of migraine and mild brain trauma.

Allostasis model

Clinicians and researchers are close to reaching a consensus about the description of the dynamic variables that create persistent post-concussion problems. It has been accepted that the medical and biological model is inadequate for explaining causes and consequences. It is vital to overcome simplifications of causal associations between a pre-trauma psychiatric history and a prolonged response to head or brain trauma. The individual genetic make-up, developmental experiences and concurrent psycho-behavioural responses are tightly networked with key biological players (e.g., chemical messenger systems: neurotransmitters and hormones, inflammatory substances, etc.) of the dynamic and complicated stress systems.

Comprehensive models based on an integrative biopsychosocial theory encourage explorations of the early stages of a person's life in view of physiological adaptations to possibly unfavourable psychosocial conditions. Such a perspective allows the understanding of the development of a fragile nervous system, which may have led to dysregulated emotional, cognitive and social/behavioural experiences.

The assumption is, therefore, that complex posttraumatic headaches that persist beyond the expected recovery period are rooted within the accumulated layers of vulnerabilities, which, in turn, affect the psychophysiological resilience of the individual.

The section above elaborated on the notion of stress as a phenomenon that arises due to an imbalance between environmental demands, internal bodily inputs and physiological resources, and as something that can result in physical symptoms, particularly if such an imbalance persists. The brain and the nervous system act as mediators between physiological activation by a stressor and the behavioural and social adjustment to it.

The Diathesis-Stress or vulnerability model examines the relationship between biological or genetic predisposition (i.e., diathesis) with the environment and life events or stressors. This understanding encouraged research into psychosomatic medicine and helped explain organic (e.g., cardiac conditions, arthritis, etc.) as well as psychological (e.g., mental illness, particularly depression) conditions. Eventually, these theories were succeeded by the Allostasis model, which appears to underpin the current understanding of stress mechanisms.

Allostasis describes a process of the activation of neurobiological systems to ensure the health and survival of the individual. Allostatic load is the consequence of long-term maladaptation to chronic demand that can potentially lead to damage of bodily systems. Human bodies are ill-equipped to deal with long-lasting stressful challenges as, from an evolutionary point of view, they developed primarily to successfully respond to acute stress events that signal a survival threat. Such events trigger a cascade of changes in the nervous, cardiovascular, endocrine and immune systems. Currently, it is believed that such initially adaptive stress responses in humans are generated by two systems.

The first of these two is the sympathetic-adrenomedullary system (SAM), part of the autonomic nervous system. Dysregulations at this level have been at the core of explaining stressful mental health conditions (e.g., anxiety disorders or, more specifically, panic attacks). The autonomic nervous system regulates homeostatic functions. The sympathetic nervous system is associated with rapid activation of metabolic resources, which provide the energy for the immediate responses to the subcortical alarm or "fight or flight" signal. The SAM stimulates the adrenal medulla to produce catecholamines (e.g., adrenalin; see the worksheet *effect of stress on the body*). The parasympathetic nervous system, on the other hand, promotes functions associated with growth and restoration. Such mechanisms are suspended during acute critical events and may become dysfunctional in the case of chronic stress. Pain stimuli and higher-level pain perception systems indicate an assumed threat to survival and, as a result, may promote a massive withdrawal of parasympathetic function whilst the sympathetic nervous system provides metabolic activation to deal with such challenges. The role of parasympathetic responses in the case of chronic negative experiences may have been underestimated in the past. Stress and negative health outcomes have mainly been associated with overactive sympathetic function. It appears that an unbalanced parasympathetic response also contributes substantially to physical and psychological disorders, which may prolong pain conditions or lead to additional complex health problems.

The second system believed to be responsible for generating adaptive stress responses is the neuroendocrine system. This consists of interlinked glands and cells that communicate via hormones released into the blood stream, which also fulfil a signalling function. Within these, there are two major axes: the HPA-axis and the hypothalamic-pituitary-gonadal (HPG-) axis. Hormones produced by the endocrine glands influence metabolism, growth and development, immune function, sleep, mood and cognition, whilst also regulating bio-behavioural stress systems.

The hypothalamus and the pituitary gland produce substances that stimulate the adrenal cortex to release cortisol. Cortisol and catecholamines have distinct regulatory functions during a stress reaction whilst also promoting the conversion of stored energy into immediately available glucose. This energy is then distributed to organs that need it most. In the case of active physical demands (running, fighting, doing something, etc.), a myocardial mechanism is utilised to optimise cardiac output. A vascular mechanism is activated in the case of mental challenges (including worries, cognitive or emotional overload, confusion, etc.), which is perhaps similar to the overlap between cognitive and pain disturbances. This involves a vascular response, which is based on increased vigilance and inhibited muscular-skeletal activity, which also shunts blood away from the periphery to the internal organs (i.e., in preparation for minimising potential bleeding in the case of a physical attack).

Furthermore, it is vital to understand the role of the HPA-axis in so-called "functional" or complex symptoms or, in other words, in body-brain disorders caused by and resulting in maladjusted body-environmental interactions (also allostatic load).

The processes activating the HPA-axis as a result of persistent environmental demand can be described with reference to the sequelae of events that both follow on from, as well as occur in parallel to, the stimulation of the autonomic nervous system. This results in the production and release of corticosteroid hormones (e.g., glucocorticoids and mineralocorticoids) and arginine vasopressin by the adrenal gland. The hypothalamus and pituitary gland release corticotrophin into the circulation. By passing the blood brain barrier, these hormones interact with receptors, particularly in the hippocampus, amygdala and prefrontal regions. Eventually corticosteroids act on target tissue via gene transcription. This process has a prolonged impact on physiology and behaviour as it is intended to enable adaptation to long-term demands. The permanent physiological changes following ongoing demand, anticipation of distress and delayed termination of stress responses, thus, help account for the development of physical and mental health symptoms over time.

The current understanding of posttraumatic headaches, especially of migraine patients and those with additional trauma histories, is based on observations of significantly increased HPA-axis activity in the form of hypercortisolism. This suggests that HPA-axis activity can provide an important biomarker for such patients.

It is without question that prolonged stressful life experiences during early individual development shape the reactivity and plasticity of cortical systems. The cortico-limbic pathways are vulnerable to childhood neglect or maltreatment. For instance, children who have experienced persistent maltreatment may present with smaller cerebral volumes, a smaller corpus callosum, less asymmetry of the prefrontal cortex and/or larger amygdalae, amongst many other physiological maldevelopments. As a result, these maladapted cortical structures and neurophysiological processes shape the interactions between the brain and the environment in a suboptimal way. Thus, such a predisposed and vulnerable system is represented by heightened allostatic load and, hence, bodily malfunctioning and symptom sensitivity (e.g., lower pain threshold). These psycho-biological components are important to consider when reflecting on premorbid social and psychiatric risk factors for people with brain trauma and persistent posttraumatic headaches.

Additionally, it is widely accepted that the impact of a long-term release of glucocorticoids leads to neuronal atrophy or -loss in the hippocampus. This has consequences for cortical network functioning and hyper-excitability, which can interrupt neuropsychological information-processing and, in turn, result in dysregulated pain processing and potentially delayed recovery from the pathological mechanisms of concussion.

Posttraumatic headache – a functional disorder?

The term "functional," or "psychogenic," disorder refers to complex health problems rooted in long-term, severe, stress-based experiences. These conditions are neither unexplained nor mysterious. They are well understood in science and applied clinical domains, including stress research,

developmental and biological psychiatry, behavioural medicine, neuropsychiatry and clinical and neuropsychology. The scope of this book can only
touch a little on the clarity that has already been established about the
mechanisms of such long-term and complex conditions that do not fit with
traditional and medical diagnostic labels.

As mentioned already, amongst clinicians and researchers, it is agreed
that mild brain trauma and post-concussion symptoms should disappear
after approximately three to six months. Additionally, it is understood
that the purely "organic" mild brain injury symptoms contribute very little to the development of persistent posttraumatic headaches as part of the
post-concussion syndrome (Figure 1.1). This assumption is based on the
clinical knowledge about bodily repair mechanisms after a *one-off, acute*
injury. In contrast, accumulative mild brain injuries and traumas, and the
lasting impact of substantial and persistent lifestyle stress, present risk factors for long-term problems and a poor prognosis.

In general, human bodies have the ability to overcome severely stressful and traumatic events and heal from most injuries without recurring or
lasting physiological or psychological disturbances. Nevertheless, different
types of stresses or stressful events can result in different patterns of stress
experiences. Additionally, the processing of stress also depends on vulnerability and protective variables between individuals.

In line with a dynamic biopsychosocial model, it is postulated that *chronic*
posttraumatic headaches develop as a result of early acquired vulnerabilities
due to genetic, physiological, psychosocial and environmental mismatches.
That means that the "story" of *chronic* posttraumatic headaches begins long
before the trauma event and the headache onset.

Patients with persisting and secondary symptoms need education and
support in order to fully understand their condition. It is a delicate matter to
explore which personal experiences and physiological maladjustments have
affected them in their earlier history. Patients may find it difficult to grasp
how their ongoing headache is not considered a purely medical or physical
disorder and rather might be the secondary effect of complicated long-term
issues, aggravated by recent trauma and the associated overlap between
vegetative, primary emotional, neuro-cognitive and pain processes. Sometimes, they might express the view that no one believes them or that they feel
like a nuisance to the health service. They may have been told that it's "all in
their head" or their pain may have been labelled as "psychogenic."

The allostasis paradigm may provide a starting point for understanding functional disorders. Functional disorders are complex health presentations rooted in a genetic predisposition or physiological vulnerability,
early attachments with the primary care-givers and the development of
neurophysiological/neuropsychological systems that determine cognitive,
psycho-motor, behavioural and social abilities.

The allostatic paradigm also uses the term "stress" to describe stimuli that exert a demand on bodily systems as well as physiological responses and processes. Some of these enter conscious awareness as they are experienced as unpleasant stress symptoms. Stress typically occurs within a complex interpersonal or environmental context that poses psychological and physical challenges to the individual.

The allostatic load is considered low or balanced if the individual feels safe and has the capacity to face the challenge. A threat, however – especially one that cannot be resolved with the existing response patterns or resources – will activate the stress system. The biological mechanism of the autonomic nervous system and the neuro-endocrine system (e.g., HPA-axis) are mobilized.

A head pain indicates a threat from within the body. In the case of recurring and persistent posttraumatic headache, it is likely that the SAM quickly interacts with the HPA system and challenges the allostatic load.

The biopsychosocial model of stress describes a continuum of added layers of vulnerability (Figure 1.8):

• Genetic constitution, early health and physiological sensitivity:
  Vulnerabilities can develop as early as during pregnancy if the embryo is exposed to certain stresses. Micro-physiological adjustments at this stage affect all body systems. The young child may be less robust when faced with additional social-environmental challenges during the very early years.

  Neonatal animal studies have shown how different maternal nurturing patterns influence the serotonin–glucocorticoid interaction, thus demonstrating a behaviourally induced genetic expression, which, in turn, affects stress and anxiety responses.

  Headache research (specifically that related to migraine) postulates a genetic vulnerability in association with the development of a nervous constitution. A genetic defect of the serotonin transporter gene (e.g., 5-HTTLPR) is believed to be related to physical and emotional irritability.

  Particularly vulnerable are those individuals who grow up within insecure attachment environments or with caregivers (mainly mothers) who may also have fragile psychophysiological resilience. It has been shown that early attachment distress and early childhood maltreatment results in elevated HPA-axis and SAM arousal. These individuals develop maladjusted endocrine systems, structural changes to the nervous system, risks for medical illnesses and, importantly, hypersensitive neurophysiological emotion and cognition networks to enable early detection and protection from harm, including pain. Such individuals tend to show larger and more frequent stress responses. This is related to

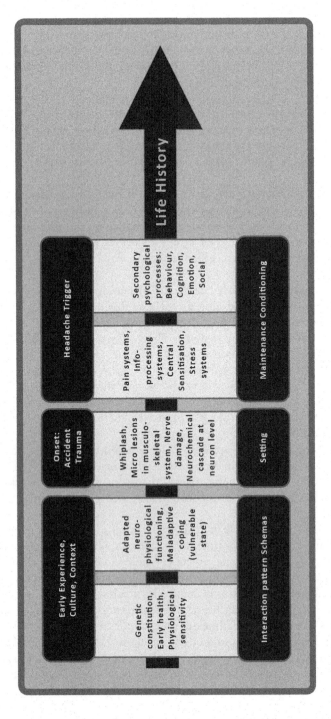

Figure 1.8 Integrative model of long-term impact of early vulnerabilities.

the neuropsychological changes described by the Central Sensitisation model. Additional adaptions in response to chronic stress happen within the immune system. Head injuries may sometimes initially involve head wounds. The temporary increase of circulation of immune cells facilitates healing. In chronically demanding situations where stress hormone levels are constantly elevated, the immunity of the individual is suppressed. Consequently, chronic stressors (e.g., due to past dysregulation/vulnerability, chronic head pain, secondary psychosocial problems, etc.) are associated with increased vulnerability to viral infections or other health problems, slower wound healing or recovery from surgery or poorer antibody activity following vaccinations.

In contrast, in patients with pre-existing autoimmune disease, prolonged stress can lead to an overactive immune system response or dysregulated proinflammatory cytokine production. Cortisol plays a regulatory role in physiological stress, activating resources in a similar way to how a fire crew regulates its available resources in order to extinguish a fire without causing too much damage. An overactive immune system downregulates the involvement of cortisol with the effect that proinflammatory cytokines are produced indefinitely and prolonged inflammation persists. In headache patients, inflammations may affect muscles, ligaments or neck and shoulder joints. In addition, neurogenic inflammatory processes affect intracerebral blood flow and result in nerve and glia cell changes. These processes have been observed in non-traumatic migraines as well as following lesions to the trigeminal nerves due to mild brain injury.

During times of illness, the inflammation is signalled back to the nervous system and symptoms of fatigue, malaise and low drive are produced, which may appear similar to depression. In the short term, sickness behaviour promotes rest and recovery, as energy is preserved and exposure to further risk or stress is reduced. In the long-term, however, such behaviour can have a negative impact on active coping and can reduce self-management motivation and skill, as well as the benefits to be had from social support. As a result, such long-lasting sickness behaviour complicates the "functional" scenario.

• (Mal)adaptive coping, vulnerable state:
   It is believed that a complex interplay of insecure attachment style, inconsistent protection by caregivers and pre-existing neurophysiological weakness gives rise to an anxiety-prone or threat-vigilant neurophysiology. An insecure social base appears to be associated with inappropriate social role modelling, which can result in poor social skill acquisition and emotional incompetence. These vulnerability factors further predispose the person to an increased likelihood of abuse linked with poor interpersonal efficacy and susceptibility to stress. The resulting personal style is used by the individual to navigate a challenging

social environment to ensure stability, the absence of uncertainty and the avoidance of threat. Stable interactional patterns or schemas emerge, which may be adaptive in the unsafe and challenging circumstances, but not in the majority of common social interactions. As personality styles are robust patterns, the individual may struggle with the dilemma of inconsistent threat perception, fluctuating personal response patterns and the general perception of normal behaviour. Such dilemmas can result in additional complications and may heighten a person's risk factors. The stress spiral escalates and secondary behavioural, psychological, psychiatric and long-term somatic disorders follow.

- Secondary psychological processes:
  Illness behaviours, misattributions, avoidance, misdiagnosis and mistreatment are among the many factors that perpetuate the chronic pattern. Such factors involve interaction between:

  - early vulnerability, biased perception and action patterns in response to threats
  - sustained injury representing a real threat and the related psychological trauma
  - individual expression of short and long-term stress mechanisms and psychological strategies (e.g., avoidance versus endurance)
  - extremely complex social interactions and environmental contexts.

  Evolution has provided us with reasonably effective mechanisms for dealing with short-term stressors. Not everyone who has experienced head trauma will develop chronic or complex symptoms. The adverse effects of the aftermath of head trauma are related to the human capacity for worry, for repetitive recall and thinking about a distressing event and for rehearsing anticipated catastrophes. Such mental processing activates all stress systems in the same ways as real threat-events do, i.e., it triggers cognitive attention to the threat, as well as the arousal and anxiety responses and associated symptoms like headaches, leading to the observed secondary complications.
  Integrative neuro-behavioural models allow the formulation of a patient's long-term vulnerabilities and their likely impact in the case of acute life and health events.

- *Emotional processing models* describe the somatic and neuropsychological pathways behind the behavioural dynamics that eventually heighten the risk for adverse symptoms to cause lasting damage and reduce the restoration of emotional resilience. The key elements include an acquired hypervigilance and learned bias towards negatively appraised stimuli, inaccurate perception of physical symptoms and maladaptive emotional regulation (see Figure 1.9 and neuropsychological models below).

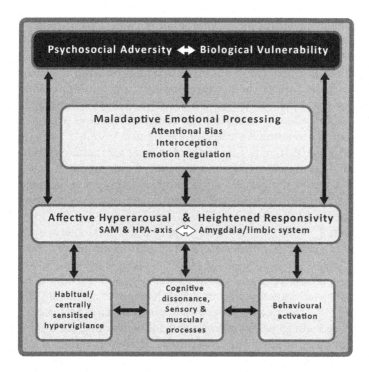

Figure 1.9 Emotional processing in complex disorders.

Early genetic and/or critical social-interactive challenges can result in maladaptive social-emotional cognition. Such sensitisation enables a person to quickly identify a perceived threat due to enhanced mechanisms, which decode facial expressions and quickly respond to them. The endocrine stress and subcortical cognitive-emotion systems (e.g., thalamo–amygdala–hypothalamus network) remain elevated at baseline to sustain ongoing and required vigilance. Over long periods of time, especially if the person remains exposed to unsafe social scenarious, such processes can lead to a significant reduction in the size of the thalamus, amygdala and other involved structures. Such changes have been linked to mental health problems and generalised anxiety, which are also key predispositions for chronic posttraumatic headaches.

The persistent expectation of danger and a trained cognitive-emotion network which is super sensitive to the detection of threatening environmental signals (e.g., aggressive expressions of a potential attacker and misreading facial expressions in non-attackers) creates a cognitive dissonance that is mediated by the anterior cingulate cortex and prefrontal regions, which are closely linked with limbic emotional centres.

A person who misperceives social and environmental stimuli encounters cognitive confusion because, in most cases, their experience represents either the exaggeration or absence of an actual threat. Prefrontal systems aim to resolve this mismatch by recruiting further attention networks in order to obtain more information from the environment about the nature of the danger. However, any additional information may overload the information processing capacity (which may be slowed due to concussion), resulting in an additional surge of arousal and possibly of malfunctioning attention-perception systems. These processes are also linked to pathways in the motor cortex that are responsible for stimulating muscle activation and behavioural responses.

As a result, the person may feel increasingly tense, aroused and irritated, fatigued with loss of concentration and, thus, highly likely to experience headaches.

Overall, emotional-somatic experiences and neurocognitive responses appear inappropriately integrated, meaning that people with such long-term complex issues have reduced interoceptive awareness. Raising the awareness of bodily experiences and learning to be in tune with internal stressors and external demands may be another helpful strategy to offer people with chronic posttraumatic headaches.

These seem to be the mechanisms following long-term sensitisation on the basis of early predispositions. However, should a person encounter a real threat (e.g., become the victim of an assault or an accident leading to head trauma), all predisposed systems fire instantly and the aforementioned neurophysiological pathways are activated and reinforced.

Considering the models that have been explored so far, persistent posttraumatic headaches can be described as the result of the added layers of psychophysiological vulnerabilities laid bare by a traumatic event, which threaten the healthy functioning of an individual. This event is embedded within the social and environmental context that either supported or hindered adjustment.

The majority of people who sustain a mild brain trauma do recover, perhaps benefitting from an early psycho-educational headache clinic session. The symptoms subside swiftly when they represent a one-off event, which, after brief intense stress-arousal, subsides to normal levels. Our stress systems have no problems with short-term stressors. However, predisposed, maldeveloped physiological systems do not return easily to the baseline after a traumatic health event. This is simply because they have not been at baseline before, as long-term bodily changes, attention-arousal systems, emotional processing and behavioural dynamics were altered due to the aforementioned early challenges and vulnerabilities.

Such multifaceted processes appear complicated, as not every one of the contributing elements can be clarified over the course of the individual's development or before, during and after the onset event. Nevertheless, clinically, it is vital to achieve a shared understanding of the participating elements, especially the contribution of aforementioned early vulnerabilities and contextual influences, as they help explain the physiological maladaptation that created the chronic symptoms. This helps the patient understand their personal attitudes toward the headache experience and explore their options regarding the different treatments available.

Taking the above explanations into consideration, the term "functional" may no longer be necessary nor helpful. Perhaps it is then time to explore the complex conditions that have developed due to long-lasting physiological adaptations affecting several bodily systems (example Alice). Medical professionals need to become more confident in working with such complicated, dynamic bodily mechanisms and the associated uncertainties. Medical science has become highly detailed as well as multifaceted. It is no longer possible for a single doctor to have all this knowledge, nor is that necessary. Treatment can shift towards understanding patients' journeys and the stages of the symptom development with the aim of supporting their efforts to manage their own well-being, improve their quality of life and move towards a gradual reduction of their symptoms.

Neuropsychological models and posttraumatic headaches

Neuro-behavioural learning

Acute headache represents a threat to the integrity of bodily systems and instantly alerts the subcortical alarm response, which is felt as fear and anxiety. The pain stimuli and associated primary emotions trigger the SAM, which accelerates systemic bodily reactions. The release of stress neurochemicals (e.g., noradrenalin and adrenalin) enhances the imprint of memories of the pain, trauma and associated fear. Therefore, the mental and physical elements of the flight or fight experience lead eventually to the neurobiologically determined prosocial or defensive behaviours, which maintain the whole vicious cycle of stress, tension, headache, fear and avoidance. It is essential to emphasise that it is not only the sensation of an acute headache and the fear triggered at the moment when it hurts that contribute to the persistence of the pain-stress condition. It is also the associated memory of previous episodes that causes an anticipation of severe discomfort. Behaviourally, people rehearse the headaches in their mind permanently and the psychophysiological systems are constantly ready to respond to emerging signs of head pain. This creates the prolonged tension, which fires off the complex stress systems described above.

According to the principles of classical conditioning, a number of associations may be established within headache pathways.

Explanations for headaches after brain trauma based on conditioned learning allow for a number of combinations. The memory of the accident, the aftermath of the brain trauma and the headache itself all represent real experiences that could be conditioned to related consequences. Psychological distress that originated from the accident and/or brain trauma could potentially be triggered at any time by simultaneously encoded environmental or social stimuli, thereby leading to conditioned responses.

Additionally, patients can experience recurring intrusive accident-related memories and images and begin to fear situations that could trigger them. The same is true for anxiety or worries about potentially getting a headache and the development of a fear of situations that are believed to cause them. Headache fear can result in avoidance and self-restricting behaviours, just as the pain itself can.

The behaviour therapy elements should offer relief from the headaches as well as a de-conditioning of the fear of headaches.

How do the conditioned connections of associated networks remain active over time? Depending on signal strength and frequency of exposure, the complex neurochemical processes acting on synapses and neurons increase the efficiency of signal transmission between participating neurons. Modulations take place within neurons, which facilitate further synaptic and pathway strengthening processes. Such reinforced pathways form the basis for cognitive networks that regulate our memory for traumatic events, social interactional responses or coping behaviours.

Once connections are manifested in neuronal structures, they cannot easily be undone, although they may weaken if the exposure to a stimulus disappears. However, in the case of repeated exposure to the stimulus or a mental image representing it (as in chronic head pain), the conditioned reaction will recur.

The aim of headache therapy following brain trauma is to encourage learning alternative strategies that dampen the firing subcortical flight or fight response. Cortical networks representing healthy adaptive behaviours and attitudes can override the conditioned fear and tensions and desensitise the autonomic system.

Neuropsychological processes

Central Sensitisation refers to the activation of higher-level systems that maintain the chronic pain experience. This includes attention networks, which remain vigilant so that the slightest indicator for potentially developing head pain can be noticed. These sensations can be amplified by emotions and worries, which are motivational drivers for optimising attention further to detect new or unusual pain signals. Higher-level memory systems get involved so that the pain can be compared with previous experiences. The memory of previous pain is matched with beliefs, appraisal and coping patterns that, in parallel, recruit actions and behaviours intended to reduce or avoid the pain. Such cognitive pain systems play a vital role in the perpetuation of chronic headaches. These can determine future behaviours and impact on sufferers' lives, regardless of whether a headache is present at the time or not.

Cortical activation

Neuropsychological processes can, via the interaction of a range of cortical systems (see the neuro and pain matrix), influence the circuits that control nociceptive neurons. Attention and expectation alone can increase pain perceptions, even in the absence of noxious stimuli. Neurons responsible for pain transmission are modulated by somatosensory, cortical and limbic structures and brain stem regions, all of which can be engaged by psychological modulations that take control over pain transmitting neurons. This means that psychological mechanisms not only contribute to the perception of acute pain, but also influence the development and maintenance of headache after brain trauma. These mechanisms are also referred to here as Action Systems and their pain-modulating ability is utilised in headache therapy and lifestyle modulations in order to dampen and override maladaptive pain.

Information-processing

Research supports clinical experiences that suggest that chronic pain is associated with, and leads to, neuropsychological disturbances.

A neurophysiological pathway can carry various messages or can activate the firing of associated and distant networks, which ultimately leads to a new experience, i.e., emotion, cognition, motivation or perception. If cognitive processing is modulated due to interference from pain messages, then this also slows processes such as alternative decision-making or emotion–motivation regulation.

Neuromechanical and neurophysiological changes inherent to headaches and brain trauma result in neuropsychological disturbance and physiological arousal that generate somatic symptoms. Particularly following concussion, this means that malfunctioning and slowly performing neural pathways might not keep up with decoding and analysing the fast stream of incoming environmental stimuli. The resulting cognitive overload activates frontal cortical areas, especially the anterior cingulate cortex, which acts as a resolution centre for mismatching or unusual information. Projections passing through the anterior cingulate are linked with emotional arousal, cognitive functioning, motoric regions, behaviour systems and subcortical stress regulation.

The discrepancy between the physical headache experience and the absence of an obvious injury can lead to a confusion of brain systems such as the anterior cingulate. Persistence of such cortical dissonance escalates subcortical processes further to provide optimal alertness and cognitive resources for resolving the dissonance. The resulting arousal might be

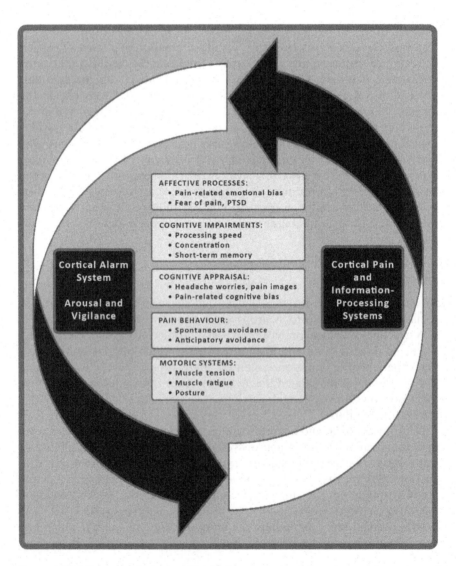

Figure 1.10 Neuropsychological headache processes.

experienced as raised physiological distress, anxiety or anger and may lead to somatic responses (e.g., muscle tension and headaches) or other sensory disturbances (e.g., vertigo, hypersensitivity to light or sound).

The above-mentioned neuropsychological overload and discrepancy between stimuli aggravate the physiological headache pathways, maintaining the chronic condition. The pain symptoms trigger the cortical alarm system and primary fear responses. The limbic system and the amygdala in particular, which might already be pre-sensitised by the brain injury or accident, contribute to the generation of secondary anxiety disorders such as agoraphobia or posttraumatic stress. Such responses and bodily arousal are reactions to a perceived threat. Nevertheless, external stimuli indicating danger are missing, because the acute injury was in the past. Cognitively, there is no reason to be frightened, but the body betrays the mind. The anterior cingulate registers this mismatch also as cognitive dissonance. Further activation of sensory systems is initiated to provide additional information so that the assumed and potentially threatening stimuli can be detected and the mismatch can be resolved. However, additional sensory data accelerate the information-overload due to pathway weaknesses, resulting in an escalation of the stress response. This vicious circle, thus, heightens a person's vulnerability with regard to the generation and persistence of postconcussion symptoms, including headaches.

Personal style and interactive pattern

Headaches following brain injury have also been linked to abnormal psychological presentations. Personal factors (coping styles, perception of the self, the world and others) usually do not, in themselves, cause a headache. However, they can play a role in symptom development, response to injury and headache management.

Individuals with headaches after brain trauma appear to exhibit more psychological problems than individuals with a type of idiopathic headache or healthy people. This might be due to a nervous predisposition associated with an individual's pain perception or vulnerabilities associated with early and maladaptive attachments or reduced health management literacy. It appears that psychologically unbalanced people have a lower threshold for headache perception, less robust coping skills and reduced learning and motivational ability to adopt strategies for regulating their pain experience.

It follows that psychological mechanisms and patterns need to be seriously taken into account in headache treatments. Patients who are anxious and distressed with regard to the imminence of headache episodes during the interval between headaches take anticipatory actions to reduce the pain or to eliminate triggers. Sufferers restrict their level of activity and functioning even in pain-free periods, which reduces their quality of life and even predicts chronic disability. Physical sensitisation and psychological fear of pain are associated with analgesic overuse and consequent drug-induced headache, as well as medication dependency. People with chronic headache often take medication during pain-free periods. This is also an avoidance behaviour and indicative of secondary psychological dependency and signals how the headache is controlling the individual's life.

Resilience: It is vital to understand each individual person and their own particular way of reacting to internal and external events. Premorbid factors – such as the motivation to deal with challenges, health behaviours, health role models, locus of control and social support – play a role in the development of chronic pain syndromes. The relationship between personal styles and environmental adversity is certainly bidirectional. Protective factors include coping, social support and, most importantly, finding meaning. People with a higher self-esteem were found to have lower stress hormone levels and performed better in the face of an acute stressor, such as a traumatic event. They can be described as having better psychophysiological resilience.

Furthermore, the circumstances of the accident also need to be considered. The setting in which the brain trauma-related headaches occurs include internal factors such as coexisting post-concussion problems, cognitive disorders, anxiety disorders (e.g., posttraumatic stress disorder) or external factors such as family dynamics and work-related issues.

Headache triggers are short-term experiences that can be related to the immediate onset of a headache and that set the scene for a cascade of unpleasant symptoms. However, it may be rare to identify headache triggers reliably. Patients might also find it hard to process the pain experience appropriately due to slowed or distorted information-processing, memory or concentration dysfunction. Furthermore, negative perception of consequences, irrational beliefs and thoughts (e.g., blame, self-blame, guilt, feeling of failure or letting down of others), and external locus of control may hinder proactive coping strategies. Emotional reactions include fear of recurrent pain, fear of severe illness, generalised anxiety and heightened stress levels. People may become irritable, frustrated and angry, or, ultimately, might feel like giving up altogether and become hopeless and depressed.

Social interactions: Fragile emotions (e.g., outbursts of frustration) and an inability to plan life proactively around the pain or apply coping strategies might lead to withdrawal from social contacts or disengagement from previously enjoyed past activities. In contrast, health behaviours could include social attention seeking. This might not always happen on a conscious level as concerned friends and relatives might want to be helpful and caring. Sometimes, it could increase carers' sense of control and self-esteem if they are able to provide support and help, but they might not realise that this can also maintain the problem. Alternatively, patients might wish to protect their carers and they will, as a result, attempt to hide their pain. Suppressing or ignoring the pain can lead to missed opportunities for positive health management.

Hypervigilance and hypersensitivity: Pain behaviours are the consequence of internal neuropsychological sensitisation and external social-environment interaction. Avoidance behaviour in the widest sense might be applied to prevent or reduce the pain experience, at least in the short-term. The constant flow of headache signals related to cognitive processing, fear reaction, pain appraisal and interactional dynamics maintains the cognitive bias, i.e., the formation of beliefs about imminent, unpredictable danger and threat to the body and the self. The increased activity of all associated circuits stimulates and maintains autonomic stress. Consequently, the person never feels safe and never feels relaxed.

Psychotherapy models and headaches

Cognitive behavioural approaches

The applied cognitive behavioural approach connects theoretical concepts about headaches and mild brain trauma with therapeutic interventions involving the person. The following sections are structured according to the cognitive behavioural format and reflect a patient's psychological experience with their headache.

Cognitive behavioural therapy (CBT) is based on the idea that thoughts, emotions, behaviour and social-environmental context shape the experiences of each individual. CBT methods are designed to help patients overcome their dysfunctional psychological experiences and adverse responses to contexts, people or events.

The developmental and life story approach applied here is well suited to offering an understanding of posttraumatic headache in association with concussion and mild brain trauma.

Stress associated with past experience of a brain injury represents a predisposition to unregulated responses in expectation of real or feared adverse events. Pain is a fundamental bodily signal that normally indicates a lesion or inflammation, which could threaten the health or the survival of the body. Both systems, stress and pain, overlap when people experience headaches after brain trauma. This represents a challenge for interventions aimed at optimising people's well-being. Psychotherapy might not achieve this alone, although it can play a powerful part in integrated packages and services promoting self-management.

Cognitive behavioural formulation

Formulation is a term used by clinical practitioners to describe an interpretation of a psychological or health phenomenon underpinned by theory and research.

The clinical formulation summarises and integrates all background information and findings about the patient's situation. Consequently, the clinical

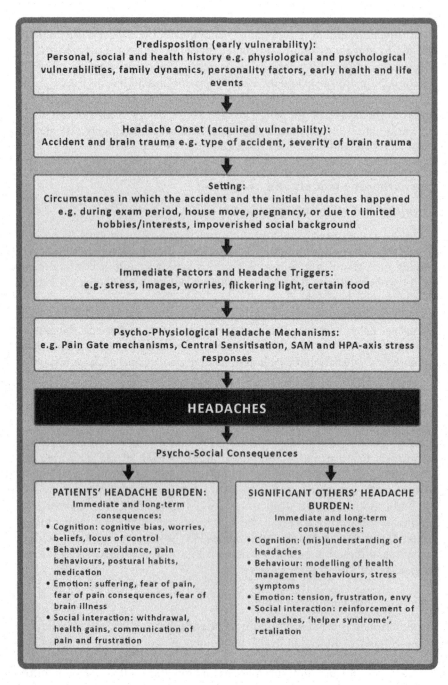

Figure 1.11 Cognitive behavioural headache formulation.

formulation describes a framework of the patient's condition that is unique to that individual as well as grounded in science.

The biopsychosocial underpinning of the cognitive behavioural formulation illustrates that persistent headaches after a brain injury are the result of complex interactions, which may have their roots in the early development of the individual.

Predispositions

Patients presenting with a headache or mild brain trauma might initially have the immediate circumstances of the brain trauma at the forefront of their mind rather than developmental components or life scenarios in general. However, it appears that the genesis of posttraumatic headaches begins long before the onset event. Therefore, the assessment should start with presenting symptoms, followed by an exploration of predisposing factors and early vulnerabilities.

What are the crucial predisposing factors for headaches?
- Personal and psychological predispositions

  Personal elements include thinking styles, health beliefs, motivation and attitudes. For instance, which problem-solving strategies, attributions or resources would the person be most likely to choose in critical life or health scenarios? Which beliefs about their health, about staying healthy or overcoming an illness did they form when they were younger? What has been their attitude towards doctors and the health system? What about their motivation to continue with activities and responsibilities in the case of minor or, indeed, major illnesses? Have they been able to focus on their remaining strength? Have they been perfectionists who took everything that happened to them or others too seriously?

  Health beliefs, locus of control, cognitive thinking and coping styles are developed early in life and will affect the response to any occurring health event later on and also influence the residual consequences of brain injury and related headaches.

  In trying to understand the person coping with posttraumatic headaches, it is also vital to investigate emotional regulation and resilience. The assessing clinician should be attentive to the expression of emotional needs related to feelings of security, stability of attachment, sense of environmental control and absence of pain. Insecurity on these primary levels can predispose people at a very young age to physiological distress and survival fears, which perhaps intensify health anxieties and cognitive bias for somatic symptoms.

  Exploration can also be made of patients' social and interactional styles. For instance, some people enjoy sharing their emotional needs with family or friends, whereas others attempt to conceal their emotions for fear of unhelpful social responses or stigmatisation. Mental health problems that may have emerged during adolescence can be an indication of early violation of attachment needs or maladaptive and emotional processing. Emotional awareness might be a critical component in the tailored posttraumatic headache intervention.

- Pre-existing and comorbid health conditions

A person who experienced long or recurrent periods of ill health as a child might be less well-equipped to cope with an added injury and might, thus, be predisposed to develop headaches as well. A person may have experienced headaches before the brain trauma and, in such a case, it is important to understand what the headaches were like and how they were dealt with in the past.

The mental, emotional and physical development of any young child is influenced by the responses of early caregivers (usually mothers). The nature of such care often depends on the stress-tolerance of the mother herself. Unstable attachments and insecurity are often the consequence of an imbalance between the nurture needs of the child and the resilience of the mother. Children with additional needs (e.g., Attention Deficit Hyperactivity Disorder) require stable and robust parental styles in order to establish a good enough sense of emotional security.

- Early interpersonal interactions and mutual attachment behaviours

Attachment experiences are encoded in the maturing neurophysiological pathways of an individual. They, thus, provide a basis for the regulation of behaviour and the processing of further experiences in the form of personality patterns or coping styles directed towards others and towards the self (including the body). Such patterns (also referred to as schemas) can help or hinder a patient in engaging with and implementing psychological headache management strategies.

Clearly, it is essential to understand a person's family history and family dynamics. Family members might have served as role models for dealing with health and illness. They might have responded in reassuring, caring ways to the child or young person when they were unwell and, in such a way, encouraged healing to take place. Alternatively, if the early caregivers themselves had a tendency towards stressful overreactions or avoidance of responsibility in demanding situations, the patient might have developed distorted perceptions of illness.

Onset

The development of posttraumatic headache is related to three overlapping onset scenarios: the event involving injury to the head and the onset of concussion/mild brain injury symptoms; possible psychological trauma associated with the injury event and, lastly, the onset of the headache itself. Whilst concussion problems occur almost immediately following the event and are expected to improve quite quickly, headaches may only develop after days or weeks and may persist for some time. In order to establish a detailed formulation of the conditions, it is useful to separate the onset scenarios.

Clinicians, traditionally, tend to view the onset of a health problem as an isolated fact. They meet the patient at the point of their first presentation of the symptoms. The impulse is to guide the patient to well-being from that initial point. Some, however, require being "picked up" from a very different place. Rather than focusing on the headaches and the aim of overcoming them, patients might be stuck in their memories about the accident and injuries. Trauma images might even trigger the resurfacing of troubles from their earlier life.

The onset experience is most certainly associated with a psychologically critical event. Brain traumas are unpleasant experiences. The emotional and cognitive responses to such circumstances are, thus, heightened. Survivors often attempt, mentally, to recreate the injury event with a view to restoring their sense of self ("getting the old me back"). Images of injury scenarios and behaviours might be sequenced or emphasised in a self-preserving or self-restoring way. Incongruent personal experiences might be externalised and responsibilities projected onto the circumstances or onto other people. This applies to the description of headache onset as well. Patients at the onset of posttraumatic headaches might want to emphasise the state of their good health prior to the injury.

It is also important to note that headache onset might not coincide with the beginning of the headache *problem*. The initial headache symptoms might have been understood as part of the concussion or simply as part of recovery. Only their persistence may have transformed the status from a transient into a problematic condition.

Setting

The circumstances around the injury also require detailed clinical investigation. Accidents resulting in brain trauma are normally unexpected events and even the most robust person might be physically and psychologically unprepared for a significant disruption of their life plans.

In hindsight, patients often discover that the setting or associated life events at the time of the injury did enhance the likelihood of an unfortunate event. Setting events are often associated with critical phases in an individual's life such as completing education, starting a new job or preparing for retirement, moving house, getting married, having a child and many more. The elevated stress or attention focused on such events can distract people in such a way that they might have an accident.

Fact and fiction need to be separated in order to gain a workable understanding of the setting as this may represent an overlap of a vulnerable stage in life, an accident and the onset of pain problems. Personal roles with family and work plus financial situations are often at the heart of the setting in which the headache and brain trauma symptoms develop. Emotional reflections and "good old days" biases are also embedded setting variables.

Leaflets in accident and emergency departments about mild brain trauma and post-concussion symptoms, including headaches, can contribute to diagnosis biases, thereby heightening the likelihood of a patient reporting symptoms in line with their expectations. It is at this point that the psychological mechanisms inherent within the predisposing variables become apparent. Patients' beliefs and illness perceptions concerning the negative consequences of post-concussion symptoms need to be assessed, as they are independent predictors for the development of persistent conditions. Fear of being diagnosed as "brain damaged," associated with inappropriate worries about stigmatisation, could determine the way in which a person responds, e.g., by initiating an over-hasty return to work.

Scenarios might surface that highlight complex social pressures, hidden social difficulties, mental health problems, forensic histories or even financial issues. These can pose an additional demand on the already weakened physical and psychological resources of the person and may, in fact, be related to the headache onset rather than the brain trauma *per se*.

Vulnerable personality styles impacting on the efficiency of adapting to change include overachievement, dependency, insecurity, grandiosity and borderline personality characteristics. People with good organisational skills and proactive coping skills may be able to utilise those and find ways to reorganise their lives. However, such skills also depend on neuropsychological functioning, which might have been affected due to the concussion.

Socioeconomic setting factors are additional vulnerability factors. Often it is found that people from low socioeconomic backgrounds have insufficient life skills or health literacy and feel less competent in accessing health-promoting activities.

Headache symptoms

Most people who experience a concussion recover within a few days. Nevertheless, many develop, or continue to experience, various symptoms, with headaches being the most prominent. For a while following the event, they might begin to worry a bit. However, after a month or two, the headaches begin to control their lives.

The person might then be at a stage in recovery where they have to deal with enduring post-concussion problems on a daily basis. The brain trauma onset lies a few weeks away, but the shock of the accident or other cause of injury is still very much felt. Concentration problems, dizziness or light-headedness, emotional liability and worrying all add to the daily grind of coping with the demands of work, family and social life. The brain trauma survivor may not yet know how to find their way out of such a situation. They might find it difficult to sleep and, during the day, might feel overwhelmed with the demands of keeping up with chores and routines. This appears to be very fertile ground for the development of a chronic and complex headache condition.

Patients can be quite uncertain about the onset of their headaches. Concussion symptoms change over time, so they might have noticed new symptoms emerging or headaches growing into more compact tension and localised pain. Few people remember a first "out of the blue," full-blown headache or migraine. Nevertheless, there is usually a point in time when they become aware of their headaches beginning to be a problem.

In the case of acute headaches, people rarely adopt a "wait and see" attitude. Common sense tells them initially to take medication and rest. If the pain persists, then people begin to search for explanations for how the headache might have come about. This is done in the hope that, if triggers can be found, then both they and the headaches can be avoided in the future. Patients produce endless lists with a number of perceived triggers, including exercise and head movements, light (especially fluorescent light), stress, anger, anxiety, noise, nausea, fatigue, alcohol intake, hunger, food, concentration, relaxation, thunderstorms, dehydration, hormonal rhythms and so on.

However, headache causes, onset and maintenance factors rarely fit together exactly. Patients need to learn about the components that maintain their headaches and how to overcome them. Herein lies the difference between treatment, where medical interventions are expected to fix the problem, and therapy, which requires active participation from the patient to improve their health management.

Consequences

COGNITIVE CONSEQUENCES: THINKING ABOUT HEADACHES

The "cognitive" component in CBT terms encompasses thoughts, ideas and beliefs that a person has about their headaches at that time. Thinking styles develop at an early age. In order to understand a person's attempt to cope with their headaches, it is extremely important to examine their conscious thoughts about their headache condition.

Immediate thoughts may focus on physical pain sensations in order to observe their intensity, their type and the pace of their development. By paying attention to the symptoms in this way, the person aims to compare them with previous headache experiences. This is thought to help the person to judge how the current headache episode may turn out. By doing this, one can weigh up whether or not to ignore the pain and carry on, take medication now or later, as well as whether or not to take precautions and inform work, family and friends about potential unavailability, etc. Pain observations are commonly represented in verbal self-talk. By doing this, the person chooses certain linguistic descriptors for the pain experience, its location and its intensity. Such descriptions can, thus, be remembered and called upon if the pain experience changes later on. Furthermore, verbal representations are related to the individual's thinking style. A person might say, "When I was at the meeting, I had a pulsating pain at the temple area, but when I got home it moved to the forehead and my eyes." In this way, it is possible to compare new headache experiences with previous ones and plan management strategies. However, another person might use very different attributes which could also trigger strong emotional responses and lead to a different mental appraisal e.g., "I had this blasting headache that went on forever and I didn't know what to do."

Depending on the direction of thinking, a person might be able to change their behaviour in such a way as to relieve the pain. They may think, "I remember that last time it got really bad after half an hour, so I'll quickly get this phone call out of the way before I am unable to do anything else." Alternatively, they may think, "I recognise this headache. The last time it got really bad after a while, so I'd better cancel my commitments now and take painkillers before it gets unmanageable. This way I might be able to prevent it from getting worse." A more pessimistic person may think, "Oh no, here we go again, I can't do anything now, this will never go away," and might feel helpless and at the mercy of the pain.

Thinking styles determine how a person might plan to get over the pain in the short term. As the thoughts are verbally mediated and remembered, they also influence how the headache can be coped with in the future.

A person's locus of control is a very important element regarding their interpretation of the pain and their ability to deal with it. People who develop an internal locus of control believe that they are responsible for their own health. Those with an external locus of control believe that external forces, such as luck or doctors' treatments, determine their outcomes.

The locus of control in headaches after a brain injury may be influenced by the attributions made to the brain trauma. For instance, a victim of an accident or assault might want to blame others for having caused so much distress. They might want their situation corrected by the person who caused it rather than accepting that, in order to feel better, they have to make an effort to help themselves. Illness attributions contribute to the kind of action a person might take, e.g., resigning to helplessness ("Poor me, I am always ill, I always have these strange symptoms, the doctors can't explain it either, I am a special case," etc.) or throwing themselves into over-activity ("there is nothing I can do about it, I have to work through it," etc.).

Health specialists are often sandwiched between such perceptions or assumptions. Patients might expect doctors or clinicians to restore them to their previous condition. This way, they can "get over" it and forget the event. If that is not possible, then often doctors and clinicians are asked to take responsibility for the patient's health, including the whole onset scenario and its consequences.

If the trauma event and the resulting headache were caused by the individual themselves, perhaps through carelessness, then other negative emotional experiences such as guilt, self-blame, shame, anger or ignorance could aggravate the situation. These are cognitively generated feelings that can create vicious traps, especially if conditioned with the headache experience and associated pain memories.

Sometimes, people who are experiencing intense negative thoughts attempt to hide their headache. This is done in the hope of preventing others from commenting on the cause of the accident, which might risk forcing them to accept their own responsibility for it. The underlying presumption might be that communicating about headaches will elicit verbal punishment or direct attention paid to mistakes that may have caused the accident. Patients might over-generalise their presumptions, which can result in low self-esteem and feeling like a failure. Such core thought patterns can be the product of personal styles and interactional schemas developed in the early years of life.

According to the "good old days" bias, many people overestimate their well-being before the accident or think that they have never felt such pain before. This might not be the case. Most adults have experienced illness or health problems at some point during their lives. However, the presence of headaches and the unfairness of the onset event can be so overpowering that previous problems may appear minor in comparison.

COGNITIVE CONSEQUENCES: PROCESSING HEADACHES

The term "cognitive" further refers to the mental processing systems that deal with any information, including pain sensations.

Patients who have experienced a mild brain trauma frequently report cognitive difficulties related to short-term memory, processing speed, divided attention or concentration. These might be due to the primary micro-pathophysiological changes or due to the aforementioned range of secondary influences. Regardless of the underlying mechanisms, psychotherapeutic work aimed at altering unhelpful thoughts and beliefs requires efficient cognitive functioning. This could prove a challenge for some people with mild brain trauma. A well-functioning working memory is a key prerequisite for therapeutic interactions dependent on linguistic discourse and the generation of behaviour change. Short-term analytical skills are required for regulating a perceived mismatch between environmental, sensory and internal stimuli, so that a person can respond most effectively to such stimuli.

This relates to what we describe as frontal action or activation systems. These consist of cortical association areas, which analyse the perceived stimuli for their relevance. The outcome of this analysis determines the motivational goal of the individual (e.g., getting pain relief). In addition, cortical networks are responsible for maintaining vigilance. This allows for the comparison of the constant flow of pain-related sensory information with long-term memories about similar experiences. Memory content is further activated so that temporarily absent, but expected, pain sensations can be recognised. As a result, actions can be directed towards a pain management goal and its achievement.

Headaches and the subsequent pain pathway activation hijack the working memory for the purpose of effective processing of all related elements and for resolving the sensory mismatch whilst dealing with arousal and stress systems. Headaches, because they are interpreted as a potential threat to the individual, take on immediate priority and use the cognitive capacity of pathways concerned with learning, adaptation and coping.

Often people with mild brain traumas avoid cognitive tasks or cognitive efforts as they perceive these as triggers for headaches. This can result in cogniphobia, a fear of engaging in mentally challenging tasks. People may actually present with reduced memory performance after mild brain trauma, because they avoid using their memory, thereby losing their skills.

By means of therapy, patients should be supported in optimising their mental abilities and using cognitive compensation aids. A number of headache therapy techniques require cognitive flexibility, whereas headache or task monitoring are based on attention and awareness.

Information-overload, confusion about mismatching sensations and slowed mental processing all require extra efforts from the individual to apply therapeutic strategies. Mental stimulation and cognitive supports are thus important adjuncts to the headache therapy programme. These can also improve confidence in attending to practical organisation of the chaos that sometimes follows a critical event, thus relieving pressure.

EMOTIONAL CONSEQUENCES

Headaches hurt
Pain is one of the most intense and unpleasant experiences we can have. However, if there was no pain, humankind would probably be extinct by

now, as would most animals that have at least a primitive nervous system. The emotional processing of pain takes place along several well-integrated neuropsychological pathways.

Pain and fear
The experience of pain alerts our consciousness to serious injuries, prompting us to take instantaneous action to examine the body and to seek remedies and relief. Acute pain is intensely linked with fear. What is meant by "fear" here is not a broader kind of anxiety, but, rather, the core subcortical alarm and emergency system that is activated in response to any kind of threat. The emotions linked with pain or acute headache are generated on this primary level.

Headache behaviours are fundamentally driven by survival anxiety, which is spontaneous and outside conscious control. This is because the associated subcortical mechanisms, the amygdala in particular, have projections to most areas of the cortex, especially the frontal cortex, which allows those primary emotions to act fast on our consciousness. However, there are fewer effective projections from the prefrontal cortex to the amygdala. Thus, the emotional impulse is regulated rather slowly. Headache fears are quickly felt, but it is not easy to talk or think oneself out of excessive anxiety. In order to dampen overwhelming emotional responses, a detour needs to be taken. This transpires via frontal networks and our Action Systems, which involve focused training of adaptive and health-enhancing behaviours.

Emotional appraisal of headaches
Secondary, higher-level evaluations of bodily responses often take the form of worries about the state of the person's health and the immediate consequences of impediments caused by the headache.

Acute pain can feel like punishment. Most people will try anything to get away from feeling intense pain. Beyond the immediate fear linked to the acute pain experience, people with persistent headaches might develop complex emotional reactions. They fear the consequences of the pain, as well as the pain itself. For instance, the condition could hinder regular attendance at work. If taking time off is necessary, they might fear the negative judgement of employers and colleagues. Making lifestyle changes, such as adjusting a work schedule, can trigger assumptions about being stigmatised. While headaches and brain trauma symptoms can remain hidden, lifestyle changes or the use of compensatory aids make the disabilities visible to others. As a result, some people might be reluctant to engage in therapy tasks that are designed to promote necessary lifestyle adjustments.

On the other hand, relief from pain is an obvious positive reinforcer. Successful headache management optimises patients' well-being and this is a powerful motivational driver for the implementation of longer-term lifestyle changes.

Patients often refer to their pain as being inside their head. Pain severity might be understood as being directly linked with the severity of an assumed underlying cause, i.e., the worse the pain, the more dangerous must be an underlying brain illness, and, thus, the patient might fear that they could die. Despite reassurance, investigations and scan images, their expressed fears and health anxiety might not shift easily. In particular, patients who have been informed about potential secondary brain injuries might worry about a delayed bleed, a rupture of blood vessels or some other structural damage. Some people find it hard to trust their doctor and have continuing doubts as to whether or not a sinister brain disorder might have been over-looked. Additional investigations or frequent medical follow-ups are often demanded to satisfy the need for reassurance that their brain is functioning normally and that their personality has been preserved.

The term "brain injury" holds not only a stigma, but also the connotation that there might be something seriously wrong with the person. Humans apparently hold an archetypal fear that they will "lose their mind" or that they are "not right in the head." This is known as "dementophobia." People can fear a perceived change in their sense of self and worry that others might notice differences in their personality. The brain is the one organ that humans associate with the place where the "self" is located. The sense of self is probably the highest level of psychological integrity. The brain represents the organic substrate for all mental and emotional experiences and the sense of identity enables the individual to consciously reflect on these. Brain traumas lead to a disruption of the life story. Such events are perceived as catastrophic because they do not easily fit with the flow of normal experiences. Hence, trauma images and symptoms need to be modulated to enable a dynamic reshaping of the sense of identity. Most people have a strong dislike of change, particularly if it affects the core substance of the self.

Head pain can also act as a trigger for memories or flashbacks of the accident that might have threatened (or was believed to have threatened) the survival of the person. In this case, people fear that they are not safe in their environment or that an accident or attack might be imminent.

On a biological level, headache fear is maintained by recurrent activation of primary emotions linked with physiological arousal of the SAM (fight or flight), which is triggered by unpredictable headache episodes. Ongoing and persisting anxieties involve the HPA-axis and the release of corticoid stress hormones that are neutralised by the hippocampus, which has a large number of receptors for these. This means that the hippocampus is performing a double act as a key player in the stress systems as well as in the pain-processing and working memory pathways. Working memory disturbances are common in chronically distressed or traumatised people, resulting in perpetuation of emotional dysregulation and cognitive lapses. The strong association between pain, fear, cognitive processing of such emotions and stress demands to be a crucial feature of headache management. Decoupling the fear and stress responses from the pain enables patients to move a huge step closer to improved well-being.

Suffering with the headache is a longer-term consequence that indicates the helplessness of the individual. Commonly, people overcome adverse life events by reorganising their daily routines and by finding ways of solving any problems that might arise. What feels different and uncomfortable initially can eventually become the new reality and the new routine. Such adjustments prove particularly challenging for people with brain trauma due to the aforementioned cognitive weaknesses. Slowness in encoding new information and reduced learning ability also means that subtle changes in personal performance are not properly absorbed and recognised. Therefore, some people find it harder to be mindful of adjustments or compensatory strategies until mistakes are made. Impairments in the ability to think and plan ahead also make learning from mistakes difficult. Such lapses and the experience of personal dysfunction feel unfamiliar and attempts to overcome such situations often lead to a dead end.

Depression is a real risk factor that often contributes to the maintenance of headaches. The neuropsychological pattern of negative thinking and poor goal maintenance in depression may further aggravate brain trauma-related cognitive difficulties and cognitive elements of headache processing.

Irrational or rigid thinking patterns associated with depression can have a significant impact on the outcome of a headache programme based on psycho-education and health management. Patients trapped in helplessness might be blind to the exit routes demonstrated in a purely education-based programme.

Third-wave CBT approaches such as Acceptance and Commitment Therapy or Emotional Resilience Training guide patients to reflect on their strengths and flexibly re-evaluate their chronic headache condition and all its facets.

BEHAVIOURAL CONSEQUENCES

Naturally, headache sufferers will try anything they can to avoid pain. Short-term strategies, like taking painkillers, may lead to counter-productive, longer-term problems. Often people are unaware of how many ways their life has changed, as the headache can be all-consuming.

Behaviour therapy traditionally looks at the predispositions as well as the consequences of the problem and associated actions. Using a cognitive behavioural headache formulation, it is important to undertake a detailed analysis of behaviours leading to, and following, headache episodes.

Furthermore, the timelines of behaviour patterns developing from the headache onset require in-depth explorations. In cases of slowly emerging headache onset, patients may just be trying to continue with their daily lives in the hope that the headache might soon disappear again.

Rapid and intense headache onset often prompts behaviours concerned with immediate pain relief, such as taking medication, resting or total discontinuation of activity.

If headaches reoccur more frequently, patients begin to think ahead and try to avoid the pain occurring in the first place. The search for headache triggers becomes a new sport and a dominant topic in conversations. Such practices maintain self-defeating behavioural patterns, while the headache remains the centre of the person's life.

The driver for avoidance of activities is fear of anticipated pain and fear that any activity could result in pain. "Fear-based activity avoidance" is a maladaptive, but powerful, coping strategy, which maintains the chronicity of posttraumatic headaches and predicts long-term disability associated with it.

Pain, fear and stress also increase the irritability and aggression often reported by people experiencing post-concussion problems, which reflect the hyperactivity of the subcortical systems. Unfortunately, although social interaction and support are vital remedies for aggression-causing symptoms, aggressive responses can severely strain social bonds. Patients may feel trapped in this dilemma. They may sacrifice their longing for support and understanding and may regulate aggressive outbursts by further withdrawing from contact with others.

People also attempt to avoid overstimulation. They might have noticed that, due to information-overload and increased cognitive efforts, social commitments are challenging scenarios that can result in breaching the headache threshold. Patients might believe that recovery from brain trauma can only be achieved by resting a lot. They might try to cut back rigorously and reduce involvement in their usual roles and responsibilities. For some people, this might mean cutting working hours or even changing their career path if they perceive their job to be related to the worsening of their condition.

Avoidance and social withdrawal contribute to feelings of guilt, as patients predict that friends and colleagues might feel let down by them. Alternatively, headache patients might feel left out while others are perceived to be having a great time without them.

These are unpleasant experiences, potentially adding to subjective psychological stresses, and it is vital to take into account how, by withdrawing from activities, people de-skill themselves. People might "lose touch" with the practical aspects of day-to-day tasks. This can be very detrimental in view of the chances of recovery.

Following brain trauma, people often say, "I've lost my confidence," or "I want my confidence back." So, where has it gone? If we disengage from any activity, we lose familiarity with previously routine tasks. If headaches prevent people from meeting each other, from being involved with shared household chores or from participating at work or leisure clubs, then the familiarity with such tasks and activities becomes rapidly lost. Reinitiating them is often riddled with obstacles and uncertainty. Consequently, the person might choose to remain inactive and do nothing.

Opposite to fear-based activity avoidance are endurance coping strategies wherein people endeavour to "push through the pain," to "carry on regardless." Often such strategies are related to early acquired health beliefs. Some people may have been rewarded for being tough when they were younger. Alternatively, some claim to be proud for "never having been to a doctor in their life before." However, such statements may be made in an attempt to disguise the sense of shame, even guilt, and sometimes low confidence in facing a health professional and admitting that they have a problem like a troubling headache. It's important for the headache therapist to be mindful about the personal beliefs and coping styles associated with such endurance behaviours. People may attempt to distract themselves from the headache and persist with activities to the point of exhaustion. This can lead to a vicious "boom and bust" cycle. People "crash out" completely in such situations and require prolonged rest, which increases the sense of failure and symptoms of anxiety and depression. It's these intense psychological experiences that manifest and prolong the headache condition.

There might be some gains for patients in perpetuating their headaches. The scope of the head pain might be offset by the benefits of being looked after and the opportunity to avoid unpleasant activities. However, such gains may be short-lived. In the long run, feelings of exclusion, loss of involvement, jealousy, fear of stigmatisation and a loss of purpose may overshadow the situation. A newly established social dynamic may also be resistant to change as it involves other people, who might also benefit from the arrangements (at least, initially). Eventually, everyone who is part of the pain network might feel burdened by the situation as they become stuck in their dysfunctional social interactions.

One of the most crucial insights for headache therapists is to be aware how patients *become* their headaches by *doing* them most of the time. During and after headache episodes, they are concerned with immediate pain relief and pain monitoring. In headache-free periods, they are concerned with preventative measures, including medical appointments, stocking up on medicines or searching a wider range of resources for alternative remedies. Health behaviours, even if carried out in a proactive way, mean that the headache condition has become a main focus in the person's life. Headaches have developed a meaning and headache behaviours have significance.

SOCIAL CONSEQUENCES: SHARING THE PAIN

Belonging to a social group is a fundamental human desire. The fulfilment of the need for inclusion and attachment creates one of the most powerful stimulants for stress relief, which has the intrinsic potential to initiate healing and the restoration of physiological balances. The most effective therapeutic variables are built on the premise of empathetic unconditional understanding in order to facilitate personal growth.

We develop as human beings as part of families and social groups. Our sense of self develops through involvement with, and getting feedback from, our social environment. People shape their social environment by interacting with, and influencing, others.

The quality and shape of social networks and social support has been associated with longevity and expressions of numerous physical and psychological conditions or, if positive, health benefits.

All behaviour within a social context is a type of communication. Even passivity and withdrawal indicate an approach or attitude within a social situation.

Caregivers may at times be concerned about the development of sickness behaviour. In line with the discussed concept of stress theory, it is suggested that cumulative increases in allostatic load are embedded in the adaptive responses by the neurophysiological stress mechanisms. In order to promote resistance to the impact of trauma, sickness behaviour is understood to facilitate recovery. Similar to the responses displayed by mammals, sickness behaviour limits exploration, mating or hunting for food so that energy can be preserved and dangerous encounters can be avoided (i.e. further injuries prevented). However, prolonged sickness behaviour can become maladaptive. If posttraumatic headaches become persistent, the interplay of behaviours along with pain pathways, cognitive and mood variables and neurohormonal mechanisms complicates the behavioural conditioning or Central Sensitisation of the condition.

It is therefore important to consider the kind of social interactions along the timeline of a person who has experienced a brain trauma. The significance of the critical event in relation to an accident, assault, or other cause does intensely affect family and friends. On one hand, they may feel empathy and care for the person and, on the other, their lives likewise are suddenly disrupted. They might have had to be available to help initially (maybe for medical check-ups) and, later on, might have had to take over some responsibilities from the person.

The provision of care and nurture can elicit intensely pleasant feelings in some caregivers. Family members or work colleagues might seize the chance to take over control of longed-for responsibilities. Disrupted relationships and additional demands can lead to stress and illness in caregivers. In the long term, this could contribute to unhelpful dynamics, perpetuating headache behaviours and increasing the burden on caregivers.

Alternatively, significant others may have to keep their lives on hold until there is more certainty about recovery and, sometimes, they might have underestimated the challenges of living with a person with persistent headaches. Eventually, they are able to make practical adjustments to either carry on with their own lives or to restore the balance of shared responsibilities.

How everything is connected

This chapter has illustrated a range of formulation models, all aiming to facilitate the concept shift towards a perspective that recognises that all facets of the posttraumatic headache syndrome are interrelated in feedback and forward mechanisms, which mutually reinforce and influence each other. Many variables, before and after the mild brain trauma, contribute to the development of persistent posttraumatic headaches. There is no single identifiable cause. Network analysis – a research method for analysing and describing the range of connections between symptoms and the weight or importance of the links – has been applied to the mild brain trauma syndrome. This approach has been shown to have high therapeutic value as clinicians and patients try to come to grips with the interdependence of the impact of the trauma event, headaches, mood, personality, lifestyle, past and present.

Bibliography

Agorastos, A., Heiniga, A., Stiedl, O., Hager, T., Sommer, A., Müller, J. C., Schruers, K. R., Wiedemann, K., & Demiralay, C. (2019). Vagal effects of endocrine HPA axis challenges on resting autonomic activity assessed by heart rate variability measures in healthy humans. *Psychoneuroendocrinology, 102*: 196–203.

Bartsch, T., & Goadsby, P. J. (2003). The trigeminocervical complex and migraine: Current concepts and synthesis. *Current Pain Headache Report, 7*: 371–376.

Bendtsen, L. (2000). Central sensitization in tension-type headache – Possible pathophysiological mechanisms. *Cephalalgia, 20*: 486–508.

Borsook, D., Sava, S., & Becerra, L. (2010). The pain imaging revolution: Advancing pain into the 21st century. *Neuroscientist, 16*, 171–185.

Brosschot, J. F. (2002). Cognitive – Emotional sensitization and somatic health complaints. *Scandinavian Journal of Psychology, 43*: 113–121.

Bryant, R. (2011). Post-traumatic stress disorder vs traumatic brain injury. *Dialogues in Clinical Neuroscience, 13*: 251–262.

Christensen, M. B., Bendtsen, L. Ashina, M., & Jensen, R. (2005). Experimental induction of muscle tenderness and headache in in tension-type headache patients. *Cephalalgia, 25*(11): 1061–1067.

Cnossen, M. C., Winkler, E. A., Yue, J. K., Okonkwo, D. O., Valadka, A. B., Steyerberg, E. W., & Manley, G. T. (2017). Development of a prediction model for post-concussive symptoms following mild traumatic brain injury: A TRACK-TBI pilot study. *Journal of Neurotrauma, 34*(16): 2396–2409.

Crtichley, H. D., & Garfinkel, S. N. (2017). Interoception and emotion. *Current Opinion in Psychology, 17*: 7–14.

De Bellis, M. D. (2005). The psychology of neglect. *Child Maltreatement, 10*(2): 150–172.

Erickson, J. C., & Theeler, B. J. (2012). Post-traumatic headache. In: J. W. Tsao (Ed.), *Traumatic Brain Injury: A Clinician's Guide to Diagnosis, Management and Rehabilitation* (pp. 149–166). New York: Springer.

Fields, H. F. (1997). Pain modulation and headache. In: P. J. Goadsby & S. D. Silberstein (Eds.), *Headache (Blue Book of Practical Neurology)* (pp. 38–57). Boston, MA: Butterworth-Heinemann.

Ganzel, B. L., Morris, P. A., & Wethington, E. (2010). Allostasis and the human brain: Integrating models of stress from the social and life sciences. *Psychological Review, 117*(1): 134–174.

Gilkey, S. J., Ramadan, N. M., Aurora, T. K., & Welch, K. M. A. (1997). Cerebral blood flow in chronic post-traumatic headache. *Headache, 37*: 583–587.

Glaser, D. (2000). Child abuse and neglect and the brain: A review. *Journal of Child Psychology and Psychiatry, 41*(1): 97–116.

Goadsby, P. J., Holland, P. R., Martins-Oliveira, M., Hoffman, J., Schankin, C., & Akerman, S. (2017). Pathophysiology of migraine: A disorder of sensory processing. *Physiology Review, 97*: 553–622.

Ham, L. P., Andrasik, F., Packard, P. C., & Bundrick, C. M. (1994). Psychopathology in individuals with post-traumatic headache and other pain types. *Cephalalgia, 14*: 118–126.

ICD-11 Classification of Mental and Behavioural Disorders Diagnostic Criteria for Research. Geneva, World Health Organization, 2018.

International Headache Society (IHS) Headache Classification Committee. (2013). The international classification of headache disorders (3rd ed.) (beta version). *Cephalalgia, 33*(9): 629–808.

Iverson, G. L. (2019). Network analysis and precision rehabilitation for the post-concussion syndrome. *Frontiers in Neurology, 10*: 489.

Iverson, G. L., Lange, R. T., & Brooks, B. L., V.L. Ashton Rennison (2009). "Good old days" bias following mild traumatic brain injury. *Clinical Neuropsychologist, 24*(1):17–37.

Jacobs, B., Beems, T., Stulemeier, M., van Vugt, A. B., van der Vliet, T. M., Borm, G. F., & Vos, P. E. (2010). Outcome prediction in mild traumatic brain injury: Age and clinical variables are stronger than CT abnormalities. *Journal of Neurotrauma, 27*(4): 655–668.

Juruena, M. F. (2014). Early-life stress and HPA axis trigger recurrent adulthood depression. *Epilepsy Behaviour, 38*: 148–159.

Kay, T., Newman, B., Cavallo, M., Ezrachi, O., & Resnick, M. (1992). Toward a neuropsychological model of functional disability after mild traumatic brain injury. *Neuropsychology, 6*(4): 371–384.

Lambru, G., Castellini, P., Manzoni, G. C., & Torelli, P. (2010). Mode of occurrence of traumatic head injuries in male patients with cluster headache or migraine: Is there a connection with lifestyle? *Cephalalgia, 30*(12): 1502–1508.

Lambru, G., & Matharu, M. (2012). Traumatic head injury in cluster headache: Cause or effect? *Current Pain and Headache Reports, 16*: 162–169.

Langdon, R., & Taraman, S. (2018). Posttraumatic headache. *Pediatric Annals, 47*(2): e61–e68.

LaRocca, D. (2017). Molecular and functional biomarkers of mild traumatic brain injury. *Brain Injury, 31*(6): 899.

Lazarus, R. S., & Folkman, S. (1984). *Stress, Appraisal, and Coping.* New York: Springer.

LeDoux, J. (2003). *Synaptic Self. How Our Brains Become Who We Are* (2nd ed.). New York: Penguin.

Lucas, S., & Ahn, A. H. (2018). Posttraumatic headache: Classification by symptom-based clinical profiles. *Headache, 58*: 873–882.

MacFarlane, M. P., & Glenn, T. C. (2015). Neurochemical cascade of concussion. *Brain Injury, 29*(2): 139–153.

Martelli, M. F., Nicholson, K., & Zasler, N. D. (2013). Psychological assessment and management of post-traumatic pain. In: N. D. Zasler, D. I. Katz, & R. D. Zafonte (Eds.), *Brain Injury Medicine: Principles & Practice* (2nd ed.) (pp. 974–987). New York: Demos Medical.

Martelli, M. F., Zasler, N. D., Bender, M. C., & Nicholson, K. (2004). Psychological, neuropsychological, and medical considerations in assessments and management of pain. *Journal of Head Trauma Rehabilitation, 19*(1): 1–28.

McEwen, B. S. (1998). Stress, adaptation, and disease. Allostasis and allostatic load. *Annals of the New York Academy of Sciences, 840*(1): 33–44.

McEwen, B. S., & Gianaros, P. J. (2011). Stress- and Allostasis-induced brain plasticity. *Annual Review of Medicine, 62*: 431–445.

Melzack, R., (2001). Pain and neuromatrix in the brain. *Journal of Dental Education, 65*: 1378–1382.

Melzack, R., & Wall, P. D. (1965). Pain mechanisms: A new theory. *Science, 150*(3699): 971–979.

Melzack, R., & Wall, P. D. (1983). *The Challenge of Pain*. New York: Basic Books.

Mullally, W. J. (2017). Concussion. *The American Journal of Medicine, 130*: 885–892.

Neut, D., Fily, A., Cuvellier, J.-C., & Valleé, L. (2012). The prevalence of triggers in paediatric migraine: A questionnaire study in 102 children and adolescents. *Journal of Headache and Pain, 13*(1): 61–65.

Packard, R. C., & Ham, L. P. (1994). Post-traumatic headache. *Journal of Neuropsychiatry and Clinical Neurosciences, 6*: 229–236.

Packard, R. C., & Ham, L. P. (1997). Pathogenesis of post-traumatic headache and migraine: A common pathway? *Headache, 37*: 142–152.

Pick, S., Goldstein, L. H., Perez, D., & Nicholson, T. R. (2019). Emotional processing in functional neurological disorder: A review, biopsychosocial model and research agenda. *Journal of Neurology, Neurosurgery, and Psychiatry*, 90: 704–711.

Pielsticker, A., Haag, G., Zaudig, M., & Lautenbacher, S., (2005). Impairment of pain inhibition in chronic tension-type headache. *Pain, 118*: 215–223.

Polinder, S., Cnossen, M. C., Real, R. G. L. Covic, A., Gorbunova, A., Voormolen, D. C., Master, C. L., Haagsma, J. A., Diaz-Arrastia, R., & von Steinbuechel, N. (2018). A Multidimensional Approach to Post-concussion Symptoms in Mild Traumatic Brain Injury. *Frontiers in Neurology, 9*: 1113.

Read, S., & Grundy, E. (2012). *Allostatic Load – A Challenge to Measure Multisystem Physiological Dysregulation*. National Centre for Research Methods. NCRM Working Paper.

Recommendations for diagnosing a mild traumatic brain injury: A National Academy of Neuropsychologyeducation paper. *Archives of Clinical Neuropsychology, 24*: 3–10.

Roozenbeek, B., Maas, A. I. R., & Menon, D. K. (2013). Changing patterns in the epidemiology of traumatic brain injury. *Nature Reviews Neurology, 9*: 231–236.

Ruff, R. M., Iverson, G. L., Barth, J. T., Bush, S. S. & Broshek D. K. (2009). Saper, J. R. (2000). Post-traumatic headache: A neurobehavioural disorder. *Archives of Neurology, 57*(12): 1776–1778.

Sapolsky, R. M. (2003). Stress and plasticity in the limbic system. *Neurochemical Research, 28*(11): 1735–1742.

Sapolsky, R. M., Romero, L. M., & Munck, A. U. (2000). How do glucocorticoids influence stress responses? Integrating permissive, suppressive, stimulatory, and preparatory actions. *Endocrine Reviews, 21*: 55–89.

Schipper, S., Riederer, F., Sándor, P. S., & Gantenbein, A. R. (2012). Acute confusional migraine: Our knowledge to date. *Expert Review of Neurotherapeutics, 12*(3): 307–314.

Selye, H. (1952). *The Story of the Adaptation Syndrome.* Montreal: ACTA.

Selye, H. (1956). *The Stress of Life.* New York: McGraw-Hill.

Sharp, D. J., & Jenkins, P. O. (2015). Concussion is confusing us all. *Practical Neurology, 15*(3): 172–186.

Silverberg, N. D., Martin, P., & Panenka, W. J. (2019). Headache trigger sensitivity and avoidance after mild traumatic brain injury. *Journal of Neurotrauma, 36*(10): 1544–1550.

Silverberg, N. D., Panenka, W. J., & Iverson, G. L. (2017). Cogniphobia in mild traumatic brain injury. *Journal of Neurotrauma, 34*(13): 2141–2146.

Silverberg, N. D., Panenka, W. J., & Iverson, G. L. (2018). Fear avoidance and clinical outcomes from mild traumatic brain injury. *Journal of Neurotrauma, 35*, 1864–1873.

Solomon, S. (2009). Post-traumatic headache: Commentary: An overview. *Headache, 49*: 112–1115.

Stratakis, C. A., & Chrousos, G. P. (1995). Neuroendocrinology and pathophysiology of the stress system. *Annals of the New York Academy of Sciences, 771*: 1–18.

Teasdale, G., & Jennett, B. (1974). Assessment of coma and impaired consciousness: A practical scale. *The Lancet, 2*(7872): 81–84.

Ursin, H. (1997). Sensitization, somatization, and subjective health complaints. *International Journal of Behavioural Medicine, 4*(2): 105–116.

Valet, M., Sprenger, T., Boecker, H., Willoch, F., Rummeny, E., Conrad, B., Erhard, P., & Tolle, T. R. (2004). Distraction modulates connectivity of the cingulo-frontal cortex and the midbrain during pain. An fMRI analysis. *Pain, 109*: 399–408.

Webb, T. S., Whitehead, C. R., Wells, T. S., Gore, R. K., & Otte, C. N. (2015). Neurologically-related sequelae associated with mild traumatic brain injury. *Brain Injury, 29*(4): 430–437.

Werner, C., & Engelhard, K. (2007). Pathophysiology of traumatic brain injury. *British Journal of Anaesthesia, 99*(1): 4–9.

Whittaker, R., Kemp, S., & House, K. (2007). Illness perception and outcome in mild head injury: A longitudinal study. *Journal of Neurological and Neurosurgical Psychiatry, 78*: 644–646.

Willer, B., & Leddy, J. J. (2006). Management of concussion and postconcussion syndrome. *Current Treatment Options in Neurology, 8*: 415–426.

Wood, R. L. (2004). Understanding the 'miserable minority': A diathesis stress paradigm for post-concussional syndrome. *Brain Injury, 18*(11): 1135–1153.

Young, J. E., Klosko, J. S., & Weishaar, M. E. (2003). *Schema Therapy: A Practitioner's Guide.* New York: Guilford Press.

Zasler, N. D., & Etheredge, S. (2019). Post-concussive headache. In: B. Eapen, & D. Cifu (Eds.), *Concussion: Assessment, Management and Rehabilitation* (pp. 59–75). New York: Elsevier.

Zasler, N. D., Katz, D. I., & Zafonte R. D. (Eds.) (2013). *Brain Injury Medicine: Principles & Practice* (2nd ed.). New York: Demos Medical.

Zasler, N. D., Leddy, J. J., Etheredge, S., & Martelli, M. F. (2019). Post-traumatic headache. In: J. M. Silver, T. W. McAllister, & D. Arciniegas (Eds.), *Textbook of Traumatic Brain Injury* (3rd ed., pp. 471–490). Washington, DC: American Psychiatric Publishing, Inc.

Zasler, N. D., Martelli, M., & Jordan B. (2019). Post-concussive headache. In: J. Victoroff & E. Bigler (Eds.), *Textbook of Concussion and Traumatic Encephalopathy* (pp. 728–742). Cambridge: Cambridge University Press.

Chapter 2

Implementation of a practical biopsychosocial approach

Introduction

What does the headache patient want from their clinician? The obvious answer would be pain relief, and the common assumption is that this can be achieved with a prescription of pain medication.

Research has found out, however, that most patients rather want information about self-management that offers them control over their own health in the long term. Psycho-education has, indeed, proven to be effective in prophylaxis and treatment for persistent post-concussion problems.

In addition to the informative approach, interventions should enable patients to be actively involved in a process that should, apart from pain reduction, aim at improvements of quality of life and psychosocial functioning, as well as the long-term reduction of disability. The emphasis is on a graded return to regular activity. This prevents secondary mood disorders and the prolonging of post-concussion symptoms. Graded and guided activity maintains skills and restores mastery. These are prerequisites for a confident return to previous roles and responsibilities. Enriched environments involving cognitive and physical stimulation also encourage neurophysiological recovery.

Cognitive behavioural programmes that target persistent post-concussion symptoms and posttraumatic headaches in that way showed that patients can achieve substantial improvements in their quality of life and can reduce their symptoms.

The educational component of a biopsychosocial approach in headache therapy cannot be overemphasised. The person with brain trauma wants to understand the interwoven brain and behaviour pathways, the functioning of the nervous system, the physiology of stress, cognitive and emotional processing and the influence of social interactions. In particular, patients need to be made aware of the vicious circle of pain, whereby the headache causes emotional (fear, helplessness, etc.) and physical (tension) symptoms and leads to inappropriate coping (avoidance, endurance, etc.), which eventually perpetuates the condition. Once patients share the understanding of how all such factors contribute to their headache condition, they are easily motivated to engage in a cognitive behavioural intervention.

Integrative biopsychosocial therapies recognise that persistent health problems are the result of long-term maladaptive dynamics between the body and the environment. The argument here is not about the superiority of one treatment model over another, but, rather, about the necessity of a paradigm shift towards holistic approaches so that the health condition can be understood in its entirety.

Assessment guidance

Getting to know the patient and their headache

So, what does the patient actually know about their headache? How have they understood their doctors? How do they explain the fact that their medication does not help? The patient has had plenty of opportunities to reflect on the causes of the headache and the maintaining factors since the initial injury, headache onset and referral to the headache therapist. It is crucial for the therapist not only to be aware of the referral journey, but also of the understanding that patients have about their own health, what they deem useful in helping themselves and where they have failed in their self-care.

The patient's primary concern is the health of their head. Medical specialists will have undertaken investigations and will have concluded that structural and organic changes can either be excluded or that the mild brain trauma has settled and does not effectively explain persistent headaches. Patients who have been successfully treated with medication are rarely referred to a psychological headache programme.

Initially, patients might be suspicious about meeting a non-medical headache therapist. At times, they can express the feeling that their doctor is passing on responsibility; they might fear being diagnosed with a mental illness or might simply see the headache therapist as a cheaper (and less qualified) medical practitioner. It is, thus, very helpful to begin an assessment by asking the patient what they know about the referral and what their doctor has explained about the purpose of the headache therapy. On the same note, it is essential to share with the patient what a biopsychosocial and cognitive behavioural headache treatment is all about and how it fits with their expectations.

We all process our life experiences in ways that enable us to create a continuous story. The coherence of one's sense of self is created by the constant evaluation of the stream of events passing through one's consciousness. We emphasise certain experiences by means of cognitive and emotional reflections, while less relevant or inconsistent information moves to the outskirts of our mental representations. In this way, we create a consistent framework of our life that steers us through the various experiences we encounter.

Events resulting in brain trauma and persistent posttraumatic headaches cause a disruption to the otherwise apparent smooth flow of life, as we perceive it. The coherence of events may need to be re-created in hindsight in order to get across what might be incomprehensible and non-chronological.

The patient might not have paid attention to certain symptoms at a certain time. They might have tried to find a reason for the accident or a link to the circumstances, even though there was no causal association. Responsibility of the individual for the onset of symptoms, the setting situation or, indeed, the accident itself might be either over- or underemphasised. In a consultation with a therapist, patients face the dilemma of wanting to present themselves in a way that preserves their personal integrity, while at the same time asking for help with a headache problem. Furthermore, patients might initially assume that their headaches can be dealt with in isolation from their life history or social setting, and that disclosure of additional very private information might not be required (e.g., undisclosed alcohol abuse, marital conflict, issues in the workplace, debt). The belief that headaches can be treated as a separate medical symptom is also linked with a patient's hope that their former sense of self can be quickly restored and that the bumps in their life journey can be smoothed out.

The key reason behind why a patient attends a headache clinic and why they want to interact with a therapist is because they are in pain. Initially they understand this to be a purely medical symptom. The headache therapist needs to meet the patient at this stage in order to form an interactive collaboration. As part of this, it is imperative to encourage the patient to describe their headaches in as much detail as necessary, which would be similar to a medical setting.

The patient's headache, a *subjective* experience, therefore, is at the heart of the investigation. A discussion of headache factors such as the type, location, frequency or intensity of the headache is an attempt to objectively describe a very individual pain experience.

Nevertheless, there are some reasons why it is useful to attend to specific headache characteristics. The headache therapist must be absolutely sure that underlying neurological causes (e.g., tumour, hydrocephalus, infections, haemorrhages or other medical problems) are either very well controlled or can be excluded. In this regard, the therapist is reliant on medical reports and good communication with treating specialists.

Furthermore, detailed headache characteristics are useful outcome variables within the therapy. Patients do like to know how they are progressing and clear feedback can be powerful in reinforcing their motivations.

Readiness for change

The headache therapist may have great plans for the patient, but there is no guarantee that the biopsychosocial approach can substantially reduce their pain. The therapist will guide the patients to look after themselves in a healthier way so as to enable the lifting of the headache burden. Crucially, patients must reclaim those headache-free periods that have been spoiled by intrusive thoughts and restrictive headache behaviours.

Patients' readiness for engagement with, and adherence to, therapy can be described with the Transtheoretical model of Change. The stages of this process – precontemplation, contemplation, preparation, action and maintenance – each require specific therapeutic strategies. The paradigm shift from pre-contemplation to contemplation has two facets in the headache therapy.

First, the patient comes to realise that lasting changes regarding their headache experience require a shift from the expectation of being medically, and therefore passively, treated towards a personal engagement and the practice of self-management strategies.

Even cultural issues may shed some light on how people process, communicate and deal with their headaches. For instance, the role of medical practitioners is perceived very differently in different cultures or social groups. Patients from traditional cultures might tend to prefer the advice of doctors and expect a medical cure or medicine. If patients feel reluctant to trust a psychosocial approach, then the explanation and justification of such an approach might need to form part of the engagement process.

Litigation and compensation-seeking is considered to be a serious obstacle to therapeutic engagement. Patients may find themselves in an entrenched conflict between the desire to improve their symptoms and the need to find satisfaction in the defence of their rights (see example Susan).

Second, the patient has to acknowledge how the brain trauma, the headaches and past and present circumstances are woven together with their physical systems, their personal styles and the complexity of secondary symptoms. Headache therapy might touch on a number of intimate experiences that may also have to be considered if the patient wants to succeed.

The therapeutic relationship and emerging psychosocial themes are meant to offer the patient a new perspective. Carl Roger's therapeutic variables (congruence, empathy, respect) are crucial in enabling the patient to trust the support of their therapist. This authentic rapport appears to be one of the most powerful mechanisms in aiding the patient in the healing their pain and letting go of fears and maladaptive coping practices. If a social interaction is perceived as supportive and comfortable, the neural circuits actively inhibit the alarm system and dampen immediate defensive behaviours. The presence of a trusted person, the development of a bond and social engagement facilitates the soothing of pain-fear responses, which, in turn, enhances a sense of safety and the de-escalation of neurophysiological stress. These are the neuro-social components of a healing therapeutic relationship.

Even though patients may request information first of all, a therapy programme should not be seen as merely an educational curriculum. Giving patients knowledge and information does not enable them to rearrange their lifestyles independently and in such a way that their quality of life and health can be automatically improved. Long-term behavioural change depends on the empathy, encouraging guidance and support from a clinician who is an expert in the field.

Example: Nick

What happens if a patient is not yet ready for such a therapeutic approach?

Nick was in his late fifties. His doctor had heard about the headache therapy programme and was convinced that he deserved relief after 18 years of suffering headaches and other symptoms. As it had been such a long time since the car accident associated with these symptoms, it was difficult for the specialist to establish whether or not the symptoms were related with a brain trauma. The hope was that the holistic headache therapy would complement previous medical treatments, as they had not achieved the desired pain relief for this man. Nick eventually attended the headache clinic on doctor's orders. He presented many additional physical problems – he used a walking stick, experienced tinnitus, had sleep problems and severe daytime fatigue and struggled with an unreliable memory.

He participated in the clinical interview and described a long list of headache symptoms and headache events that made going to work and providing for his wife impossible. He felt that in the aftermath of the accident he had ruined the life of his wife as he was aware of the burden he had been for her. Despite this, he had not made any healthy changes in his lifestyle since the accident and had resigned himself to being on incapacity benefits. The interview and questionnaire outcomes revealed that he frequently did not following simple common sense guidance regarding healthy behaviour. Nevertheless, he described the headaches as torture. He said that he had been sentenced to suffer such pain as a form of punishment because he had caused his injury by having driven his car irresponsibly.

It was clear from listening to the way he told his story that he was not ready yet to let go of his "deserved" punishment. He had given himself a life sentence and said that that period was not yet over. He described how he expected his suffering to last for at least 25 years. There was no point in any health professional offering support and relief. He did not feel that he deserved it, because deep inside he was convinced that he had not yet suffered enough. He agreed to meet with the therapist again at another time, when the self-imposed life sentence had been served – in seven years.

Posttraumatic headache and legal scenarios

Persistent post-concussion symptoms following an accident or assault often result in legal disputes. Researchers are divided in their findings whether the pursuit of legal compensation has a substantial impact on the individual's experience and reporting of symptoms.

Clinically, it is important to be mindful of whether or not a patient has initiated a legal claim to compensate for the headache and other injury-related symptoms that might have prevented them from returning to their former responsibilities. Initial headache assessments might have pointed out such socio-environmental factors like compensation-seeking.

Patients who participate in headache therapy at the same time as engaging in a legal procedure might be hindered in exploring their predispositions and settings around their mild trauma and headache-maintaining interactions. Their own participation in proactive headache management requires a lot of personal effort, which they might not be willing to apply if someone else can be blamed.

Some people in certain circumstances may chose short-term gains, and legal compensation may be perceived as offering immediate and powerful rewards in the form of:

- retaliation against whoever is perceived to have caused the loss of health
- proof as to who is in the right and who is to blame
- lifting of stigma and easing of guilt and shame
- expectation that a financial pay-out will compensate for persisting symptoms and distress
- hope that normality and health can be restored.

Nevertheless, legal procedures are often complicated and take a long time. Commonly, they reinforce trauma experiences or other personal challenges, thereby hindering desensitisation, which all adds to the stress levels of headache patients. These dynamics happen in a non-therapeutic environment that risks the manifestation of maladaptive coping and loss of control, as the case is out of their hands.

Example: Susan

Susan was a 76-year-old lady. One day, while shopping in her local supermarket, she tripped and fell backwards on her head. Her husband discovered a small grape under her shoe and showed it to the staff at the supermarket. The assumption was that Susan had slipped on the grape, which had caused her fall.

Susan described her experience after the fall in the following way. She fell flat on her back without having been able to save herself. She did not lose consciousness. While still on the floor, she screamed for help and suddenly felt very cold and began shivering badly. She was taken to the local accident and emergency department and admitted to hospital for full investigations.

Assessment of onset scenario: Susan contacted a solicitor and engaged in a claim against the supermarket. As part of that process, she saw a medico-legal expert to provide evidence of her injury and persisting posttraumatic headaches.

She described the onset of extremely severe headaches immediately after the fall. Apparently, these continued for a number of weeks, if not months. She truly believed that she had torn a nerve or blood vessel. She was convinced that she would cause further damage if she slept on the back of her head, which had become very hypersensitive. She did not dare to wash her hair and was extremely cautious with a hairbrush.

She reported a number of cognitive disturbances, such as concentration problems while reading and short-term memory problems. These required her to write many lists as aides memoires.

Susan mentioned the distress involved in attending appointments and meetings with her solicitor. She said that she felt very unwell with her headaches, so that she was not able to travel to all meetings. This was associated with her fear of walking outdoors. Therefore, she was no longer able to accompany her husband on outings to London and visits to the museums, as in the past. Nevertheless, she undertook a number of trips to their property in Spain during the litigation period. She said that she felt most sorry for her husband, as she was no longer able to properly fulfil her role as his wife.

Medical information: An MRI scan following her fall showed lacunar infarcts and small vessel disease. One or two additional lesions were noted within the deep white matter of the brain and cerebellum. One tiny haemorrhage was noted in the right frontal lobe. The most plausible explanation for the latter incidental finding was subclinical hypertensive haemorrhage.

Her health history included mentions of other episodes of falls prior to the event in the supermarket. A range of entries highlighted her difficulties in coping with life events and, when she was younger, problems in managing her demands at work. There was an indication that her long-standing concentration problems and ongoing stomach illness were linked to chronic stress.

Predispositions: Susan seemed to present a range of early vulnerabilities including long-term stomach problems, hypertension, psychosocial challenges at work, sensitivity to stress symptoms and suspected vascular dementia.

Setting: Susan appeared unaware of the vascular changes happening in her brain, but might have experienced increasing concentration and short-term memory lapses. These worried her as they reminded her of past situations when she had struggled to cope at work. She had experienced her past "mental breakdown" as a personal failure. The compensation claim offered her the opportunity to project her symptoms into an objective framework and, thus, enabled her to divert from her perceived personal weaknesses.

Did Susan really "try it on" to gain some financial reward? It can be assumed that she genuinely believed that her past nervous constitution and physical vulnerabilities were unrelated to the symptoms that unfolded after her fall.

Symptom dynamic: Susan held the genuine belief that she had caused a serious blood vessel rupture or nerve injury and so avoided touching her head. As a result, she did not habituate to her symptoms and did not experience her bruise healing. Constant worrying possibly aggravated her physical tension, which might have maintained the peripheral sensitivity, which was then perceived as headache. Her underlying vascular dementia might have limited rational reflections about her intrusive worries. Her anxiety and intense arousal fuelled her avoidance of walking outdoors and fear of falls. Hypervigilance and attention to the risk of potential falls reduced the capacity of her working memory and concentration functions, thus limiting her cognitive potential even further and closing the vicious cycle.

Additionally, Susan seemed sensitive to social performance pressure and to her ability to meet the expectations of her husband. She described regret that she made her husband unhappy by not engaging in their previously enjoyed pleasures.

Interpretation: It appeared that the fall in the supermarket was unconsciously utilised by Susan to associate her health anxieties with the critical event. The "grape under her shoe" created an objective scene that allowed her to project her headaches, cognitive weaknesses and fears.

The litigation procedure reinforced Susan's and her husband's misattribution of her difficulties to a head injury. They missed the opportunity to understand and reflect on the meaning of the underlying onset of dementia in the context of a long-standing stress disorder.

Clinical interview

The psychosocial interview provides a tool for establishing a solid understanding of the headache condition with a view to planning the headache intervention.

The clinical interview is a qualitative method to obtain information about the health condition in the context of the personal history.

The cognitive behavioural approach is applied from a life history as well as from a current "cross-sectional" perspective. This means that the cognitive, behavioural, emotional and context variables of the headaches and their impact are of equal value as the early or past experiences relating to health and psychosocial aspects of the individual.

As will be highlighted in the case examples that follow, it is crucial to investigate:

- all headache and post-concussion variables
- early psychological and social (i.e., family) history in reference to the development of the headache disorder
- early health (including pain) and social vulnerabilities
- past stress-related, critical or traumatic events
- available life skills, personal efficacy and emotional robustness as well as
- health-damaging maladaptive habits such as smoking, poor diet, reduced activity or poor sleep hygiene.

The intention of the first interview is to listen fully and have time for the patient, to validate their suffering, to investigate coping behaviours that will be targets for later therapy and to obtain explicit examples of the headache symptoms (see Headache Interview).

Empathetic listening is a primary therapeutic variable that actually facilitates healing. Patients have a great need to offload their burden. Their significant others might have tried to be very supportive, but it's the skilled practitioner who can best catalyse a shift towards understanding alternative headache attributions and health behaviours. The interview has, therefore, systemic components as well. It disentangles the headaches from the tight association with the onset event and places it in a reframed context of a life story. The headache therapist must therefore have a good knowledge of headaches as a clinical condition, as a brain trauma-induced problem and as a biopsychosocial condition embedded in the person's history.

As mentioned above, the first interview also serves the purpose of engaging the patient. As the example of Nick illustrates, not every patient who attends the initial meeting is ready to give up his or her headaches. Apart from assessing the patient's readiness for change, it is also important to explore their existing abilities and resources for committing to a therapeutic process. The assessment of psychological variables, especially personal attitudes and coping styles, can provide crucial insights into such abilities and resources. Patients might have dealt successfully with challenges in the past, but might no longer have the same resources available. Some might have overused coping strategies, whereas others might have overlooked how their coping style has become counter-productive or why they have not benefited from previous interventions.

Psychological headache investigations can be thoroughly planned if the patient can share a few detailed examples of their headache experiences. These can be analysed using the cognitive behavioural formulation, which concludes with demonstrations of exit routes out of vicious circles and habitual responses. Additionally, detailed information about the pain experience allows the measuring of changes and the monitoring of therapy successes. In cases where the pain worsens, or there is a suspicion that there might be organic reasons for the pain, the therapist must discuss those observed changes with medical colleagues.

A CBT-based, semi-structured interview investigating antecedents, headache symptoms and behaviours associated with posttraumatic headaches is introduced in Chapter 3.

Example: John

John, aged 32, was referred with severe headaches following an industrial accident. He was not very well educated and worked as a refuse collector. He had acquired his injury from being hit by some heavy machinery. He had experienced mild brain trauma and had felt disorientated for a couple of days after the accident. Two to three weeks later, he developed severe headaches, spreading across his forehead and straining his eyes. This affected his work performance. Blurred vision and dizziness accompanied the headaches. As the firm he worked for had to investigate liability in this case, he was referred by his occupational health officer.

John described a severe psychological reaction to the headaches. He said that he felt badly depressed; he was not able to cope with the headaches at all and had suicidal thoughts. Although he still attempted to go to work, this drained all his energy so that he required the rest of the evening to recover. As a result, he was unable to undertake household chores and food preparation, so he had to return to living with his elderly parents.

Such presentations describe the intense and life-consuming consequences of a mild brain trauma in the context of a person with reduced premorbid personal efficacy and resilience. Unexpectedly, the interview about John's health and lifestyle revealed that he consumed between 25 and 28 cups of coffee per day. As a result, he experienced a number of physiological disturbances. He was not able to sleep most nights. Further explorations revealed that John was extremely traumatised by the experience. This was related to his lost sense of orientation and his incoherent recollection of events over the two days following his accident. John did not understand what concussion and mild brain trauma were about. The mild short-term memory lapses and word-finding problems troubled him as they reminded him of his school days when he had been bullied for being stupid. He worried extensively about the functioning of his body and mind. He became hyper-observant during the daytime, as he was determined to make sure that he remained alert and in control at all times.

Most of all, he was afraid of going to sleep out of fear that he might not wake up again. In order to stay alert during the day, he consumed very large amounts of coffee and in order to remain awake during the night, he drank even more coffee.

This example illustrates a number of elements. John reported his headaches as the most noticeable and troubling symptom to his doctor. The doctor concluded that these fit into the model of post-concussion syndrome. The change of interpretation by the headache therapist came about by investigating John's history and headache coping behaviours, but also by being mindful of one other essential detail, i.e., his excessive caffeine intake. However, the coffee consumption was also a secondary component. John did not comprehend the meaning of his symptoms. The uncertainties he faced triggered his fundamental fear of loss of control. He worried that being absent-minded or even going to sleep would re-trigger the experience of disorientation. At the core of his anxieties were his early experiences of being bullied and outcast from his social groups at school.

The combination of these elements led to hyper-vigilance and physical tension. This had most likely irritated his trigemino-cervical complex, which resulted in the described face and head pain.

His therapy plan focused on disentangling these misattributions and helping him comprehend his experience. Central to his therapy was the practice of relaxation strategies, reduction of coffee consumption and the building of resilience. It further included confidence enhancing support to enable him to learn that most of life's situations can be mastered even in cases of uncertainty or diminished control.

Psychometrics and questionnaires

There is good evidence about the effectiveness of questionnaire administration in obtaining essential headache information. According to research, patients might even be more likely to accurately report their symptoms on questionnaires rather than in clinical interviews. Questionnaire items may prompt patients about symptoms they might have forgotten to mention in an interview. Some people may feel shy during an interview and worry about inadequate verbal interactional skills, anxieties or misunderstandings.

Headaches are subjective symptoms. It is not possible to objectively quantify pain experiences with scans or tests. Nevertheless, questionnaires and rating scales may give the patient a chance to rate the headache according to the way it feels to them. Self-report questionnaires enable the clinician to cover a number of questions in an efficient way. The results and scores on subscales and individual items can be compared with interview responses; discrepancies can be highlighted and explored at the appropriate point in therapy.

The most obvious reason for using questionnaires and headache rating scales is the ability to utilise them as statistical outcome measures and the opportunity they provide to compare individual patients against available normative data. When choosing questionnaires, it is important to understand their qualities (e.g., theoretical underpinning and psychometric properties) and respondents' variables (e.g., expectation bias, symptom exaggeration). The type of questionnaires must, of course, fit with the therapy methods and aims.

Numerous pain and health questionnaires are available. Nevertheless, there are few, if any, specifically designed and validated for headaches after mild brain trauma. Clinicians shouldn't let this stop them from administering a well-chosen selection of self-report measures (see examples in Chapter 3).

The practical administration of assessments requires careful planning. The therapist and the patient are engaged in an interaction where both need something from each other. The patient needs understanding and pain relief, while the therapist requires detailed personal and health information in order to formulate and plan the therapy.

Throughout this process, the patient requires support in the form of empathetic encouragement, practical teaching and cognitive support. For instance, they might find it hard to concentrate for the length of time that is required to complete questionnaires. They might have trouble reading due to blurred vision or slowed language processing or they might worry that concentrating on the questionnaire gives them a headache. Guidance during the questionnaire administration can improve the compliance with their completion. The purpose of the measure can be explained. Questionnaires can also be administered verbally in the form of facilitated interviews. Instructions may be repeated, rephrased or broken down. The advantage of a supported questionnaire administration is that the patient does not feel left alone with this tedious task; they can be guided if they do not find the right box to tick or don't comprehend an item. In cases of ambivalence, the administrator can explore in detail what the patient means with their response. Supported questionnaire administration also ensures that it is the patient who gives the answers and not their caregiver.

For all these reasons, it might be helpful to book separate sessions for the administration of lengthy questionnaires.

Psychometric questionnaires are not only vital assessment tools, but also have immediate therapeutic value. Patients like receiving clear feedback about their scores and the meaning of assessment outcomes. This allows for a fresh and more distanced perspective on their condition and might help disentangle headache symptoms from other contributing factors.

Observation methods

Observations find their use in headache assessments and as therapeutic strategies. Methods include recording headache episodes and variables in diaries, on monitoring sheets, on analogue pain scales or in mobile apps. Diaries have their place in monitoring patterns regarding onset and length of headache episode, frequency and/or intensity. Such records enable the systematic comparison of changes in pain sensations and benefit patients with additional attention and memory problems. Analogue ratings of headache can be completed very quickly and can be combined with ratings of emotional distress and coping abilities.

Headache observations within interventions enhance symptom awareness, challenge inaccurate illness perceptions and provide positive reinforcement of therapy participation. Patients learn to monitor their headaches in a controlled way during the symptom-focused stage in therapy. Planned monitoring can counteract the preoccupation with intrusive headache worries and other inappropriate headache behaviours. Weekly reviews of observed headache symptoms disentangle them from behavioural and contextual variables and provide direction for therapeutic tasks.

A combination of monitoring headache symptoms and psychological variables fits with the lifestyle focus of the therapy, which promotes a shift towards the observation and recording of well-being activities and the modification of inappropriate behaviours.

The therapeutic benefit of headache diaries was evidenced in research that showed that migraine patients who recorded therapy activities as well as migraine episodes experienced greater reduction of symptoms than those who participated in therapy without monitoring their outcomes.

Headache experiences and health improving activities can be recorded using event sampling or interval sampling methods. The event sampling method involves the recording of all target episodes and activities within a defined observation period. For instance, all headache episodes occurring during a day or week are sampled. The interval sampling method enables monitoring of headache episodes within a regular time frame. For instance, headaches or activities are monitored intermittently for an hour each morning and afternoon. This allows the patient to have time off from monitoring tasks. Additionally, this method can establish gaps between headache episodes, which has value for therapeutic reflections (e.g., understand what the person did during pain-free times).

The use of structured headache observations and ratings should be part of the comprehensive assessment at the start of the individual programme, at the review and in follow-up sessions.

The therapy philosophy shifts eventually from an initial focus on the pain towards a focus on values in life and purposeful activities. The recording of those activities that orientate the patients towards their health values and improvements in their quality of life will eventually replace the observation of headache problems.

Headache monitoring or observation methods need to be practised prior to sending the patient home with instructions to carry them out. As with all strategies, patients should be encouraged to use recording devices they are familiar with (i.e., pen and pencil versus digital tools). This can also help avoid information-processing overload.

Assessment case examples

Headache setting

Example: Sean

There is never the right moment to have an adverse life event.

Sean was involved in a motorcycle accident just as his wife was due to give birth to their first child. As a result of the subsequent moderate brain trauma, he had to spend some time in the hospital. Obviously, he was most impatiently awaiting his discharge. However, his initial weeks at home turned out to be an ordeal. He felt guilty for having been absent during the birth and worried that he had abandoned his wife. He also had missed the first few days with his baby and the transition to becoming a father had been very abrupt. He felt useless at home as he was unable to get a grasp on his new responsibilities as quickly as he felt he should. Although he tried as hard as he could to be involved, he had to give in eventually due to feeling completely exhausted. The emotional pressure as well as the daily demands were believed to have contributed to the onset of his severe tension headaches.

Therapist's notes: Sean had participated in neuro-cognitive assessments at his local brain trauma clinic. The reports indicated some slowness in his speed of information-processing and reduced working memory. Sean's family setting confronted him with completely new responsibilities and very different routines. It was suggested that the headaches developed due to the unusual demands on his organisational skills whilst his neurophysiological systems were still settling down, as expected in the early stages after a brain trauma. His headache therapy involved simplifying and structuring his daily tasks alongside the implementation of pacing strategies and regular relaxation practice. The latter also optimised his mental focus. His wife realised that she could not fully rely on Sean's support during his recovery and arranged for help with childcare and the housework.

Example: Rebecca

Rebecca was hit by a taxi when was attempting to cross a road during her last term at university. She managed to complete her course with good results, but experienced a severe migraine attack upon starting her first job. As a result, she had to leave early that day. A couple of months later she experienced a further severe attack at a party where she witnessed a fight. More frequent migraine attacks followed, which, at the time of her headache appointments, completely controlled whether she was able to work or not.

Therapist's notes: Rebecca went through a vulnerable stage in life towards the end of her degree. She was substantially more stressed about obtaining her degree and taking up her first job. Noting the similarity to Sean's situation, one might also wonder whether the added pressures of forthcoming life challenges increase absent-mindedness that might result in people getting involved in accidents. The accelerated stress responses were most likely related to the onset of Rebecca's first migraine episode. Her ongoing worries about her work performance created vicious cycles, which were also represented by her self-defeating thinking. The Central Sensitisation theory comes to mind here, which probably led to increased vigilance of migraine symptoms. These appeared to be conditioned to events triggering fearful anticipation of danger or performance failure.

Headaches and secondary consequences

Example: Sofia

Sofia experienced a mild brain trauma due to a car accident. Additionally, she sustained physical injuries. She participated in residential rehabilitation to work on mobility and to improve her practical functioning, for example, getting dressed and preparing meals. During this time, her husband sorted out her finances and, in checking her credit card account, discovered a large amount of debt. However, Sofia claimed that she could not remember anything concerning the debt and said that the questions she faced from her husband caused her to have very bad headaches and sleepless nights.

Therapist's notes: The substantial marital dispute linked to the debt situation became a public scenario during her rehabilitation. It later surfaced that Sofia had been responsible for the car accident and that the victims had lost their car as a result. Therapeutic meetings that included Sofia and her husband revealed that the financial arguments served as a projection of her husband's anger and mistrust towards her. She found her guilt too much to bear and felt helplessly trapped in an unsupportive relationship. Her tension headaches were likely related to the pressures of attending to the financial aftermath of her accident. Moreover, they seemed to be maintained so she could describe herself as the victim – of her headaches – which diverted her self-blame and guilt.

Headache maintenance

Example: Connor

Connor, a 25-year-old man, was referred to the headache therapist by his neurologist. He complained about constant headaches that had begun around the time he had taken his GCSEs. His history seemed very vague and he gave very little detail about his upbringing or present activities. He was on social benefits at the time of the assessment and did not reveal what he had done in the years following school. He complained about long-term ill health associated with chronic migraines and fatigue. He had apparently sustained a mild brain trauma less than a year prior to his consultation. Questionnaire outcomes revealed very high scores for the experience of physical and headache problems, as well as depression symptoms. He complained about constant low energy and severe fatigue. Connor described how he had fallen from a ladder when he was attending to the house's gutters. He said that his injuries had intensified his head pain. The only way he was able to cope with them was to stay in his darkened bedroom most of the time. He took medication to prevent migraines and smoked marijuana during acute attacks. He knew of no other helpful coping strategy. He rarely left the house, but said that he was at ease in social situations.

It was very difficult to engage Connor in any kind of exploration of his headaches and current circumstances. He appeared very distant and flat emotionally. The therapist, in trying to engage him in a creative dialogue, asked the "miracle question" – that is, what he would do if the headaches suddenly disappeared? His face lit up and he said that this would be so wonderful. He would invite all his friends and throw a huge beach party. In order to elaborate on this image that had obviously sparked some reaction, he was asked about the details of this possible party: where exactly it would be, what time of day it would take place, what type of entertainment it would involve and who would be invited. As he had used the phrase "all my friends" earlier, he was asked about these friends, who they were, what they meant to him and what they had in common. It turned out that Connor had no friends, not a single one, and that even if the headaches disappeared, there would not be a party. He would not be able to tell anyone about it and it would not make a difference after all whether he stayed in bed all day or got up, because there was no one to care about him. The headache was all he had. The headache was his only loyal companion.

Therapist's notes: It was concluded that Connor's headaches had very little to do with the experience of his brain trauma. The long-standing headache was connected to his depression and withdrawal from almost all activities, including social ones. His therapy plan focused on overcoming his social isolation and searching for a purpose in his life.

Example: Brian

Brian was a middle-aged engineer hoping to retire in a few years. He had been injured as a pedestrian in a "hit and run" accident. He responded with extreme anger towards the drunken youngsters who had gotten away with a stolen car. Although he had only experienced minor head and physical injuries, he was suffering emotionally due to the unfairness of the accident.

Furthermore, he felt he was entitled to compensation, but, owing to the absence of good witnesses, litigation attempts had been unsuccessful. The additional distress had contributed to memory and concentration problems, disturbed sleep patterns and, unsurprisingly, recurrent tension headaches. Furthermore, he had experienced panic attacks when walking outside and soon developed agoraphobia. As he began avoiding leaving the house, he became depressed. He had received help from a psychiatrist to some extent, but his anger had not subsided. The anger and his headaches soon developed a reciprocal relationship. Angry outbursts triggered by daily hassles generated headaches. Headaches reminded him about the unfairness of his accident and triggered angry outbursts. In trying to distance himself from the experience and escape from the severe distress, he went to stay on his own in his French holiday home. Soon after his arrival there, he experienced a heart attack.

Therapist's notes: It had been difficult for Brian to adjust to the experienced unfairness. His health deteriorated significantly, eventually resulting in a heart attack that further caused an anoxic brain injury. At this point, Brian was referred to a psychologist for a thorough assessment. The anger–headache dynamic appeared to have trapped him and prevented him from moving on. It also surfaced that this scenario enabled him to avoid involvement with other major life decisions. He had delayed taking early retirement, which caused financial problems. He avoided making decisions about his properties in England and France, which caused significant marital disputes. Having his headache was a good excuse to avoid facing his responsibilities. However, it hurt, a lot.

Interpretation of assessment outcomes

The assessment outcomes and background information can be summarised and interpreted in combination with an understanding of the development of posttraumatic headaches.

The cognitive behavioural model also offers a practical method for organising assessment findings, and examples are the "cognitive behavioural headache formulation" in Figure 1.11, the *mild brain trauma worksheet* or indeed the headache report.

The psychological interpretation or clinical formulation of headaches provides the basis for the feedback discussion with the patient. The worksheet *my headache formulation* could be used or, indeed, could one of the biopsychosocial formulations introduced in Chapter 1. The formulation allows structure and engages the patient, as it interprets their head pain from different perspectives whilst making sense in their individual day-to-day experiences.

The feedback and formulation session is very important for the patient, as it outlines the direction of their therapy. It should be a planned separate session (or two) after the completion of all initial assessments and prior to the commencement of the therapy.

Patients experience great benefit from detailed discussions of assessment findings, the description of the dynamics between headache symptoms, health behaviours and social reinforcers. Some may achieve a high level of insight from this and may be able to carry on with their health management independently. Patients can be encouraged to return for follow-up reviews or further psycho-education "boosters." In that sense, the feedback and formulation session can be understood as a stand-alone intervention. This approach is implemented in headache clinics for people with mild brain trauma.

Referring specialists and family doctors also benefit from the formulation and related recommendations as it allows them to offer appropriate support in their own reviews with the patient.

The interpretation provides an opportunity for the therapist to guide the patient through the transition from a medical to a health management and lifestyle approach. At the point of formulating the headaches in their dynamic interaction with all biopsychosocial components, both the therapist and the patient can become really creative. Examples of this are illustrated in the presented cases.

Interpretation – headaches and the meaning of life

Example: Harry

Harry developed chronic tension headaches following a sports accident during the second term of his final year at university.

Handover information: Harry had sustained a concussion as the result of a rugby scrum. He said that he could not remember much about the actual event or what had happened immediately afterwards. He was told that he had been confused for a number of minutes at the scene, but regained orientation when he was moved to the first-aid room. He was taken to the Accident and Emergency department and, following investigations and checks, was discharged with a leaflet explaining the consequences of mild traumatic brain injury.

Harry felt reassured by the staff at the emergency department and, following a weekend at home during which his parents looked after him, he returned to university. The days following that apparently went by in a haze and he felt emotionally disconnected. He explained that he had been a very ambitious student, but suddenly he was unconcerned about his final exams. Nevertheless, he forced himself to focus on his studies and research in preparation for his final exams, which were a few weeks later.

At the start of the exam period, he experienced a sudden onset of severe headaches. He described intense pain spreading from his ears and up to his temples. He described that the headaches, once they started, would remain all day and keep him awake at night so that he found it hard to get up in the morning to resume his exam preparations. He said that the headache episodes had carried on throughout the exam period. Due to his endurance attitude he completed his course as one of the top students despite the severity of his headaches and his lack of enthusiasm.

He was nevertheless thrilled about receiving an immediate job offer as a geologist. He was interested in this well-paid job, which would take him on field studies in the African desert. In the hope that the headaches might eventually disappear, he took up the new challenge. He lasted five weeks working in the desert under extreme conditions. Eventually, the headaches, aggravated by the heat and sleep problems, made it impossible for him to continue. He took sickness leave and returned to England in the hope of "sorting his head out."

He was in significant pain and very worried that the initial injury had caused further damage, which he had made worse by exposing himself to extreme conditions. On one hand, he became very worried about his health and, on the other, he did not want to risk losing his well-paid job.

The handover medical report indicated that Harry had possibly sustained a concussion initially.

Many months after this initial event, upon his return to the UK, he underwent thorough neurological examinations and scans to investigate the underlying cause for his headaches. The investigations did not reveal any physical injuries. His medication was changed and he took part in physiotherapy. However, neither the medication nor the physiotherapy treatment had any positive effect. Eventually, his doctor referred Harry to a headache specialist.

Harry demanded a "quick fix" from therapy. It was uncertain whether he would want to engage with an integrative self-management approach. Harry was informed during the interview that the assessment outcomes were intended to help plan for a CBT-based headache programme. He was told that this would require attendance at the health centre and, following the assessments, participation in eight to nine sessions. Harry firmly explained that he did not have that much time available. He said that he was not able to concentrate in the suggested sessions in addition to the car journey, due to his constant pain. He decided to decline to participate in headache therapy for people with mild brain trauma.

Two months later, Harry called again. He described the intensity of his daily headaches and added that he had not been able to return to work as he had planned. He was at the point where he wanted to "try anything" to get better. He agreed to an assessment of his headaches and coping styles.

During this, he elaborated on his story, which revealed patterns that enabled a better understanding of the underlying mechanisms of his symptoms.

Predispositions: When Harry was young, he was sent to a private junior school. He vividly described the Victorian manner of the matron at the school, who had a firm, shrill voice that scared everyone out of bed in the morning.

It appeared that his traditional family expectations were about good education and it had been expected that he would deliver good results. He struggled at school due to his dyslexia. He had seen specialists in the past and had undergone special tuition. His dyslexia presented him with minor information-processing and mental flexibility weaknesses. This vulnerability was challenged by academic demands mentally and possibly also physically due to neck and eye strain whilst focusing on written tasks. Knowing that he could not stand out academically he transferred his ambitions to sports. However, the types of sport he had chosen included swimming – mainly breaststroke – and rock climbing, which aggravated his vulnerability to neck strain. Harry's lack of academic ambitions was further contrasted in his brother, who was very hard working, had studied music at a prestigious university and had achieved high professional rewards.

Owing to the lack of a better idea about what to do in his life, he followed the advice of a family member and decided to study geology. He assumed this would be a less rigorous academic subject as well as quite practical. Nevertheless, his studying involved reading, research and writing reports. These tasks exposed him to the weakest of his abilities and he managed to avoid them as much as he could throughout his course. However, his exams required writing and the research included significant reading. During the period of intensive final studying he had sustained his concussion, which set off his chronic headaches. Luckily, his competitiveness and endurance coping strategy helped him "push through" and finish as one of the top students. Harry had also hoped that the headaches had simply been aggravated by the demands of his final studies and exams and would eventually disappear.

Setting: The therapist also learnt that Harry had been in a long-term and serious relationship during his time at university. His girlfriend's mother had died due to cancer shortly before his rugby accident. During those difficult times, he had supported his girlfriend emotionally and had spent much time with her and her family. However, not long after the mother's death, the girl ended the relationship, having found a different partner. This coincided with the beginning of Harry's examination period.

Around when Harry called the headache therapist for a second time, his ex-girlfriend had made contact again, which was not welcome. She had requested a restoration of their friendship, but not their intimate relationship. Thoughts about his ex-girlfriend, the emotional investment he had made and the pain of the separation intruded into Harry's mind constantly.

He went through some extraordinary turmoil during his time on sickness leave. He experienced daily headaches and felt trapped and helpless because his attempts to relieve the pain had not worked. He tried forcing himself to think about his future, but often stayed in bed for most of the day.

He complained that he was unable to get up without his mother screaming at him. He said that he saw no purpose in his life and wondered if he really wanted to be a geologist. In his fantasies, he saw himself being some sort of craftsman, manufacturing beautiful luxury items. The sickness episode created feelings of uselessness and despair as he was under pressure to resume a career that he seemed cut-out for but one he was unsure about.

Onset: Harry's vulnerabilities seemed to have added up all around the same time. He was dyslexic, had an adversity to being pressurised and was exposed to university exams. The rugby accident possibly also caused neck and shoulder bruising along with a concussion, and the emotional intensity related to the break-up with his girlfriend was probably the "final straw."

Harry had strained all his resources in order to succeed in his course and to get his lucrative job. His working conditions had proved to be hostile to his health and aggravated his headaches.

Interpretation of lifestyle consequences: This case story sounds surprising in the sense that the concussion and head trauma seemed not to be part of Harry's worries at all. He was more concerned about other areas in his life that had longer-lasting and more severe consequences for his emotional well-being and self-esteem (e.g., the break-up of his relationship, the fear of losing his job, questions about his chosen career, overcoming perceived weaknesses). However, the accident-related headache onset, probably exaggerated by exam stress, required therapeutic attention now.

Personality: The strong theme about having been sent to a boarding school to be looked after by a nasty matron and feeling the need to conform to ambitious family expectations raised questions about Harry's core personality pattern. He completed the Young Schema Questionnaire and the analysis revealed schemas such as "Fear of rejection," "Unrelenting standards" and "Self-sacrifice." It appeared that he conformed to his family's unrelenting expectations, because their values were familiar to him and, by complying, he had achieved their support.

The headaches finally made it impossible for him to follow the path laid out for him. The associated social and emotional pressures increased his tension and distress.

The headaches, nevertheless, had a message for him. They kept him away from a life he did not want to lead.

His therapy proceeded with an exploration of his values and a practical search for solutions regarding the next steps to take towards becoming a skilled craftsman.

The above case examples illustrate how engaging with patients can reveal surprising insights, as the dynamic components and trajectory of posttraumatic headaches are better understood. For the therapy, this means that, besides the focus on headache management, there may be other factors that need to be addressed as well if a lasting reduction of pain and distress is to be envisaged.

Interpretation – persisting headaches due to maladaptive personal style and avoidance behaviour

The psychological presentation of a person develops during their upbringing. Interaction patterns that evolved out of a family history and also early vulnerabilities shape the psychological factors that may either help or hinder adjustments to be made after a critical event such as a mild brain trauma. Examples are the already explored "good old days" bias, cogniphobia, avoidance or endurance behaviour, fear of a certain diagnosis or health-based locus of control. Over and above these are more rigid and stable personality characteristics that are associated with a vulnerability to posttraumatic headaches and also with persistent challenges to adjust and overcome the symptoms. Examples for these include traits related to high sensitivity towards anxiety and neuroticism, alexithymia, strong trends towards perfectionism, egocentricity, disagreeableness, unconscientiousness and a whole catalogue of negative affective and socially problematic personality styles such as narcissistic, histrionic, dependent or passive-aggressive (see example Anthony).

Interpretation of headaches – a complex functional presentation

---

Example: Alice

Alice was a lady in her mid-fifties who had been a victim of a pedestrian accident.

Handover information: Alice saw a medical specialist for head trauma as she continued to experience extreme headaches four years after the event. Medical investigations ruled out structural or organic lesions. As the initial medical history pointed to a complex presentation, she was referred to the headache clinic.

Headache assessments: During the clinical interview, Alice mentioned her headaches most of all. She said that she had not experienced headaches prior to her accident, although she had had a range of health problems in the past.

Her posttraumatic headaches emerged about two to three weeks after the event, some days after she had returned to work. She described almost daily episodes with a slow onset of head pain, which affected the temple areas of both sides of her head. A sense of tightness would eventually spread around her head so that it felt like a ring was strangulating her brain. This sensation caused her substantial anxiety that her brain might suffocate and she often experienced "black-outs." At this point, she would be unable to carry on with what she had been doing and would have to leave work and take a rest. Usually, she regained some control over her physical functioning after some hours.

Alice also described a number of body pains that affected her sleep. She mentioned hyper-arousal interfering with her concentration abilities and slowed information-processing functions, which seemed related to mild acquired dyslexia. She said that she tended to misspell words when she was under time pressure. Apparently, such experiences had increased since the accident.

As a result, her daily activities became much more difficult to master than in the past. She felt that her strong endurance and survival spirit had been broken.

She also experienced balance problems and the sudden onset of severe fatigue with the urge to close her eyes immediately. Tiredness was a constant problem and sleep had not helped her to feel refreshed.

Her results on a health screening questionnaire, the SF-36, indicated that she perceived herself to have a very low quality of health overall and, specifically, in the domains of physical and emotional role-functioning. She considered her health to have deteriorated over the previous year and she reported substantial levels of head pain. Interestingly, her score in the mental health domain was the highest. She desperately tried to keep her spirits up.

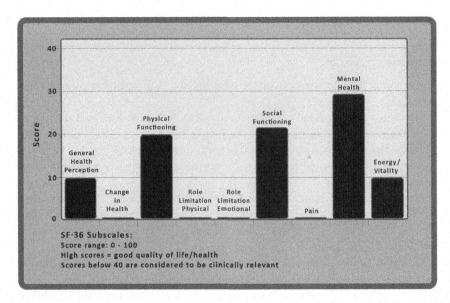

Figure 2.1 Alice's health-focused quality of life outcomes on the SF-36.

Predispositions and physical vulnerabilities: Alice had experienced severe asthma as a baby and child. She mentioned that she had to be hospitalised several times due to life-threatening lung failure. She described how her father had supported her as a child by teaching her techniques to cope with asthma attacks and the associated panic.

With her father's support she managed to control her panic and learned how to slow down her breathing, which calmed her so much that she was even able to join a fencing club and participate in swimming events as a teenager.

Alice described how she had become dependent on her father's coaching and had worried whether she would survive an episode when he was absent; for instance, when he had to go to work and she attended school.

Nevertheless, her health was also compromised in several other ways. Beginning at the age of 11 and continuing into adulthood, she suffered unusually intense menstrual pains. She had experienced a complicated miscarriage that had required hospitalisation in her mid-twenties. It was also discovered that she had endometriosis, as well as ongoing gynaecological and urological symptoms.

Attachment vulnerabilities: Alice experienced a challenging upbringing. Insights into her background put her childhood illnesses in perspective and help to understand her chronic problems, including the posttraumatic headaches.

Her parents divorced when she was at junior school and she was sent to live with her mother. Although, her father had been supportive with regards to Alice's lung problem, he was an alcoholic and was often an unreliable parent.

A few years later, her mother remarried and she gained a step-sister with whom she didn't get on. It appeared that the onset of her menstruation pains coincided with this life episode.

Even though she had stayed with her mother since the divorce, she actually did not spend much time with her. She recalled that she did her homework on her own and had to prepare her own food in the evening. Her mother worked away and was busy with her new partner. She remembered that she felt alone a lot. Most of all, she worried about her health and her survival of asthma and panic attacks, as she had lost the close support of her father.

When she was about 12, she openly expressed that she wanted to be with her father again. This resulted in a very traumatic court case during which she witnessed her father being escorted away in handcuffs. Apparently, her father had attempted to meet her during a break in the legal proceedings. As this was against the rules, he had been forcefully removed. She recalled how traumatic this had been for her as this had been the last time she had seen him for a long time. Alice's mother was from Brazil. It sounded as if there was always a threat that Alice might be removed from her home and taken to Brazil permanently.

Eventually, when Alice was a young teenager, she somehow managed to obtain her own solicitor and achieved permission to live with her father.

However, as a result of this, her mother developed stalking behaviours and continued to follow her against court orders. Her mother had tried to meet her at her school, which apparently scared Alice dramatically due to her fear of being taken to Brazil, and she suffered ongoing nightmares as a result. Such scenarios severely affected her mental health and she attempted to take her own life. As part of the mental health risk management, she was placed with an uncle. However, at his house, she again had to look after herself and was on her own mostly. Alice described her uncle as a reclusive person, who might even have been depressed. Both of them were socially isolated.

Eventually and by applying her endurance attitudes, she finished college and found work as a waitress. Still a teenager, she decided to move away from her unhealthy family environment. She met her first partner, but unfortunately the relationship turned violent and ended in divorce in her mid-twenties, soon after her miscarriage.

Personal style: Alice had lost her father's protection when she was very young and was made to live with a mother who appeared to have personality problems. Alice became highly determined in order to survive neglect and uncertainty. The ongoing strain and effort, however, further challenged her already vulnerable health. Each time she struggled with another health problem or family issue, she adopted a "be strong against the odds" and "I will do it no matter what" attitude and sought a proactive solution. However, she never showed her struggles or her emotional fragility to others. Holding her head up high was also meant to show her family that she was not easily defeated.

Setting: Earlier in the year, prior to the accident, Alice had experienced additional family stresses that she described as the "straw that broke the camel's back." She had been required to support two terminally ill distant relatives, which required overnight visits and presence at several hospital admissions. Eventually, in order to rest and optimise her sleep, she decided to take a holiday with a female friend. The accident happened as she was unloading her heavy suitcase from her taxi and she was run over as she crossed the road towards her hotel. Alice had very vivid memories about the accident. She described the scene in fine details, including light and sound effects, and as if in slow motion. She knew exactly how her body was positioned as she was pulled away from the middle of the road. It became apparent that she had experienced symptoms of posttraumatic stress and she had been highly vigilant in busy environments for a long time afterwards. Due to this overwhelming experience, she felt constantly nervous and scared, which re-ignited her fears of recurring asthma and panic attacks. She perceived the breakdown of her emotional resilience as a setback of her coping and adjustment ability, which led to feelings of depression and frustration.

Alice had been checked over during her Accident and Emergency admission after the accident. Luckily, she had not sustained any major injuries and was discharged the following day. However, having felt severely shaken and bruised, she and her friend decided to abandon the holiday. She returned home and used her leave period to recover. Immediately following that, she returned to work. Due to shame and a sense of failed coping ability, she did not reveal to her colleagues what had happened to her. Soon after commencing her work, she developed severe headaches. Her office job began to challenge her concentration and mental processing abilities, which were already fragile, in association with her PTSD and past traumatic experiences. This and the stress following the accident added to her reduced physical functioning overall. She mentioned flair-ups of stomach pains, which affected her sleep as well. In the past, she had had a range of abdominal problems and recently she had associated her stomach pain with intolerance of certain foods.

Following the accident, Alice filed a legal claim, which was still ongoing at the time of her visit to the headache clinic and which kept re-igniting the trauma for years after the event.

Interpretation of lifestyle consequences: This case clearly illustrates the diathesis of added layers of early vulnerabilities and adversities and the allostatic load on Alice's psychophysiological stress systems, still failing to maintain her body's integrity.

Alice experienced a head injury resulting in post-concussion and post-traumatic stress symptoms. The circumstances of her accident seemed highly distressing, but she escaped without serious head injuries. In straightforward cases, such injuries would resolve within a short period of time.

Alice's situation highlights that the headache, although a severe and key symptom, represented only a small part of her complicated long-term condition. Alice had reflected on her history in the assessment session and it became quite clear that she had good insight into the interdependence of her health and upbringing and how this made her more sensitive to adjusting to an additional adverse and traumatic event.

Initially, she interpreted her ongoing headache symptoms, black-outs, sleep disturbances and fatigue, fears and cognitive weaknesses as a failure to apply her endurance and survival strategies. However, as her situation continued to persist over several years, they offered her a chance to find health management methods she had never tried before. She was also fortunate to have met a very understanding and supportive partner in the meantime. They planned to move in together. This enabled her to let her own house to tenants and resign from her job. She said that she envisaged exploring a completely different way of life and wanted to try courses in photography or even train as a mindfulness coach. She said that she felt that her whole life had been about overcoming adversities and she wanted to take an opportunity now to engage in something that was more focused on creativity and well-being.

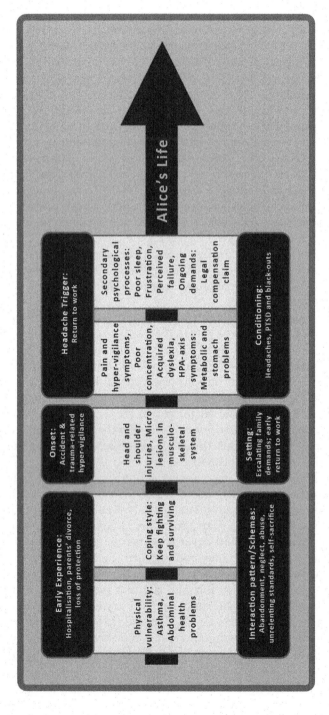

Figure 2.2 Example Alice: complex functional presentation and headaches.

From a psychophysiological point of view, her case falls within the biopsychosocial explanations of complex functional disorders. It can be described by applying the Allostasis model and adding theories about the neurobiology of attachment disorders. Right from her childhood, her body was required to adjust to severe violations of her safety. All her early symptoms, lung condition, gynaecological problems and mood disorder may be linked to neurobiological features adjusting to attachment violations. Her personal determination and intelligence helped her survive highly adverse social environments. Nevertheless, her endurance strategies challenged her stress systems further.

As an adult, she had developed a high level of insight into her condition and had made further attempts to balance her lifestyle. Just at the moment when she had wanted to mitigate additional stress by taking a holiday, she had an accident. This represented a huge setback for her and she struggled to recover.

Yet again, the persistent problems, especially the headaches that were so severe that they caused her to black-out, helped her take a different turn and change her lifestyle for the better. She benefitted from a shared exploration of the biopsychosocial approach and was reassured that neither her head nor her brain had been severely injured in the accident. She explored her new lifestyle vision with the headache specialist. She was excited to direct her focus to activities that would really make her feel well and comfortable. The range of her proactive ideas included:

- Relaxation and pacing herself: she had acquired material about relaxation and coping and used the *Headspace* app.
- Friends and family: she was a sociable person and instead of cancelling most of her social gatherings, she made arrangements to meet friends more often on a one-to-one basis. She enjoyed quality time with her best friends. As the meetings were shorter in duration, she also found them more manageable.
- "Me" time: Alice was surprised how she felt really spoilt when she visited a nail technician. She noticed that being treated kindly and surrendering to the care of another made a real difference to her well-being.
- Home and financial: Alice and her new partner moved in together. This not only strengthened their bond, but also reduced the amount of activities she had to undertake when she used to live in both their households. Financially, she was better off as she managed the income from her tenants wisely. This enabled her to resign from work and explore new opportunities.
- Diet: Alice planned to see a dietician to relieve her stomach symptoms.
- Fitness: she was going to return to swimming, Pilates and mindfulness.

This seems like a long list of good intentions. Hopefully, Alice can apply her proactive and positive outlook and enjoy the support of her partner to achieve better health outcomes and well-being after all.

Cognitive behavioural headache therapy

Headache service within an integrated health organisation

Modern healthcare is embedded in a network of local health services that collaborate with each other. Clinics for people with posttraumatic headaches can probably be found in Accident and Emergency departments, or in brain trauma rehabilitation or pain management centres.

Hence, it seems important for the clinicians working in interlinked departments to share an agreed treatment philosophy. This is often grounded in the term "rehabilitation." The World Health Organisation (WHO) model for rehabilitation also applies the classification of functioning, disability and health to headache disorders. This means that headache conditions are given the same attention by health and rehabilitation services as any other condition (Figure 2.3). Most importantly, the WHO's description of rehabilitation needs has eliminated the distinction between conditions with an established pathology and those caused by environmental factors, cognitive/ emotional disturbances or stress. It is acknowledged that people's presenting problems are associated with multiple factors, of which physical pathology might be just one.

The cognitive behavioural formulation for posttraumatic headaches appears to fit perfectly into this WHO rehabilitation model. Starting with the description of the health problem, this approach moves through a process that focuses, first, on the physical problems, then on the implementation of therapeutic activities and, finally, on participation in meaningful roles. The components of a health condition such as headaches and mild brain trauma, as well as past and present personal and environmental factors, determine the type of rehabilitation activity and the direction of adaptive lifestyle changes. Such a framework is helpful in easing the communication of patients' progress between involved doctors, headache therapists, linked support services and, of course, the patients themselves.

An integrated and networked healthcare system can mean that patients with posttraumatic headaches may work with a range of specialists during their journey from injury to well-being. Programmes for people with posttraumatic headaches may be an integral part of a brain trauma or pain management service. The therapy components – assessment, formulation and intervention – may be offered in one-off headache clinics and/or headache therapy alongside other rehabilitation programmes. They may involve individual and group work and could include the patient's family.

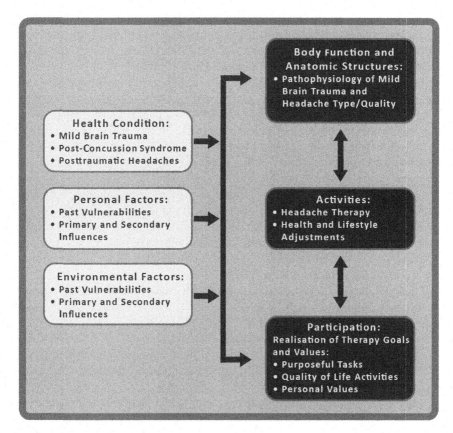

Figure 2.3 World Health Organisation model applied to headache therapy.

Focus shift in headache therapy

The overall intention of headache therapy is to optimise physical well-being and proactive coping in order to enable participation in meaningful life activities.

The psychotherapeutic elements of this approach aim to reduce physiological stress experiences in order to increase the pain threshold and resilience. Cognitive-behaviour therapy has been shown to optimise psychosocial stress-related conditions and benefit overlapping neural pain mechanisms.

Specifically, the interventions for posttraumatic headaches must focus on pain avoidance behaviour and the reduction of headache fear and distress. These two components are the main drivers for the condition persisting. CBT offers numerous methods and strategies to help a person address these issues as part of their pain management.

Most patients desire a reduction of headache intensity, duration and frequency, most of all. As mentioned above already, a number of associated variables, such as reduced self-efficacy, maladaptive social patterns, and difficulties with personal organisation and life skills in the widest sense, emerge from the comprehensive headache assessments.

The course of adjustment following a mild brain trauma often runs from an initial focus on medical management and physical recovery, followed by a "wait and see" or "it might get better on its own" period, to a stage when patients notice that their headaches have started to rule their lives and they then feel desperate for help. Just like Harry in our example, people are keen to reinitiate contact with the headache service when their own attempts to cope have been exhausted or have failed.

In the meantime, they may have found ways of achieving short-term headache relief, either using medication and by avoiding potential triggers and mental or physical activities. Such short-lived strategies do not lead to substantial and lasting improvements. If underlying mechanisms are not addressed, then a deterioration of the health condition is likely to occur, at a huge cost to the person (and the health service).

The CBT-based biopsychosocial approach to headache treatments addresses three main areas and goals:

- headache focus: reduction of headache parameters
- coping focus: acceptance of vulnerabilities, management of headache-related anxiety and depression, optimisation of health behaviours, improvement of coping styles
- lifestyle and social focus: improvement of headache-related psychosocial interactions, realisation of purposeful activities and core life values.

The course of the therapeutic interaction begins with assessments and the establishment of robust and positive pain coping styles. After this, it moves swiftly to the therapeutic activities, addressing headache-maintaining, secondary psychological variables and underlying drivers and patterns that have prevented the patient from leading a satisfying and healthy life. The shift away from headache as a medical symptom towards personal life aims and values is a main theme of biopsychosocial therapy (Figure 2.4). This approach is grounded in research about chronic brain–body disorders that seem to be driven by the aforementioned allostatic imbalance. Physical activity and social interactions are, therefore, vital in achieving reductions in stress and pain.

CBT in combination with tailored creative therapeutic strategies is a method for leading patients along the journey from symptom to lifestyle management.

Headache specialists in trauma or brain injury units may come from various professional backgrounds, for example, they may be counsellors,

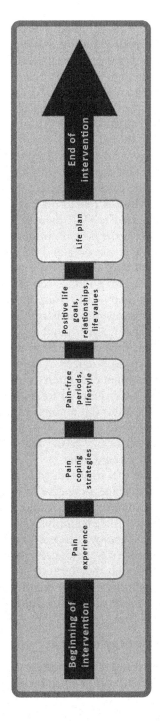

Figure 2.4 Shift of therapy focus throughout the course of the headache therapy.

nurses, physiotherapists, occupational therapists, doctors, psychologists, or psychotherapists. A well-coordinated package includes medication management, physio- and exercise therapy, diet programmes, pain management techniques, fatigue management, vocational and life-skills orientated rehabilitation. Headache therapists are advocates of such types of integrated health therapy, which is further shaped by the recovery from mild brain trauma.

Perhaps the majority of patients with posttraumatic headache only need to attend a one-off session at the headache clinic in order to understand and initiate the shift from focussing on the headache towards lifestyle changes.

A significant minority, however, present with long-term and complicated health and life scenarios. Some people affected in this way can be more reluctant to let go of their expectation of remaining a passive recipient of medical treatments. Patients are required to shift their belief that they have purely medical problems, which are in the domain of doctors, to an acceptance of the fact that their own health experiences and behaviours contribute to and manifest their headache condition. Eventually, they understand and participate in guided interventions that are, in fact, self-management approaches.

This belief shift requires two main components. First, it entails patients' own psychological components, such as the stable cognitive patterns representing the personal identity. An attempt to alter such patterns, even in therapy, temporarily weakens the person's sense of identity. The accident or injury may already have been experienced as traumatic. People talk about their "shattered self." This is often evaluated as a threat to the integrity of the personality and people have the urge to reconstruct their former self quickly. This means that a substantial amount of courage, self-confidence and a safe therapeutic setting are needed for someone to shape their new learnings about the condition into a more dynamic identity, whilst also taking up positive and healthy behaviours.

Second, the shift of focus in therapy needs to be encouraged by a clinician who can role-model and encourage a creative way of rebuilding someone's life. The therapist may need to be mindful of where in the "change process" the patient is and may have to utilise techniques to optimise motivation.

In practice, this means that therapy exercises, explorations of emotion and behaviour, pain and task monitoring, etc. need to be negotiated with each patient as they have to realise that they need to put in the work themselves. Reluctant patients may benefit from highly creative therapeutic methods to tap into their very personal "make-up" and to ignite the readiness for change.

Cognitive behavioural therapy methods

The following section illustrates how common cognitive and behaviour therapy methods can be applied within a headache programme.

The diagram "Headaches after Mild Brain Trauma" serves as template for matching psychosocial headache symptoms with suitable therapy methods.

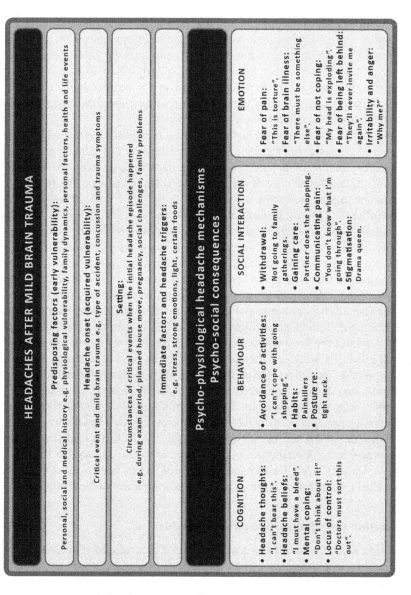

Figure 2.5 Headaches after mild brain trauma.

Headache therapy would be easier if pain processing could be separated from psychological processing. The headache itself could be more directly managed if one could regulate heightened distress, anxious worrying and behavioural preoccupation separately from the pain or its consequences. However, these processes are neurophysiologically fused together. For instance, the anticipation, the experience of adversity and headache worry, as well as mental preparation for expected pain altogether, drive the stress or allostatic processes, which prolong the condition.

Pain signals a potential threat to survival. Overriding the Central Sensitisation and encouraging relearning, de-conditioning and central reorganisation takes time, practice and, as already mentioned, dedication. Therapy aims and methods need to be clear and structured in order to modulate ingrained headache pathways.

In parallel to the management of secondary stress, the person with headaches learns to acknowledge and re-evaluate pain sensations, which can open up opportunities for positive coping. New pathways develop only as a result of well-practised adaptive strategies and actions, which ultimately should be more important than the pain. These opportunities for a healthier choice of behaviour need to be encoded in new neurophysiologically mechanisms.

In the formulation process, patients separate the multi-layered meanings of the headache from its physical parameters. The assumption is that patients who understand the headache as a redundant physical sensation can learn to habituate to it. Patients can then acknowledge the pain as a neutral sensory perception and disconnect it from their fears and avoidance behaviours.

Patients may have a preferred coping style. They may be avoiders or "pushers" with an unrelenting achievement-focused or endurance style. Theoretically, patients with an avoidance style would most benefit from exposure techniques and patients with an endurance style from a paced and graded activity approach. Nevertheless, in applied therapy and day-to-day life, such coping styles can rarely be so neatly separated. Most behavioural methods used in the headache programme contain a combination of techniques.

Relaxation and stress-reduction methods

Relaxation methods are at the core of successful headache management as proposed in this book.

Apart from the commonly known comfortable relief of muscle tension, the effect of relaxation is explained in relation to the physiology of the Action Systems and re-modulation of cortical pathways. Deep relaxation reduces patients' arousal by increasing autonomic control and optimising subcortical functioning (including in the anterior cingulate, amygdala, midbrain and hypothalamus). Headache patients should eventually notice a calming of physiological stress symptoms and anxiety, a reduced response to headache triggers and a habituation to redundant sensations associated with hyper-vigilance.

Relaxation techniques serve as positive attention diversion techniques, as the patient focuses on relaxation instructions rather than on the headaches. This optimises those neuropsychological pathways and Action Systems concerned with the strengthening of positive coping behaviours and this results in central reorganisation or the "de-skilling" of neural systems concerned with headache processing.

During relaxation, the involved sets of subcortical structures are activated to increase the ability to focus. Other brain areas (e.g., posterior parietal cortices) are calmed at the same time, which reduces internal distraction.

In order for relaxation to be effective, it is absolutely necessary for the person with headaches to master a relaxation technique that suits them. Relaxation can facilitate graded exposure programmes to previously avoided situations in order to promote desensitisation of headache fear.

With regard to headache therapy, such exposure tasks focus on:

- physical components of headache (e.g., pain descriptions as "sharp," "stabbing," "burning")
- cognitive components of headache (e.g., inappropriate thoughts and worries about headaches and associated consequences)
- emotional components (e.g., stress, arousal, fear)
- behavioural and interactional components (e.g., help-seeking, avoidance, pain communication).

Practical considerations for relaxation therapy are presented in the health management module.

Progressive muscle relaxation

Progressive muscle relaxation is a very common and effective way of learning intensive relaxation. The main principle consists of contracting and then releasing muscle groups in progressive order. The patient is meant to recognise the difference between muscle tension and muscle relaxation. The immediate sense of feedback from the muscle groups has been well received by people with mild brain trauma.

Progressive muscle relaxation is best taught in stages, introducing new muscle groups in consecutive sessions. When patients have mastered the principle and respond well, some muscle groups can be clubbed together. This can shorten the time needed for instructions, as the patient is able to achieve the relaxed state within shorter periods. The script may need to be adjusted for patients with physical comorbidities or problems with mobilising particular muscle groups.

Autogenic training

Autogenic training is a relaxation technique based on self-hypnosis principles. It was first described by Schultz, who discovered that the subjective experiences of "warmth" and "heaviness" induce a deep sense of relaxation that can be produced at will. Patients are initially encouraged to learn the technique with the aid of a coach and to continue to practise it at least once a day for about 15 minutes.

Autogenic training has a specific instruction for the relaxation of the forehead, which can be adapted for headache patients. The simple and repeated instructions can help patients with memory difficulties learn the technique easily.

Focused body relaxation

A large number of relaxation exercises use body-focused imagery, including suggestions about accepting physical sensations, disturbing thoughts or unpleasant emotions. The mindful instructions allow passive attention and facilitate the desensitisation of disturbing experiences at the same time as disconnecting associations between headaches and fear of headaches, or between headaches and worry/stress.

A focused body relaxation script was created for use in the headache therapy programme proposed in this book. It is intended as foundation relaxation practice and can be combined with a variety of imagery methods.

Abdominal breathing

Abdominal or diaphragmatic breathing is a core relaxation technique meant to slow down the breathing rhythm and optimise the breathing pattern. Structured teaching about abdominal breathing can precede the administration of a full relaxation script. Patients can be shown how to extend the time used for the out-breath, pause briefly and then take a new breath. The diaphragm expands on the in-breath and is released with the out-breath. Some patients have found it useful to hum, sigh, sing or count aloud on the out-breath to learn to relax the diaphragm efficiently.

Example: Richard

Richard was severely shaken up by his accident. He found it difficult to cope with his residual post-concussion problems. For him it was especially hard to concentrate on new and unfamiliar information. Indeed, he was only able to hold up to three components of a message in his mind.

He was also highly fearful of the outdoors, where he was not able to process the rapid stream of sensory stimuli happening all at the same time. He wanted to learn how to reduce his intense irritability, combat his agoraphobia and process what was going on around him without feeling overwhelmed by it. Nevertheless, he found it difficult to focus on and comprehend relaxation instructions like the focused body relaxation. Abdominal breathing has fewer verbal instructions, but Richard was still unable to coordinate his attention to "breathing in/breathing out" at the same time as being aware of his abdominal breathing pattern.

To reduce the cognitive demand and to make the task more natural, Richard practised abdominal breathing in combination with singing "I Am Sailing" by Rod Stewart.

- While standing up and holding his hands on his abdomen, he sang "I am sailing..." aloud with the therapist.
- Richard was instructed to extend the final line "across the seeeeeeeeaaaaaaaa" up to the point of completely emptying his lungs.

Richard was able to remember the lines of the song and combined the rhythm with his prolonged out-breath. He practised twice weekly in therapy and daily on his own for about four weeks. Eventually, he applied the abdominal breathing technique to regulate his anxiety when he left the house and when he was exposed to more cognitively demanding social situations.

Positive self-statements in relaxation

Positive self-statements are short and direct verbal instructions integral to relaxation techniques. Verbal self-instructions accompany and reinforce the relaxation experience. In order to maintain optimal concentration, patients should focus on one to two statements per relaxation practice session. The statement should be short and positively phrased. This means that spontaneous self-talk such as, "Don't panic!" is better rephrased as, "I am calm." Positive self-statements combined with imagery can be very powerful in enhancing optimal thought and belief patterns, thereby also strengthening the intentional Action Systems.

Relaxation and imagery

Psychological pain management strategies use elements of imagery extensively.

The relaxation techniques involve a person listening to relaxation instructions and focusing on the effect. Patients are actively encouraged to work with the suggestions and images in order to design a script that suits them best.

To begin with, the therapist administers a relaxation induction script. This enables the patient to settle into a state of relaxation. This is followed by visualisation suggestions that directly target the pain experience.

There are different types of pain relief imagery:

• Imagery that is incompatible with pain
• Imagery that encourages the modification of the pain sensation.

"Pain displacement," "healing paradigm," "hat anaesthesia" and other methods are examples of such techniques.

Relaxation strategies are among the most powerful psychological pain relief methods and, once mastered, are to be coupled with headache episodes. Deep relaxation has a number of positive effects. Autonomic arousal responses are directly dampened down. The self-instructions that are applied in relaxation focus on the relief of muscle tension and the slowing down of breathing rhythms. Reduced muscle tension limits the headache potential. Cognitive processes are focused on attention towards the mental image, positive self-instruction and monitoring the relaxation effect. This promotes a proactive cognitive focus while neglecting pain processing. Ultimately, healthy central reorganisation overrides hyper-sensitive pain pathways.

Example: Bethan

Bethan was a very nervous undergraduate student aiming to become a primary school teacher. She had experienced a very mild concussion at the age of 17 as the result of a rugby tackle. She had utilised a learning support coach in order to obtain good school grades, despite her persistent posttraumatic headaches. With less support available, she struggled at university. Performance pressures and her ongoing difficulties with task organisation triggered frequent tension headache episodes. She was at the point of despair when she entered the headache therapy programme and requested a "magic wand" to quickly dispel her headaches.

Bethan was a huge fan of the *Harry Potter* series. Building on this interest, the therapist commented, "The wand chooses the wizard, you know," and, with a convincing Dumbledore impression, continued, "We can find a wand that can help you to do all the tricks required to dispel your headaches. However, we first have to find the wand (the coping strategy) that works for you. When we have accomplished that, you'll have to practise. Even magic takes practice. Harry Potter had to go to Hogwarts for seven years to study the use of magic. Your headache therapy programme takes some weeks to complete and you are encouraged to practise your magic in between sessions. "

Bethan joined health management and individual therapy sessions. She combined her relaxation with the following magic images taken from the *Harry Potter* series:

• "Riddikulus": Bethan was particularly afraid about failing modules of her course due to recurrent headache episodes. She visualised her fear in the shape of a scarecrow, which she then pictured dressed up in a ridiculous fashion. Joking about it resulted in the image falling apart. Humour and laughter also helped her release the tension associated with performance anxiety. As in the novels, the creation of the image required some practice until it was powerful enough and easily remembered.

- "Reducio": Bethan used this imagery method to reduce the intensity of her head tensions during an episode.
- "Expecto Patronum": Bethan used a protective image to shield her from anticipated pressure and distress, especially if it tended to have an impact on her mood.

"Harry Potter therapy" might not yet be on the list of approved, research-based methods, but one can easily detect the cognitive reconstruction strategies promoted by such "magic spells."

Habit reversal

Another specific behaviour modulation technique is habit reversal. Postural habits are important to consider in cases of tension headaches or headaches that are triggered by the trigemino-cervical mechanisms. Patients are encouraged to learn skills aimed at reducing unhelpful postural habits and also habitual negative thoughts. Self-monitoring tasks and visualisation exercises can assist patients in noticing their unhealthy habits. Positive self-statements or achievement-focused images can be coupled with deep breathing and relaxation. All are intended to reduce physiological distress and promote healthy habits.

Patients may have internalised "rules" they have set themselves or they may have over-generalised expectations set by others, such as, "I have to wear sunglasses as I am over-sensitive to light," "I need to take two pain-killers before going out" or "if I don't lie down in a darkened room, the migraine will not go away." Patients may have experienced many changes in their routines, lifestyle or well-being during the course of their headache condition. Nevertheless, they sometimes carry on with a maladaptive "rule" out of fear that diversion from it will cause or prolong headaches. Re-assessments and tailoring of routines and coping strategies to changed circumstances are important when headaches become chronic.

Example: Christopher

Christopher had been in a car accident at the age of four. He had acquired superficial facial injuries, but no brain trauma. At the age of 11, he experienced a viral brain infection. He felt generally unwell and a lumbar puncture that was part of the investigation into his illness triggered his first migraine.

Christopher was an artistic boy. However, probably in line with early vulnerabilities due to the brain trauma, he had begun to experience recurrent migraine attacks when he performed on stage with his orchestra, choir or ballet school. Although he was often ill for a couple of days afterwards, he accepted that these episodes were related to one-off stressful events.

During his teenage years, he developed daily migraine episodes, which caused him to feel ill most of the time. He had to take regular time off school, which increased his worry about his academic performance. Such worries aggravated his perceived stress and significantly reduced his mood. Feeling more isolated from his friends due to absence from school, he involved himself in computer games for longer durations than other young people of his age. Whilst playing, he felt fully absorbed and was able to avoid thinking about school work, his loneliness and, indeed, was distracted from the migraine pain. However, it is likely that the prolonged exposure to computer gaming increased his eye strain, neck tension, bad posture and game-induced hyper-arousal – all habits that perpetuated his migraine cycle.

Cognitive techniques

Example: Holly

Holly's migraine condition developed following an assault witnessed whilst she was at university. In the weeks and month afterwards, she described herself as constantly "feeling on edge" and being worried about receiving punishment from other people. Holly's fear of migraines was twofold. First, she feared trigger events related to social conflicts and stress and, second, she worried about disapproval if she was unable to attend work due to an acute migraine attack.

One day in therapy, she became very upset when she talked about her fear that people could be nasty to her or bully her. She recalled explicit details of recent social conflicts and her perpetuating mental intrusions of these situations. She had been unable to stop replaying people's comments in her mind or reimagining catastrophic endings of argumentative interactions. In relation to migraine attacks, she was intensely concerned about missing work as people "might talk behind her back." She was also highly anxious about attending work, because she was no longer sure about her colleagues' support when she was present.

Holly applied a meta-strategy "GO SLOW" to stop repetitive and intrusive worries about social encounters. To begin with, she explored the effect of a powerful "STOP" image to halt her intrusive worries. She described a fierce Viking warrior who would stop and scare unnecessary and unhelpful worries away. This enabled her to "LEAVE" the trigger situation and "OBSERVE" how her body calmed down. This short "WAIT" helped her distance herself from her immediate fear before she orientated herself

Figure 2.6 Holly's meta-strategy "GO SLOW."

towards an alternate task. Regular practice of this thought-switching exercise helped Holly dissociate herself from cognitive intrusions and obtain a more balanced perspective on social situations. Eventually, she developed a new habit. When her negative thoughts started to become worrisome, after a moment of reflection, she left her house and went jogging in a nearby park. She added GO as a prompt to her meta-strategy. She hoped to implement and maintain, eventually, a physical exercise regime to reduce her stress in general and increase her resilience towards her migraines (Figure 2.6).

Habituation and desensitisation

Example: Emilia

Emilia was a 43-year-old lady with migraines that had developed following an accident 13 years earlier. She also experienced a premorbid sensitivity to visual disturbances. Since her youth, she had had floaters in her right eye. Floaters are the harmless results of degeneration of the gel that fills the eyes. They are visible because of the shadows they cast on the retina. Emilia had learnt that by wearing glasses, the perception of the floaters changed and she could "look through" them. Nevertheless, following her accident, she noticed that, first thing in the mornings, while still in bed, the floaters began to shiver and that they eventually turned into aura symptoms, followed by full-blown migraine attacks. She counteracted this by immediately wearing her glasses on waking up to distort the floaters. She became very preoccupied and anxious about having her glasses nearby and obsessively worried about wearing them all the time. She begun to fear that losing her glasses would cause an unmanageable migraine attack.

It happened that she had fallen ill with severe flu one year and she needed to spend several days in bed to rest. Although she felt too ill to leave the bed, she was obviously not asleep all the time. Mentally, she was now concerned with regulating her high fever and ingesting enough fluids, rather than on monitoring her floaters. Feeling drowsy and weak, she didn't have the energy to bother about her glasses. Feeling really tired, she simply noticed her floaters as she looked up at the white ceiling. Whilst observing how they floated around as she moved her eyes, she became aware that she did not develop aura symptoms. Consequently, she left her glasses on the bedside table. After a few days, she realised that as she remained calm, the observation of floaters would no longer trigger an aura or nausea. Eventually, her fear of triggering her migraines by focusing on the floaters and her obsession about wearing the glasses instantly upon waking up began to fade. She realised how wearing the glasses had merely been a safety mechanism to avoid the fear of migraine triggers. Her participation in the headache programme helped her intensify her relaxation methods and pace herself in more optimal ways.

Therapeutic storytelling

Therapeutic storytelling, as a form of enhanced work with metaphors, can play a useful part in individual therapy or the health management module to illustrate pacing and task management.

Patients who experience frequent headaches are often disappointed or feel guilty that they cannot perform their daily activities or fulfil their responsibilities to the standard they were once used to. Instead of slowing down or letting go of unrelenting expectations, they try to squeeze as many tasks into headache-free periods as they can or try to catch up with unfinished activities. The story about the hare and the hedgehog illustrates the rationale of irrational and rigid beliefs in an enjoyable, easily absorbable way to engage patients in reflecting on such unhelpful patterns or copings styles (Appendix II).

Stories and metaphors are intended for patients to interpret and ponder in their own way; however, some might require support in making sense of the inherent meaning. In applying this particular story, for example, patients are encouraged to imagine that they are the hare racing towards a limiting belief, that is, the belief that only running faster can help one win (e.g., endurance and achievement-driven behaviours). Just as it is common sense to believe that a hare is faster than a hedgehog, so too do patients, on the basis of previous life experiences, believe that they should have the capacity to always achieve their tasks. However, the acquired headache condition now limits their options and resources. The belief that they can master tasks according to pre-accident expectations is no longer valid.

In the story, the hare should have re-evaluated his progress and should have considered alternative options in the light of his experience of failure; however, he did not, and this had fatal consequences. Is it possible for patients to realise that they might be running after an illusion? Can they gain insight into the fact that it might be healthier to find a different track or a different speed? Reframing on a core level is essential for the patient who experiences that changing paths means that their identity has been undermined.

Hypnotherapy

Clinical hypnotherapy is a psychotherapy approach that aims to induce a state of deep relaxation or a trance in order to help patients form more adaptive behaviours, thoughts and feelings.

Clinical hypnotherapy can be combined with cognitive behavioural techniques in the application of pain management. The proposed headache therapy uses examples of therapeutic language patterns in discourse with patients according to the Ericksonian model. The applied clinical hypnosis methods are based on cognitive theories of hypnotic responding. Traditional approaches can be found in various combinations of deep relaxation with direct instructions and pain relief imagery. More recent developments introduced implicit and indirect language patterns into the therapeutic interaction inherent in hypnotherapy. Key features of such language patterns can be very effective in helping headache patients creatively reflect upon limiting beliefs and maladaptive behaviours. The application of such therapeutic language styles is indirect, thus unconfrontational, and helps the patient feel safe while the appropriateness of thoughts or behaviours is questioned.

The following hypnotherapy approaches can be applied in the headache programme:

- *Speaking the patient's verbal and non-verbal language in order to optimise rapport*: patients' very own descriptions of the pain symptoms can be used during the therapeutic discourse or be built into relaxation scripts.

- *Non-pathological approach*: symptoms are reframed as indications of desired personal growth. Patients begin to understand headache maintaining factors and how the headaches and pain-related habits have developed a new meaning. Reframing a secondary purpose of the pain can open opportunities to seek more positive goals.
- *Strategic and solution orientated*: the focus is on the desired outcome, rather than the symptom. This is in line with the shift of focus in therapy. Eventually, patients are guided to optimise their quality of life and to find their purpose during headache-free periods rather than being consumed by headache fear and avoidance of activity.
- *System orientated*: the headache is understood within the context in which it developed. In this programme, this is part of the biopsychosocial and CBT formulations.
- *Ambiguity methods*: metaphors, imagery, therapeutic stories and humour can help the patient make sense of their coping styles or to find creative coping strategies.
- *Action and insight*: engaging in health-promoting activities and challenging avoidance can help overcome various traps and vicious cycles.
- *Utilisation:* sometimes, the headache experience can offer completely new opportunities. In Harry's case, the headache's purpose was reframed as a means of keeping him away from a career path he had not consciously chosen for himself.

Example: Beatrice

Beatrice, a theatre nurse, had experienced chronic migraines and tension headaches since her car accident 15 years previously. She had already contemplated substantial lifestyle changes and was very open towards headache therapy. As part of her individual programme she also explored the *purpose* of her headaches (see session 5). She discovered that the headaches had been very powerful in dictating the course of her life for many years. She felt the energy inherent in the pain, but explained that this kind of energy was useless for her. Could it, perhaps, be useful for something else or someone else instead? She elaborated on that thought and imagined that the headache could have meaning for aliens in the form of fuel for their space ships. By use of mental imagery, relaxation and the pain displacement method, she removed the headache from her head through her ears (she imagined that the headache looked like tissue taken out in surgery) and placed it on her front lawn each night. This had two advantages: the aliens would have a reliable fuel station and she would be able to go to bed without a headache. What she was left with was a sore spot, just like a wound healing after surgery.

Beatrice purchased an alien toy, which she brought along to the following therapy session. Apparently, it had been assigned a place in her loft, signposting the alien space ships to their fuel station.

Hypnotherapy methods can prove supportive for people with long-term posttraumatic headaches. Hypnotic instructions are often presented slowly and repeated several times, which helps people who have poor attention ability and are quickly overwhelmed by a rapid stream of information. Patients with perceptual difficulties benefit from verbal associations and narrative techniques that are embedded in hypnosis instructions. In contrast, patients with language or verbal processing problems respond well to guided imagery and visual pain relief scripts.

The delivery of hypnotherapy increases the comfort in which the individual themes of headache therapy are absorbed by the patients. This can really benefit rapport and subsequently self-motivation.

The headache programme proposed in this book integrates hypnotherapy techniques with pain modulation imagery, reframing the meaning of pain and reflection on core values and life aims. Such future-orientated and solution-focused techniques optimise engagement with, and motivation for, behavioural change.

Hypnotherapy inductions facilitate reaching deep relaxation stages quickly. This is helpful for patients who cannot concentrate on long relaxation scripts. Direct suggestions are useful for patients with limited cognitive capacity and the repetition of hypnotic suggestions optimises memory recall.

Hypnotherapy techniques can easily be converted into self-hypnosis exercises, which give patients the opportunity to practise on their own.

Overall, hypnotherapeutic techniques have a fair potential to complement cognitive behavioural methods by adding creative, yet very person-tailored, methods to modify rigid pain behaviours.

Physical therapies and exercise

There is substantial awareness about the usefulness of aerobic exercise, particularly for migraine patients. An exercised-based migraine intervention was implemented by one sports psychology programme. Migraine patients participated in 30-minute sessions of either Nordic walking or jogging three times a week for ten weeks. Patients participating in either activity significantly reduced the frequency of their migraines. Negative coping and avoidance of social and other activities was reduced and habituation to migraine triggers and stressful stimuli was increased. Consequently, migraine thresholds and physical fitness were also improved. In addition, the influence of vulnerability factors decreased. Cognitive parameters such as working memory, mental flexibility and attention accuracy were also found to have improved. This could mean that the physiological benefits of aerobic training increased the efficiency of the nervous system, thus also reducing migraine episodes.

Pacing and fatigue management

Daytime fatigue is common with chronic headaches. Following brain trauma, associated disruptions of neurophysiological mechanisms can alter the healthy diurnal pattern, including the cortisol rhythm. A malfunctioning hormonal pattern can increase daytime fatigue, causing exhaustion and sleep problems at night. The perception of danger, especially a "social threat," is a powerful stressor. Headache sufferers often fear negative evaluation by others as much as pain. Therefore, secondary social consequences of headaches seem to be strongly associated with fatigue and sleep disorders. People who attempt to anticipate and compensate for negative feedback are at risk of "burn out" or "boom and bust."

Several therapeutic techniques that aim to optimise energy levels as well as pacing and activity management are described in the health management and individual headache therapy sections in Chapter 3.

Positive psychology and flow

Positive psychology, in broad terms, involves focusing on a person's current skills and resources in order to optimise their use in the future. The focus is on improving healthy functioning for a more fulfilling life. Personal growth following brain trauma can be an encouraging theme for a person with headaches.

The concept of "flow" focuses on a person's ability to be fully immersed in a meaningful activity. Flow takes the "being in the moment" experience up to a higher level, incorporating new personal challenges. This process involves the discovery of an exhilarating balance between panic and boredom states. A person who can accomplish this will, thus, move out of their comfort zone towards new experiences.

Headaches and brain trauma might throw a person off balance involuntarily. The shift of focus from a medical to a self-management approach that requires self-motivation might challenge a person's comfort zone. This can create a temporarily unstable experience that ultimately opens opportunities for development of the self and engagement with proactive life goals beyond the headache condition.

People experience flow when they stretch themselves a little further beyond their current limits and attempt new challenges that force them out of their comfort zones. The mastery of an extraordinary and enjoyable activity may lead to the feelings of excitement and exhilaration that are part of the flow experience.

In applying a positive therapy philosophy for patients with persistent headache problems, it is vital to guide patients towards:

- Awareness of life-traps that maintain their symptoms and hinder them living in accordance with their values.
- Insight about self-restricting behaviours and the hypersensitivity-trap associated with pain and anxiety symptoms.
- A graded and paced plan, moving them towards positive possibilities.
- Courage to apply the new and therapeutic coping strategies whilst letting go of safety-seeking and avoidance behaviours.

Chronic headache patients can feel trapped in their pain and, consequently, the visualisation of exciting life experiences might sound simply impossible. Often, patients have surrendered their ambitions due to their headaches. The paradigm shift in this headache therapy is intended to refocus patients on enhancing their quality of life during headache-free periods, to use available resources in an adaptive way and to explore how their values can be approached by gradually moving towards "possibility goals."

Acceptance and Commitment Therapy

Acceptance and Commitment Therapy (ACT) is inherently linked with positive psychology. It is an advanced concept of cognitive behavioural therapy. It encompasses therapeutic strategies for facilitating illness acceptance and commitment to behaviour change. Many techniques raise awareness of physical sensations with the aim of "defusing" unhelpful misattributions and accelerating desensitisation to such sensations.

The following key therapy principles aim to optimise choice and flexibility:
- cognitive defusion: methods used to reframe or reorganise inappropriate associations in order to discover new behaviour options
- acceptance: non-judgemental observation of thoughts, behaviours and experiences
- contact with the present moment: mindful awareness of the "here and now," experienced with curiosity and openness
- observing the self: discovering the core self in different contexts
- values: exploration of meaningful aims that give direction to one's life
- committed action: setting behavioural goals associated with values and overcoming unhelpful obstacles.

The therapeutic emphasis on language use, stories and metaphors overlaps with the hypnotherapy and imagery methods. Patients with chronic headaches might have tried for a very long time to eliminate their pain and they might have rearranged their lives according to it, often without improving either their headaches or their lives. ACT approaches facilitate a positive shift in therapy and guide the patient towards an awareness of how pain-related thoughts, behaviours and feelings can be modified and how a move towards possibility goals can be initiated (see Chapter 3). This fundamental perspective has been incorporated into the headache programme proposed in this book, along with elements such as cognitive defusion and values work.

In practical terms, the therapist may guide the patient to an understanding of how a strong identification with their headache came about. Through linguistic descriptions such as "I have constant headache," or "Because of my headache…" patients internalise the formulation, "I *am* my headache." Therapeutic exercises enable the patient to defuse associations between the self, thoughts, emotions or physical sensations.

Using another example, headache associations such as "this is killing me" or "I cannot cope" might result in avoidance and, therefore, limited choices and options. In combination with relaxation and imagery, patients can observe head sensations and learn to apply innovative verbal associations. Linguistic creativity may free a person, enabling them to explore alternative actions. The thought, "I would love to go out with you tonight, but I have a headache," is fixing a behavioural restriction. Simply replacing "but" (which indicates a contradiction) with "and" reduces the restrictive notion in the statement. It no longer implies that going out is impossible.

Most people associate their head or brain with the centre of their personality. Something going wrong with the head is, thus, one of the scariest health anxieties. Patients may worry that headaches could alter their identity. People fear that head pain might drive them crazy. The head pain symbolises a threat to the most basic of human needs – survival – in the form of fear of death, rejection and a loss of control. ACT techniques optimise the "defusion" of old and unhelpful associations and the fusion of new ones in line with current resources.

Emotional Resilience Therapy

Emotional Resilience interventions offer support for people who have additional emotional difficulties following mild brain trauma. It is informed by strengths- and resilience-based theory and related to ACT. This concept has been designed to provide people with an opportunity to reflect on their strengths, skills and values and to build their resilience in the face of distress and discomfort. People with adaptive styles and resources like resilience or grit (a passion and perseverance towards long-term goals and a strong sense of commitment and challenge) were said to adapt quickly and effectively to posttraumatic symptoms.

Emotional Resilience Therapy can be applied in the form of a course for individuals or groups, focusing on resilience, emotions, mindfulness, tolerating discomfort, self-compassion and values-focused action. The intervention is based on practising emotional coping skills and encourages reflections on individuals' experiences and stories. Reassurance-giving and challenging the concept of "normal" following significant life events are examples of embedded therapeutic methods. Effective endings of therapy sessions include relaxation and imagery exercises.

Therapeutic focus of Emotional Resilience Therapy is as follows:
- "what is working" rather than "what is wrong with me"
- ability to adapt and live with purpose even in the face of difficulties
- identification of personal strengths and how one can be resilient
- finding meaning and focus in life.

Participants are encouraged to use reflective journals to record the skills and qualities they have used; e.g., how they practised defusing techniques or made time for compassionate and self-soothing activities.

Emerging research outcomes have suggested that people who participated in Emotional Resilience Therapy improved on questionnaires validated for this intervention and ACT.

Emotional Resilience Therapy can be offered instead of the health management module for headache patients who may predominantly have difficulties with emotional coping.

Schema-focused cognitive behavioural therapy

Schema-focused cognitive behavioural therapy was developed for people presenting a challenging personal style. Schemas are robust interactional patterns formed in the early years of a person's development. As we saw in Chapter 1, our neural networks develop in response to the way in which our very core needs for orientation, freedom of pain and a protective bond are met. This is expressed in the form of communication and social attachment behaviours that are shaped according to the circumstances. People born with a vulnerable psychophysiological constitution, who are also subject to insecure and unstable attachments, may develop maladaptive schema patterns or "life traps," as well as predispositions for poor adjustments to adverse health or life events.

Personality traits associated with complex psychological recovery from brain injuries (e.g., endurance or achievement-driven styles, dependency, insecurity, grandiosity) have been found to match some known schema patterns (e.g., unrelenting standards, self-sacrifice, failure or fear of rejection).

Patients who present maladaptive schemas might find it more difficult to internalise helpful therapy suggestions. They may not easily be able to let go of their restricting life traps, as these trigger insecure attachments or the fear of abandonment. Schema assessment and schema formulation may be helpful in optimising motivation for the headache programme.

Patients who present resistant scenarios may benefit from intensive schema-focused therapy following the headache programme.

Example: Kristin

Kristin's brain surgery had optimised her severe epilepsy, but left her with recurrent migraine attacks. Owing to her epilepsy in childhood, she gained hardly any academic qualifications. In line with this, she was trapped by her perception that she was stupid. The impact of her neurosurgery led to further slowed information-processing abilities. She really struggled to keep up with discussions at work and worried about verbal abuse and social exclusion.

In order to compensate, she aimed to meet the "very high standards" set by others. This, she thought, would avoid being negatively judged and she would not have to see herself as a failure. However, her slowed verbal processing often let her down, triggering her "fear of failure" life trap after all. Such well-formed thought and behaviour patterns also began to hinder her progress in the headache programme.

To overcome her life traps, she used pictures and visual metaphors, familiar to her environment, to supplement verbal information. Using the therapy themes of developing skills and practising positive strategies in order to nurture herself, she thought of her interest in gardening. These were linked with her schema pattern in the following way:

- The schema "fear of failure" appeared to be the at the root of her problems.

  She described that it felt as if her roots were infested with pests, as she could not overcome her assumptions that she was worthless and stupid. She desired to apply some positive "fertiliser" to strengthen the core root of her sense of self. She explored the nurturing effects of her relationship with her partner and friends. She allowed herself time to absorb experiences of being loved and cared for, rather than feeling that she might not be worthy of such attention. Relaxation and imagery exercises reinforced her growing sense of physical well-being.
- Assertiveness and compensatory strategies.

  Kristin noticed how she often got overwhelmed and felt inadequate when she was unable to comprehend complicated verbal information at work. She experienced a sense of panic when multiple requests required an immediate response. She described such situations as a competition for sparse resources, just like "weeds." As she failed to satisfy the often-conflicting instructions and due to her low self-esteem, she felt low in mood and highly on guard. This situation was exacerbated because she worried that the next migraine attack might strike at any time.

She felt like she had to defend and prioritise her resources and assertively apply some "weed killer." She tried out strategies that allowed her time for verbal processing. For example, she focused on the actual verbal message rather than worrying about whether or not the message was meant as a criticism. She also used compensatory strategies more confidently, such as writing information down. Such simple alterations of her approach proved to challenge one of her schema patterns as she also believed that only stupid people take notes.

- "Environmental" boundaries.

There were times when Kristin needed to protect herself from the elements, just like a fragile plant placed in a greenhouse.

She learnt to "shield" herself from any hectic situations around her. She used positive self-talk to distance herself and practised abdominal breathing to reduce her stress response. She bravely negotiated with her manager to use big headphones, so as to indicate to others when she was too busy with work and did not want to be disturbed. By pacing her work tasks, she created "mini breaks" that gave her space to get away from distracting demands from others.

The picture of a flower on her desk was a creative way of reframing and prompting her to apply her strategies. Eventually, she got much better at regulating her distress and stayed clear of schema traps. Kristin's therapy sessions were divided into sections to focus on her schema pattern and graded practice of her coping and assertiveness skills.

Patients with posttraumatic headaches might present early vulnerabilities, which eventually emerge as dysfunctional early schemas. As these are well-ingrained in the personal style of the individual, they might aggravate secondary pain experiences as well as hinder swift progress in headache therapy. Schema patterns are not always bad. They develop to allow effective communication with others in routine social settings. However, if an unexpected event requires quick and flexible adjustment, then rigid schemas become a trap, as the associated habits and beliefs may no longer fit. People may feel at a loss of what to do and may search for ways to reinstate the former status quo.

Addressing the discrepancy between the former idealised self and the present disliked self is at the heart of the positive philosophy in rehabilitation therapy. The suggested CBT methods enable a transition from negatively experienced core patterns towards proactive life goals and possibilities. For instance, the possibility goal methods encourage a flexible exploration of personal plans along a dynamic continuum aimed at meeting people's values.

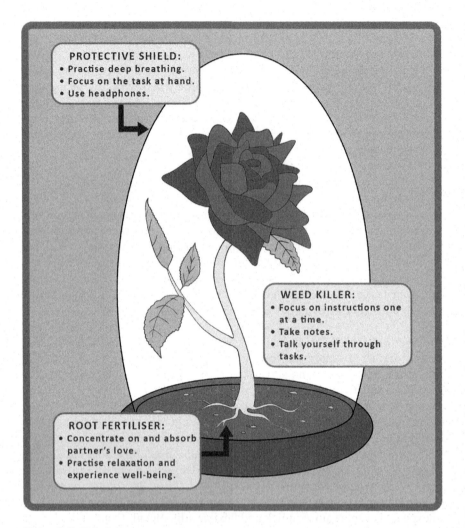

Figure 2.7 Kristin's meta-strategy.

Example: Terry

Terry was stuck in life due to his belief that there was no point in starting any activity as he would be hindered in completing it by his intense and prolonged headache episodes. He was a young man, but since his accident, he had mainly stayed at home waiting for a "good day." Due to the lack of a plan he was unable to accomplish much during times when he did not have a headache. Terry, inspired by the "miracle question," confessed that if he had all the necessary resources and fewer headaches, he would build a house on his own from scratch. The session proceeded by converting this life dream into possibility actions.

Terry was asked to rate his current resources on the "possibility continuum" (see Chapter 3). It transpired that he had already completed all the preparations necessary for building his house, down to the fine architectural details. He had expressed a strong interest in a piece of land. The headaches, however, held him back from putting in an offer and from beginning the actual project. Terry was too overwhelmed by the size of the job and too worried that the headaches would make the completion of the task impossible, which would result in a financial disaster. Using the continuum methods, he was able to reframe his over-generalisation. By tailoring his pacing and task management strategies, he created a clear overview of the stages involved in his big job.

Having mapped this out, he visibly relaxed his facial and neck muscles. He was able to envisage how the staged plan could be implemented on his good days, even if there had to be more flexibility in his schedule.

At his follow-up about two months later, he had not only put an offer in to purchase the plot, but had also proclaimed that he no longer experienced his tension headaches. He said that during the health management module and earlier individual sessions, he had not really believed in this kind of headache management. However, with his dream in mind, he had been motivated to make the therapy really work for him.

Example: Tracey and Katie

Tracey was a teaching assistant in a local primary school. The environment was hectic and noisy. Her schema traps, "Unrelenting standards" and "Self-sacrifice," prevented her from optimal task management (she did not use her break times, but instead did extra jobs for colleagues and children). She began to reflect on the relationship between her frequent migraines and her lifestyle in the discussions about the "Hare and the Hedgehog" story. Nevertheless, giving up her schemas was still too frightening for her at this point. She responded joyfully to the "miracle question" and said that she always wanted to be a famous singer.

Katie presented "Fear of rejection" and "Self-sacrifice" schemas. Owing to a fear of social exclusion, she did not allow herself to say "no" to others and engaged in numerous activities that were often not on the scale of her own values. She experienced constant headaches, severe fatigue and diminished pleasure in her activities. Her dream was to become a self-employed photographer.

It transpired that Tracey was not far off her dream. She had participated in a number of musical shows and had sung on local radio. Katie had plans to become the official photographer for a friend's wedding. Both ladies were held back, by their schemas, from rearranging their routines into healthier ones. They engaged well in headache therapy and practised coping strategies tailored to their ambitions and they both explored the possibility methods. Following the headache programme, they started schema therapy.

Rehabilitation of cognitive functions

The term "cognitive" has at least two different meanings. In psychotherapy terms, "cognitive" refers to the style and content of mental experiences such as beliefs, thoughts or the processes involved in generating ideas and an understanding of matters. Unhelpful or irrational mental processes can be approached with methods provided by cognitive behavioural therapy.

Conscious thinking is based on healthy cognitive processing. "Cognitive," in this context, concerns the quality of the functioning of neuropsychological pathways. Examples of simple cognitive functions are the ability to switch attention between stimuli with competing priorities or the ability to rearrange tasks rapidly. Working memory capacity is required when, for instance, the aim is to focus on longer-term health outcomes rather than responding to immediate disturbances. Richard, for example, needed to improve his alternating attention and learn how to focus on verbal instructions at the same time as regulating his breathing rhythm.

Breaking down conditioned pain and fear responses requires working memory, in addition to a strong conscious focus of the long-term benefits. This is often coupled with a personal vision that helps overcome and stop the instinctive conditioned reaction.

Patients who have experienced mild brain trauma can be prone to having difficulties with such cognitive functions. Therefore, some patients with headaches after mild brain trauma require working memory and attention process training as part of their headache programmes.

Executive and metacognitive abilities are important prerequisites for planning therapeutic activities and for pacing daily tasks. Meta-strategies are cognitive procedures like problem-solving algorithms that can be generalised for use with many tasks. These can include the preview of a task, research and organisation of subtasks and materials, planning and monitoring the task performance, plus revision and checking desired outcomes. Patients benefit best from headache therapy if they are given the opportunity to rehearse strategies and therapy activities with the therapist in their sessions, which is similar to what happens in a cognitive remediation programme.

Cognitive psychotherapy and cognitive re-training can be both carried out in a structured and goal-orientated format. It appears vital that the headache specialist has access to objective cognitive assessments undertaken with their patients. Attention, mental flexibility and speed may have been affected by the neuropathology of mild brain trauma. Heightened arousal due to fear and pain sensitisation further challenges cognitive abilities. Depending on personal style, some people might have developed a cogniphobia and might avoid cognitively demanding activities, thus de-skilling themselves. Others might be driven by achievement and endurance schemas along the line of the belief that the harder they work the quicker they will regain their former level of performance. This, however, might increase the strain, physically as well as cognitively, and the likelihood of tension headache as well as mental fatigue.

In applying headache therapy, it becomes apparent that cognitive flexibility training optimises a patient's sense of self-control. Working memory exercises, paced task schedules and the regulation of distractions can be implemented and patients can easily monitor their progress. Attention skills are also trained as part of relaxation practice.

Example: Josh

Juggling appears to optimise the Action Systems and dampen or divert the pain-related Central Sensitisation mechanisms. A juggler needs to be fully engaged in the activity for it to work. Attention, sensory and motor processing, as well as performance monitoring, are coordinated and fine-tuned. The activity fully absorbs large cognitive networks and needs to be synchronised with body awareness and breathing rhythm. It seems that the juggler's brain has no capacity for processing any competing stimuli, like pain, simultaneously with the complicated flow of movements.

Josh had acquired his brain injury six years previously due to an assault. As part of his brain injury rehabilitation he had been offered a shop-fitting apprenticeship, which he was about to complete when he participated in the headache programme. He said that he was very grateful for the opportunity to gain qualifications in a field he really liked, however, the woodwork areas were busy and noisy. Josh found it very hard to cope with his headaches in such an environment.

Prior to his brain injury, Josh had been homeless and had earned some money by juggling and street entertaining. His juggling skills became his most used headache coping strategy. He arranged a personalised schedule at work. Instead of having a long lunch break, he took a number of smaller breaks. During each of these, he went to the yard behind the workshops with his juggling clubs. Initially, the physical exercise component increased his circulation and helped with the release of muscle tension. The focused attention diverted him from worrying about his headaches. His improved cognitive and motor flexibility contributed to his ability to quickly switch between work tasks and coping strategies. Josh said that he would recommend juggling to all headache patients.

Example: Henrietta

Henrietta was a middle-aged businesswoman who had been in a car accident a few years prior to coming to headache therapy. Her tension headaches were associated with long drives through the country. Once the headaches had started, they would continue for a few hours, even after she had completed her journey.

She was unable to make changes to her career. It was also not possible to break down the drive and have more breaks due to the pressure of her commitments. In her headache programme, she had been thinking about an answer to the "miracle question." She said that she had always regretted that she had never learnt a foreign language. She said that despite her many foreign travels, she had always postponed learning another language. Most of all, she wanted to learn French. In the headache programme she was encouraged to explore whether or not language learning could distract her from headache monitoring during long journeys. She downloaded an audio French course that she listened to whilst driving. By the time she came for her follow-up session, she had passed the foundation stage of the course. Most of all, she was coping much better with her headaches. She said that the headaches still lasted a while after the trip, but she was much less bothered about them during her driving.

Attention diversion strategies can be recommended to interrupt the worry cycle during a headache-free period and as a positive distraction at the onset of a headache episode.

Planned and proactive interruptions of the stream of headache-related thinking and avoidance patterns provide opportunities for central reorganisation, that is, focusing on achievable meaningful goals and letting the headache run its course.

Cognitive exercises or games can rapidly override the intense fear and pain inherent in some types of headaches. With practice and determination, a person (like Bethan or Holly) can create a brief stop-gap in the fear-pain-fear cycle. This may be just enough to create a space to decide which means of coping to apply next or how to reorganise the day.

Bibliography

Barabasz, A., & Barabasz, M. (2012). Hypnosis and the brain. In: M. R. Nash & A. J. Barnier (Eds.), *The Oxford Handbook of Hypnosis. Theory, Research, and Practice* (pp. 337–363). New York: Oxford University Press.

Barnier, A. J., Dienes, Z., & Mitchell, C. J. (2012). How hypnosis happens: New cognitive theories of hypnotic responding. In: M. R. Nash & A. J. Barnier (Eds.),

The Oxford Handbook of Hypnosis. Theory, Research, and Practice (pp. 141–177). New York: Oxford University Press.

Bond, F. W., Hayes, S. C., Baer, R. A., Carpenter, K. M., Guenole, N., Orcutt, H. K., Waltz, T., & Zettle, R. D. (2011). Preliminary psychometric properties of the Acceptance and Action Questionnaire – II: A revised measure of psychological inflexibility and experiential avoidance. *Behavior Therapy, 42*(4): 676–688.

Collicutt McGrath, J., & Linley, P. A. (2006). Post-traumatic growth in acquired brain injury: A preliminary small scale study. *Brain Injury, 20*(7): 767–773.

Cramer, J. A., Silberstein, S. D., & Winner, P. (2001). Development and validation of the Headache Needs Assessment (HANA) Survey. *Headache, 41*: 402–409.

Erickson, M., & Rossi, E. L. (1980). Indirect forms of suggestion. In: E. L. Rossi (Ed.), *The Collected Papers of Milton H. Erickson on Hypnosis*, Vol. 1: *The Nature of Hypnosis and Suggestion* (pp. 452–477). New York: Irvington.

Ganzel, B. L., Morris, P. A., & Wethington, E. (2010). Allostasis and the human brain: Integrating models of stress from the social and life sciences. *Psychological Review, 117*(1), 134–174.

Glaser, D. (2000). Child abuse and neglect and the brain: A review. *Journal of Child Psychology and Psychiatry, 41*(1), 97–116.

Gracey, F., Palmer, S., Rous, B., Psaila, K., Shaw, K., O'Dell, J., Cope, J., & Mohamed, S. (2008). "Feeling part of things": Personal construction of self after brain injury. *Neuropsychological Rehabilitation, 16*(5/6): 627–650.

Grambling, E. E., Neblett, J., Grayson, R. L., & Townsend, D. (1996). Temporomandibular disorder: Efficacy of an oral habit reversal program. *Journal of Behavior Therapy and Experimental Psychiatry, 27*: 212–218.

Grimm, J., & Grimm, W. B. (1857). *Der Hase und der Igel*. Berlin: Kinderbuchverlag, 1987.

Gurr, B., & Coetzer, B. R. (2005). The effectiveness of cognitive-behavioural therapy for post-traumatic headaches. *Brain Injury, 19*(7): 481–491.

Gurr, B., & Wickes, S. (2006). The usefulness of a relaxation program for brain-injured patients. *Clinical Psychology Forum, 166*: 14–18.

Hayes, S. C., & Strosahl, K. D. (2004). *A Practical Guide to Acceptance and Commitment Therapy*. New York: Springer.

Hunt, S. M., McEwen, J., & McKenna, S. P. (1985). Measuring health status: A new tool for clinicians and epidemiologists. *Journal of the Royal College of General Practitioners, 35*: 185–188.

Iverson, G. L., Brooks, B. L., Ashton, V. L., & Lange, R. T. (2009). Interview versus questionnaire symptom reporting in people with the postconcussion syndrome. *Journal of Head Trauma Rehabilitation, 25*(1): 23–30.

Jacobson, G. P., Ramadan, N. M., Aggarwal, M. D., & Newman, C. W. (1994). The Henry Ford headache disability inventory (HDI). *Neurology, 44*: 837–842.

Jacobson, G. P., Ramadan, N. M., Norris, L., & Newman, C. W. (1995). Headache Disability Inventory (HDI): Short-term test-retest reliability and spouse perception. *Headache, 35*: 534–539.

King, N. S., & Kirwilliam, S. (2011). Permanent post-concussion symptoms after mild head injury. *Brain Injury, 25*(5): 462–470.

Lazar, S. W., Bush, G., Gollup, R. L., Fricchione, G. L., Khalsa G., & Benson, H. (2000). Functional brain mapping of the relaxation response and meditation. *Neuroreport, 11*(7): 1581–1585.

Leonardi, M., Steiner, T. J., Scher, A. T., & Lipton, R. B. (2005). The global burden of migraine: Measuring disability in headache disorder with WHO's classification of functioning, disability and health (ICF). *Journal of Headache Pain*, *6*: 429–440.

Lipton, R. B., & Steward, W. F. (1995). Health-related quality of life in headache research. *Headache*, *35*: 447–448.

Mickeviciene, D., Schrader, H., Nestvold, K., Kunickas, R., Stovner, L. J., & Sand, T. (2001). A controlled historical cohort study on the post-concussion syndrome. *European Journal of Neurology*, *9*(6): 581–587.

Mickeviciene, D., Schrader, H., Nestvold, K., Kunickas, R., Stovner, L. J., & Sand, T. (2004). A controlled prospective inception cohort study on the post-concussion syndrome outside the medicolegal context. *European Journal of Neurology*, *11*(6): 411–419.

Mittenberg, W., Canyock, E. M., Condit, D., & Patton, C. (2001). Treatment of post-concussion syndrome following mild head injury. *Journal of Clinical and Experimental Neuropsychology*, *23*: 829–836.

Nash, M. R., & Barnier, A. J. (2012). *The Oxford Handbook of Hypnosis. Theory, Research, and Practice*. New York: Oxford University Press.

Öst, L. G. (1987). Applied relaxation: Description of a coping technique and review of controlled studies. *Behaviour Research and Therapy*, *25*: 397–410.

Overath, C. H., Darabaneanu, S., Evers, M. C., Gerber, W-D., Graf, M., Keller, A., Niederberger, U., Schäl, H., Siniatchkin, M., & Weisser, B. (2014). Does an aerobic endurance programme have an influence on information processing in migraineurs? *The Journal of Headache and Pain*, *15*(1): 11–29.

Packard, R. C., & Ham, L. P. (1993). Impairment rating for posttraumatic headache. *Headache*, *33*(7): 359–364.

Padesky, C. A. (1994). Schema change processes in cognitive therapy. *Clinical Psychology and Psychotherapy*, *1*(5): 267–278.

Potter, S. D., Brown, R. G., & Fleminger, S. (2016). Randomised, waiting list controlled trial of cognitive-behavioural therapy for persistent postconcussional symptoms after predominantly mild-moderate traumatic brain injury. *Journal of Neurology, Neurosurgery, and Psychiatry*, *87*: 1075–1083.

Prochaska, J. O., & DiClemente, C. C. (1982). Transtheoretical therapy: Toward a more integrative model of therapy. *Psychotherapy: Theory, Research, and Practice*, *19*(3): 267–288.

Rogan, C., Fortune, D. G., & Prentice, G. (2013). Post-traumatic growth, illness perception and coping in people with acquired brain injury. *Neuropsychological Rehabilitation*, *23*(5): 639–657.

Roger, C. (1951). *Client-Centred Psychotherapy*. Boston, MA: Houghton-Mifflin.

Rowling, J. K. (2013). Harry Potter. *Boxed Set: The Complete Collection*. London: Bloomsbury Paperbacks.

Sapolsky, R. M. (2003). Stress and plasticity in the limbic system. *Neurochemical Research*, *28*(11): 1735–1742.

Sapolsky, R. M., Romero, L. M., & Munck, A. U. (2000). How do glucocorticoids influence stress responses? Integrating permissive, suppressive, stimulatory, and preparatory actions. *Endocrine Reviews*, *21*: 55–89.

Satir, V., Gomori, M., Banmen, J., & Gerber, J. S. (1991). *The Satir Model: Family Therapy and Beyond*. Palo Alto, CA: Science and Behavior Books.

Schultz, J. H. (1932). *Das Autogene Training (konzentrative Selbstentspannung). Versuch einer klinisch-praktischen Darstellung.* Leipzig: Thieme.

Seligman, M. E. P., & Csikszentmihalyi, M. (2000). Positive psychology. An introduction. *American Psychologist, 55*(1): 5–14.

Silverberg, N. D., & Iverson, G. L. (2013). Is rest after concussion "the best medicine?" Recommendations for activity resumption following concussions in athletes, civilians, and military service members. *Journal of Head Trauma Rehabilitation, 28*(4): 250–259.

Smith, B. W., Dalen, J., Wiggins, K., Tooley, E., Christopher, P., & Bernard, J. (2008). The brief resilience scale: Assessing the ability to bounce back. *International Journal of Behavioral Medicine, 15*(3): 194–200.

Sohlberg, M. M., & Mateer, C. A. (2001). *Cognitive Rehabilitation.* New York: Guildford Press.

Tatrow, K., Blanchard, E. B., Hickling, E. J., & Silverman, D. J. (2003). Posttraumatic headache: Biopsychosocial comparisons with multiple control groups. *Headache, 43*: 755–766. – NHP outcomes.

Thorn, B. E. (2004). *Cognitive Therapy for Chronic Pain.* New York: Guilford Press.

Ware, J. E., & Sherbourne, C. D. (1992). The MOS 36-item short-form health survey (SF-36). *Medical Care, 30*(6): 473–483.

World Health Organisation. (2001). *International Classification of Function.* Geneva: WHO.

Yeates, G. N., Gracey, F., & Collicutt McGrath, J. (2008). A personal deconstruction of "personality change" following acquired brain injury. *Neuropsychological Rehabilitation, 18*(5/6), 566–589.

Young, J. E., Klosko, J. S., & Weishaar, M. E. (2003). *Schema Therapy: A Practitioner's Guide.* New York: Guilford Press.

Zigmond, A. S., & Snaith, R. P. (1983). The hospital anxiety and depression scale. *Acta Psychiatrica Scandinavia, 67*: 361–370.

Chapter 3

Cognitive behavioural therapy for posttraumatic headaches

Introduction

This cognitive behavioural therapy manual is intended as a step-by-step guide for clinical specialists working with people with mild brain trauma. It includes a variety of assessment and therapy material that should help the busy clinician prepare efficient and effective interventions.

The therapy philosophy shifts from directly managing the head pain initially, via explorations of challenges, towards value-driven lifestyle improvements.

The proposed headache programme can be delivered in the form of one-off headache clinics, as well as individual and/or group therapy interventions.

At the core of the single-session headache clinic is the reformulation of the headache condition. Using psycho-educational methods, this clinic is an early intervention following a mild brain trauma and serves as a preventative method to counteract chronicity and secondary symptoms.

Individual therapy sessions increase opportunities for tailoring therapeutic strategies exactly to the patient's situation and headache experience. Headache therapists are invited to use the methods and material in this book creatively, as they are consistently guided by cognitive behavioural principles embedded in a biopsychosocial approach.

Group interventions offer the benefit of interactions and support between peers. The pace and the structure of sessions for five to eight participants can make a real difference for people who otherwise might struggle with low motivation or self-doubt.

Whether patients are offered a one-off headache clinic appointment, group-based health management or individually tailored CBT depends on their assessment outcomes and also on their involvement with other therapies perhaps for comorbid symptoms. It is really important that the associated team specialists are on board with the headache therapy philosophy and collaboratively explore patients' expectations.

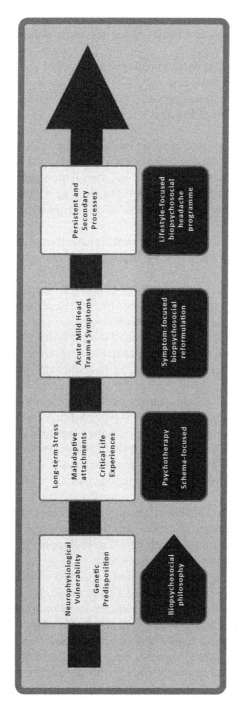

Figure 3.1 Headache stages and therapeutic approaches.

Headache therapy components

The headache programme consists of the following main components:

- Module 1: Engagement and headache assessment
- Module 2: Headache clinic
- Module 3: Health management
- Module 4: Individual therapy

Module 1: Engagement and rapport building have huge potential to facilitate a therapeutic interaction. The trust in the therapist is a prerequisite to formulate the therapy rationale in a way that is fine-tuned to the patient's psychosocial needs and headache symptoms. The importance of building motivation and getting the patient ready for change cannot be emphasised enough.

Assessment outcomes provide the tools for the therapist and patient alike to obtain a more rational overview of an otherwise psychologically intense experience.

Module 2: Headache clinics have the purpose of helping the person cope with headaches occurring immediately after the onset event and prevent secondary psychological symptoms and behaviours. They can be highly effective for many people who have sustained a mild brain trauma. The module incorporates the reformulation approach and provides tools for psycho-education, reassurance and signposting to additional health management services.

Module 3: The health management programme aims to introduce relaxation as the main coping strategy. Lifestyle advice and psycho-education about headache dynamics form the essential ingredients of this intervention. This can be delivered in the form of individual or group sessions. Small group settings feel safe for the reluctant participant. They are also intimate enough for supportive social interactions, which can optimise therapy adherence.

Module 4: Individual headache therapy follows naturally after the health management component. Patients will have acquired robust relaxation skills already, which can then be tailored to their specification.

The individual programme outlines weekly therapy sessions and follow-up. The starting point is an educational component in which the headache and trauma symptoms are further clarified and strategies for their reduction and modification are explored. Later on, patients focus on hindering lifestyle factors that encourage and maintain headaches. The shift towards enhancing the quality of life during headache-free periods becomes the priority at this stage. Eventually, the therapy reaches out to families and friends to help them respond to the patient's headaches in a health-promoting way.

Headache therapy sessions are supplemented by participants practising their developing skills between sessions. Level of engagement and intervention outcomes vary between patients and are difficult to predict. Most patients with posttraumatic headache have shown lifestyle improvements and have increased their use of proactive health management and coping strategies, preferring it to medication for the reduction of their headaches.

This therapy guide provides the therapist with a large selection of practical material including assessments, norms, session plans, worksheets and therapy scripts. It is offered as an all-inclusive manual, with the aim of optimising therapy preparations. Therapists or researchers who require additional norms or material that is copyrighted will have to refer to the original literature.

Module 1: engagement and headache assessments

The following sections are meant to highlight specific considerations regarding assessments of patients with posttraumatic headaches.

Psychosocial assessment of headaches is aimed at achieving a better understanding of the development, maintenance and dynamics of the symptoms in the context of a previous mild brain trauma and with the background of the earlier personal history. The assessment module gives the patient plenty of opportunity to reflect upon and to process the aftermath of the event that led to the injury.

It is important to bear in mind that patients may have already talked about such issues numerous times with their family and friends, as well as doctors, prior to attending a specialist clinic. This can mean that the story that has evolved in their minds, has become well-rehearsed and may not accurately reflect their headache experience and associated coping.

Hence, the assessment requires skilful disentangling of the facts relating to the symptoms and psychosocial markers. An empathetically conducted clinical interview as well as psychometric questionnaires can help patients begin to understand how the headache condition has taken hold of their lives.

The assessment process is well-aligned with the stages in therapy. A first focus is concerned with headache symptoms and facts (e.g., factors that precipitate or aggravate headaches). The second focus is on personality and lifestyle opportunities. The third important area is the investigation of social interactions.

As part of the engagement element within initial assessment interactions, patients should be assessed for suitability and expectations. It is vital to point out the crucial importance of motivation for self-management if an improvement of quality of health is envisaged.

Headache interview

Clinical considerations for conducting a headache interview were discussed in Chapter 2. The semi-structured guideline that follows facilitates the narrative assessment of headache symptoms and contextual factors on the basis of a cognitive behavioural approach.

1   The headache experience at present.
2   Description of the types of headaches that are a problem.
3   Predispositions and early vulnerabilities:
   • Childhood health including history of pain syndromes
   • Health role modelling by early caregivers
   • Adverse early life events and coping strategies
   • Psychological, mental health and personality styles
   • Social relationships
4   Presenting health and psychosocial topics:
   • Brain trauma event and injury facts
   • Residual post-concussion symptoms (physical, emotional, cognitive)
   • Comorbidities (physical: e.g., back pain; psychological: e.g., depression, sleep and fatigue problems; sensory impairments: e.g., hearing loss) and associated health behaviours
   • Therapy and/or rehabilitation received in the past and outcomes
   • Personality factors (e.g., self-esteem, schemas, emotional regulation, intelligence)
   • Coping styles (e.g., avoidance, endurance behaviours, information-seeking, problem-solving, resourcefulness)
   • Expectations regarding proposed headache intervention
   • Occupational, social and family functioning and headache impact on these
   • Lifestyle, attitude to exercise, interests, plans and ambitions
   • Diet in general, alcohol consumption, smoking, medication and drugs
   • Social support in relation to headaches and the onset event
   • Secondary gains such as compensation-seeking, sickness or benefit claims
5   Specific headache variables:
   • Headache onset, course, changes over time
   • Headache qualities (description of pain sensation, location)
   • Headache variables (intensity, duration, frequency, level of distress)
   • Triggers, trigger behaviours
   • Predisposing factors (e.g., pre-morbid headache, depression, health conditions)
   • Health behaviours and coping styles associated with headaches

- Activities that reduce, maintain and increase the headaches
- Activities following remission of headaches
- Headache attributions and loci of control
- Setting, context and modifying variables

6   Factors to take into account:

- The referral reason and procedure that set the direction for the inter-actions between patient and therapist
- The assessment details from clinical interviews, self-report question-naires, diaries, and observations, medical investigations
- The summary of the assessment information integrated with the biopsychosocial formulation (e.g., clinical headache report, Figure 1.11, *my headache formulation* worksheet)
- Expectations about the usefulness of a CBT-based headache intervention
- The relevance of the additional recommendations for the patient.

Such a comprehensive investigation can guide the headache specialist and avoid a situation in which simple, straightforward explanations may be overlooked.

Self-report questionnaires

Questionnaire outcomes can be extremely useful for enhancing the clinical history and interview details, as well as for monitoring change. Results and responses to items that the patients have highlighted can be discussed fur-ther to establish a clear formulation of the headache condition and all as-sociated behaviours. The selection of questionnaires should be in line with the format of the assessment and stages of the therapy (e.g., focus on specific symptoms, personality, quality of life or social interaction).

The questionnaires below are available in the published journals, on the respective websites or in the first edition of this book.

Headache-specific measures

IMPAIRMENT RATING FOR POSTTRAUMATIC HEADACHE

This questionnaire is composed of criteria for posttraumatic headaches. These are presented in the form of a mnemonic: IMPAIRMENT (Inten-sity, Medication use, Physical signs/symptoms, Adjustment, Incapaci-tation, Recreation, Miscellaneous activity of daily living, Employment, Number = frequency, Time = duration of attacks). The psychological items on motivation for treatment, over-exaggeration or over-concern allow for a psychological perspective on the physical headache criteria.

THE HENRY FORD HOSPITAL HEADACHE DISABILITY INVENTORY (HDI)

This questionnaire consists of two subscales: a headache symptom one and an emotional one.

Furthermore, it has been produced for self-report and independent rater use. The comparison between self- and an independent rater observations can be very useful for therapeutic discussions. Both versions can provide valuable measures of change and therapy success. The questionnaire has good validity and test–retest reliability. As a general guide, a cohort of patients with posttraumatic headaches presented on the headache subscale with a mean of 32.20 (SD 11.25) at baseline and with a mean of 22.30 (SD 11.39) at follow-up. Norms on the emotion subscale indicated a mean of 25.20 (SD 9.43) at baseline and a mean of 14.15 (SD 9.36) at follow-up. This demonstrated a significant reduction of symptoms. The questionnaire is available on the internet and in the first edition of this book.

HEADACHE NEEDS ASSESSMENT (HANA)

This is a short questionnaire consisting of seven questions. Each item is rated according to the frequency of headache-related problems and the extent of their subjective "bothersomeness." This questionnaire is very well suited for the multifaceted headache programme as the headache is described systemically amidst psychological and contextual symptoms. Individual therapy goals can be directly derived from the items' expressions. Used as a measure, it can illustrate changes of associated symptoms as well. Therefore, this tool may help decentralise the headache and establish how it is affected if other variables change. The headache needs symptoms decreased from the baseline mean 87.5 (SD 37.5) to a mean of 63.8 (SD 34.5) at the end of the headache therapy in the original norm group. A copy of this questionnaire can be found in Appendix IV.

Measures of health and quality of life

NOTTINGHAM HEALTH PROFILE (NHP)

The Nottingham Health Profile is a generic quality of life survey used, first, to measure the subjective physical, emotional and social aspects of health that are essential for a multi-dimensional therapy programme. Second, it investigates how a health problem affects life domains. The subscales on pain, physical ability, energy and sleep are useful in association with headache symptoms. Patients have found the items easy to understand and the questions quick to answer. The questionnaire is sensitive to changes in posttraumatic headache and migraine conditions. A full version can be found in the first edition of this book and online.

THE MOS 36-ITEM SHORT-FORM HEALTH SURVEY 36 (SF-36)

This valuable outcome measure investigates health-focused quality of life in two domains consisting of four subscales each. The physical health domain includes: Physical Functioning, Physical Role Limitations, Bodily Pain and General Health. The mental health domain includes: Vitality, Emotional Role Functioning, Social Functioning and Mental Health.

This questionnaire has good psychometric properties and has been applied in a vast range of health research.

Clinical norms can be found in the first edition of this book. A copy of the questionnaire can be found there, as well as on the internet.

MULTIDIMENSIONAL HEALTH LOCUS OF CONTROL

Locus of control applied to health conditions may be attributed to internal factors (e.g., self-determination of a healthy lifestyle), powerful others (e.g., a family doctor) or luck. The measures are considered to be in the public domain. The description of preferred health attributions seems vital for therapeutic discussions as part of this approach.

Measures of psychological variables

YOUNG SCHEMA QUESTIONNAIRE

Schema therapy describes 18 schemas, each of which covers a particular maladaptive belief and interactional personality pattern. Optimising such patterns is often required when individuals are trapped in maladaptive coping styles that maintain head pain and other negative experiences. Schema therapy questionnaires are available online.

HOSPITAL ANXIETY AND DEPRESSION SCALE (HADS)

The HADS has been applied extensively for screening of psychological symptoms in a wider range of settings. It has robust psychometric properties and it is useful for frequent reassessments. The headache therapy presented here showed significant reductions on the embedded subscales of anxiety and depression in a group of posttraumatic headache patients. As a rough guide, the HADS full-scale score at baseline was mean 19.4 (SD 5.95) and at post-therapy was mean 17.20 (SD 7.38) in the original norm group. The questionnaire is copyrighted and is commercially available.

Headache monitoring and rating scales

The process of headache monitoring requires systematic symptom recording that provides a focus in therapy. Patients with additional planning and organisation difficulties learn how to define their target symptoms and how to monitor them. In contrast, anecdotal and sporadic records may result in false associations between headache-related factors. For example, monitoring tasks that focus only on headache onset and duration can miss modulating variables (e.g., change of activities, a period of illness, distressing news) or changes in headache perception during a single episode.

Patients can use their usual means for recording activities, such as their headache diaries or digital apps.

Analogue rating scales are common and effective in pain measurement. They can be used to measure:

- Headache intensity: visual analogue scales
- Headache frequency and duration: analogue scales, diaries and calendars.

Headache monitoring and personality style

Headache monitoring methods can be tailored to patients' personality or coping style.

PRIMARY NEEDS ARE: INFORMATION AND "EVIDENCE"

Some patients might have an incorrect understanding of the frequency, duration and intensity of their headaches. The subjective experience of the pain can be so overwhelming that the patient's perception seems an exaggeration of the actual symptoms.

Headache monitoring can help some patients gather systematic evidence about the actual headache episodes. This is an insight-generating approach and enables patients to disentangle psychological and secondary elements from headache facts. Correct monitoring can support the realisation that the headache episodes have an impact on only parts of people's lives and that control can be regained over other areas.

Symptom monitoring is a strategy used by many people to improve their health routines (e.g., giving up smoking, drinking less alcohol or losing weight). The chosen observation strategy should fit with patients' routines to determine whether or not the pain is associated with a particular activity at a particular time. Such systematic monitoring can help identify therapeutic approaches targeting both the headache and the associated activities. The headache diary in Appendix I provides an example.

Quantifying what is essentially a subjective experience may be difficult for some people at first. With some practice, this task also has a therapeutic effect. It allows the person to take a more observant perspective to describe the headaches and associated experiences.

Headache frequency:
How frequently have you had headaches *on average* (during the previous fortnight/month)? (Figure 3.2)

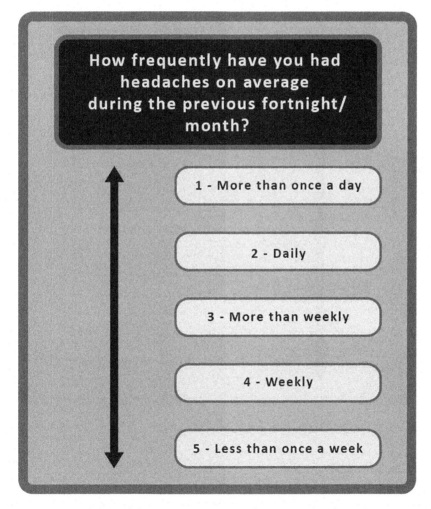

Figure 3.2 Headache frequency scale.

Headache duration:

How long did your headache episodes last, *on average* (during the previous fortnight/month)? (Figure 3.3)

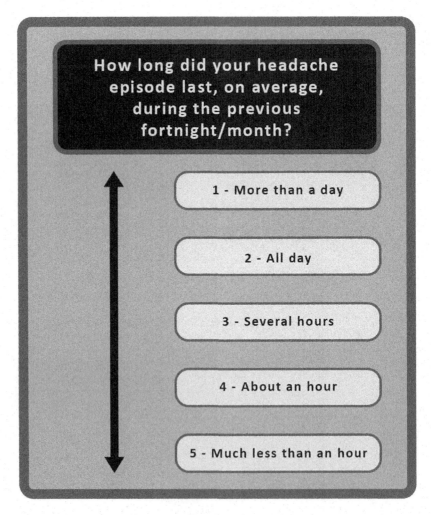

Figure 3.3 Headache duration scale.

Headache intensity:

How intense is your headache *right now*?

Or how intense were your headaches on average (during the last week/fortnight)? (Figures 3.4 & 3.5)

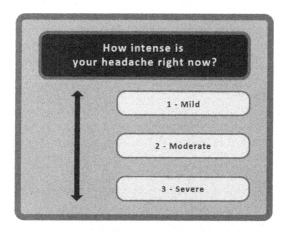

Figure 3.4 Headache intensity scale (a).

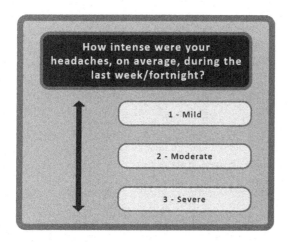

Figure 3.5 Headache intensity scale (b).

PRIMARY NEEDS ARE: SUBJECTIVE EXPERIENCE OF AND SUFFERING
WITH HEADACHES

Patients who feel overwhelmed in their helpless suffering might not benefit
so much from systematic monitoring to come to a more objective realisation
about their headache. The subjective suffering is the observation target for
these people. The headache is a symbol of their psychological need. The
monitoring can, thus, help a clearer communication of any kind of distress.
Additionally, personal styles, adjustment and coping can be systematically
observed as well.

If questionnaires are used for this purpose, then the HANA and the psychological or emotional scales on pain questionnaires (e.g., HDI, SF-36, NHP) are very useful for achieving this monitoring aim. Pain scores can be interpreted in association with outcomes from anxiety and depression scales (e.g., HADS, emotional scales of the quality of life/health questionnaires, etc.).

Headache distress:
How intense is your headache-related emotional distress right now?
Or how intense was your headache-related emotional distress on average (during the last week/fortnight)? (Figures 3.6 & 3.7)

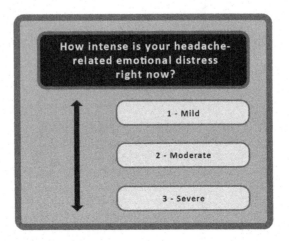

Figure 3.6 Headache distress scale (a).

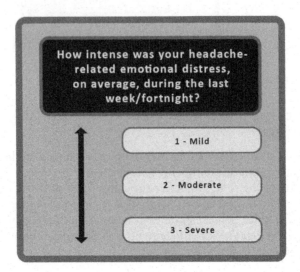

Figure 3.7 Headache distress scale (b).

Headache monitoring during therapy

Patients who have observed their headache components for a defined period of time can compare their headache scores with their psychological responses or coping attempts and utilise these for their therapy. For instance, diary or rating scale records can be explored in combination with therapy tasks as suggested in the worksheets *thinking about headaches, dealing with worrying thoughts, balancing headache thoughts* and *mind-absorbing activities.*

Eventually, patients move on to using monitoring tools for planning and recording health management and lifestyle activities (e.g., worksheet *activity planner & well-being schedule*). Such exercises become powerful therapy re-inforcers and patients get into the swing of re-evaluating their condition in view of independent health management.

The clinical headache report

Finally, all clinical information about patients' headache experiences can be summarised and interpreted so that the development and impact of the condition can be understood.

Referring clinicians may require a comprehensive explanation about the condition, its development as well as the therapy plan or other recommendations. The patients themselves will be very keen to receive feedback about the assessment findings.

The assessment summary or clinical headache report provides the headache specialist with a unique opportunity to communicate the multifaceted condition from the person's life-history perspective, spanning from pre-morbid vulnerabilities to overlapping post-trauma factors, secondary behaviours and social context. The provision of such a comprehensive report makes it possible to share the biopsychosocial understanding of such a complex condition with professionals within an integrated health service system and ensures that the patient receives ongoing encouragement of a proactive self-management approach.

Example: clinical report about a patient with posttraumatic headache

This example report describes the headache condition qualitatively whilst incorporating the assessment findings and results.

Mr Anthony P.   Headache Therapist
An Address   Headache Clinic

Dear Mr Anthony P.,

Thank you for participating in the comprehensive headache assessments in view of preparing your headache programme.

We have already begun to discuss how your headache condition and your lifestyle are related to each other. In this letter I am providing a summary of your headache difficulties, which offers the foundation for a more comprehensive understanding of how your condition has evolved and the factors that may maintain it.

- Onset Event:

  You experienced a traumatic head injury six months ago as a result of a bicycle accident that resulted in a small skull fracture. Unfortunately, it appears that your skull has not healed as expected and you are awaiting an appointment at the minor injury clinic for a small surgical correction.

- Immediate factors and consequences:

  You have noticed that any kind of head or body movement triggers a sharp head pain that starts at the site of the injury and spreads across your whole head, sometimes affecting your neck as well.

  Besides this sudden-onset pain, you also described severe, frequent and long-lasting headaches across the back of your head. You have become extremely fearful of pain and, thus, highly cautious about your head and body movements. This means that you are holding your head in a constantly tilted position and you have adopted a robot-like style of walking, rigidly moving your whole body rather than turning your head.

  You feel awkward about this because you are aware that this looks unnatural; you are ashamed and fear stigmatisation by others. As you are also looking for a new partner, you don't want to come across as odd in the presence of women. You recorded on the questionnaires that you no longer participate in any social activities and you only leave the house for your appointments. Nevertheless, it seemed that whatever you have done to try and help yourself has not worked consistently and you believe that getting better or not is just a matter of luck.

  Although social isolation does not sound like a good experience, perhaps the reduced complexity of your environment has contributed to your improved sense of energy, which was noted during your period of waiting for the appointment.

  In addition, you reported an improvement of your mood and emotional coping, because you have now been given an appointment for the outstanding minor surgery. You are also hopeful that you can benefit from participating in the headache therapy programme.

  However, because you were made aware that your scar has not formed as expected, you have become even more worried about it. You believe that the pain is associated with some bone or body particle that has come loose and might travel around your brain, i.e., following the path of your spreading head pain.

  You have also stopped leaving your house as you worry you might catch a cold. You fear that a cough or sneeze could trigger not only the headache, but might also release some bone fragments. You have even placed an enormous amount of sticky tape all around your windows and keep the house very warm in order to prevent drafts, which could cause you to catch a cold.

Additionally, you have become very obsessive with cleaning, as you fear that any crumbs on the floor might accidentally cause you to flinch, thus triggering unexpected body movements, which could set off the pain.

• Early vulnerabilities and interactional pattern:

You told me that you were an accident-prone child. You remembered numerous occasions when you fell off swings or down from trees and often sustained cuts and bruises. Apparently, your mother had been frustrated by the high levels of attention you required and ceased to comfort you or soothe your pains. Without her reassurance you often feared for days afterwards that you had perhaps seriously fractured some bones. You developed a belief that there must be something fundamentally wrong with you. These worries have made you highly sensitive to bodily sensations. When you became older you attempted to make sure that your environment was always safe and you developed obsessive tendencies to check for danger.

It also transpired that, in your adult life, you used your lively temperament to influence the staff in your firm. It appeared that you strove for a high-status role in order to compensate for the deep-felt belief that you are defective in some way. In order to present yourself as an authority figure, you described how you purposefully used your voice to "express frustrations." In particular, when others did not seem to meet your incredibly high expectations, you tried to intimidate them with your angry outbursts. In the end, your aggression and intimidation scared your partner and this resulted in the breakdown of your relationship following your accident.

• Setting and maintaining factors:

You are the director of a financial company. Due to your headaches following your bicycle accident you were unable to return to this role. In the meantime, you experienced an aggravation of your symptoms, which resulted in unusual postures and consequent avoidance of social situations. You found it very difficult to cope with your headaches and with being forced to stay at home, and your outbursts of frustration have resulted in the permanent breakdown of your relationship. This felt to you like the rejection and abandonment you experienced when you were younger, i.e., when your mother refused to provide you with her warmth and nurturing when you were hurt.

We explored the timeline of your headache development. Your accident happened six months ago and you appeared to adjust well from a practical point of view in the first two months. Nevertheless, you seemed to struggle to cope with the experienced sense of isolation from your work role and your outbursts of frustration contributed to the departure of your partner. Shortly after the time when your partner left, you reported to your doctor that you had developed severe head pains and you requested additional medical examinations.

Baseline Questionnaire Results Anthony

Questionnaire	Raw Scores	Interpretation/Norm Range
HDI Total	94	Severe: Beyond standard deviation
HDI Emotion Subscale	44	of
HDI Function Subscale	50	posttraumatic headache sample
HANA Total	84	Similar to others with posttraumatic headache
Headache Frequency	2-daily	Severe, beyond SD of sample
Headache Intensity	3-severe	Severe
Headache Duration	1-all day	Severe
Headache Intense/Weak	3-severe	Severe
SF-36	Waiting // Baseline	
General Health Perception	10 // 30	Better, but still clinical range
Change in Health	0 // 0	Severe problems
Physical Function	20 // 55	Improved, non-clinical
Role Limitation (physical)	0 // 0	Severe problems
Role Limitation (emotional)	0 // 67	Improved, non-clinical
Social Functioning	22 // 0	Reduced
Pain	0 // 11	Better, but still clinical range
Mental Health	28 // 64	Improved, non-clinical
Energy/Vitality	10 // 65	Improved, non-clinical
MHLC		
Internal Factors	14	-
Powerful Others	17	-
Luck	24	Highest attribution of locus of control
HADS Total	20	Similar to posttraumatic headache
Anxiety Subscale	10	sample and clinically in borderline
Depression Subscale	10	range
YSQ	70	'High/unrelenting standards' schema
	94	'Social isolation' schema
	85	'Defectivenes' schema

Figure 3.8 Baseline questionnaire results: Mr Anthony P.

During the recent assessments and interview, you have already in-creased your awareness about how you are using body postures and the behavioural expression of pain in order to gain the attention of doctors and the support of other people you know. Nevertheless, you experience such severe anxiety in relation to the health of your brain that you have become dependent on health care support and request almost weekly contact with your GP and, more recently, your surgeon. It appears that health professionals are giving you the reassurance and nurturing you require. However, as you are still on your own, the benefit of this soon dries up after contact with your doctors and the health anxiety builds up again.

Unfortunately, it appears that you have become stuck in a number of vicious cycles that maintain your pain, your behaviour and your interactional style with others overall.

• Initial formulation:

You sustained a head injury resulting in a small skull fracture that has not healed as expected. It appears that the scar pain has not settled and your worries about serious damage has resulted in vigilant monitoring of your head sensations as well as irrational images about bone fragments travelling through your head, leaving traces of brain lesions. The physiological arousal linked with such frightening images reinforces your pain pathways, as well as your emotional irritability.

Your innate personal style, which involves excessive control over your environment and your body, has resulted in a delayed return to work and has caused serious relationship problems.

You appear trapped in your personality pattern, because your attempts to help yourself and seek comfort and emotional reassurance have backfired. Social isolation seems to be the theme that runs through the stages of your life. The more you try to control or even surrender control by seeking help, the more your symptoms are aggravated. The more secondary behaviours you develop, the more you feel ashamed and inadequate. You are now at a loss as to how to get out of these traps because your health and the world around you seem so unpredictable.

• Suggestions:

This summary highlights some key elements that surround your complex headache condition. You are aware now that a "quick fix" or "medical repair" following the surgical repair of your skull deformation is unlikely, because your personal style and your health behaviours have led to a more permanent manifestation of your condition.

The headache assessments enabled you to explore how various factors from your past history hinder your body from adapting to your injury symptoms.

You are not quite ready to accept that the surgery to correct your scar may not be absolutely necessary, nor that this may not be the perfect solution to your pain problem.

You are keen to learn strategies to reduce your headaches, to overcome your difficulties and to making lasting adjustments to your lifestyle so that you can have more pleasant interactions with others. Consequently, it is recommended for you to:

- learn relaxation and cognitive strategies to optimise your coping with acute head sensations and longer-lasting headaches

- engage with physiotherapy and practise exercises to reverse neck tension and improve your posture
- practise cognitive and behavioural strategies (e.g., thought-stopping, meta-strategy "GO SLOW") to regulate your frustrations and outbursts
- use a graded desensitisation approach, which would enable you to remove unnecessary sealant and reverse other excessive safety measures in your home
- engage in schema-focused therapy to explore your sense of isolation, fear of rejection and maladaptive over-compensation
- explore community resources to help you learn and apply interactive strategies and a communication style that can help you form satisfactory relationships, both at work and on a personal front.

These are the coping needs you have established in our assessment meeting. Due to your difficulties in interactions with others, e.g., in a group setting, you would prefer to enrol in the 1:1 headache therapy.

I look forward to working with you.
Yours sincerely,
Headache Therapist

HANA: Headache Needs Assessment
HDI: Henry Ford Hospital Headache Disability Inventory
HADS: Hospital Anxiety and Depression Scale
MHLC: Multidimensional Health Locus of Control
SF-36: MOS 36-item Short Form Health Survey
YSQ: Young Schema Questionnaire

To sum up, the interpretation of the headache experience is at the core of the multifaceted understanding of posttraumatic headaches.

The outlined procedures – assessment, formulation, feedback and intervention – need to be grounded consistently in the theoretical model. This alignment guarantees a shared understanding of the condition, the motivation for health behaviour change and, consequently, an increased likelihood of symptom reduction and lifestyle improvement.

Module 2: headache clinics for people with mild brain trauma

What do headache patients want from their doctor? According to research, the answer is not just medical treatment, as one would expect, at least not in the long term. What patients really want from their doctors is an *understanding* of their pain.

Nevertheless, a physical examination by a medical specialist is vital at the outset, first, to check that no underlying medical issues that require immediate attention (such as haemorrhages or tumours) are present and, second, to identify the specific subtype of posttraumatic headache, upon which a subsequent formulation and therapeutic approach may be based. After such medical reassurance and clear diagnosis, patients will be much more likely to engage with therapists in an exploration of non-medical and alternative factors that constitute their headaches.

Psychologically informed early intervention for people with mild brain trauma is highly recommended and this includes prevention of persistent posttraumatic headaches. This is because people with psychosocial predispositions and complications are most at risk of developing posttraumatic headaches and secondary problems that potentially maintain and reinforce their conditions.

Specialist clinics for people with mild brain trauma symptoms, predominantly headaches, apply a manualised and tailored approach to guide both the specialist and the patient through the clinical encounter. Such headache clinics aim to facilitate the shift from the medical and symptom-focused understanding to the comprehensive biopsychosocial philosophy. This sets the pace for the engagement with headache management and initiation of proactive lifestyle changes.

The key aims of such one-off sessions include:

- Engagement, reassurance and normalisation
- Psycho-medical education and reformulation
- Motivation for ongoing self- and health management.

Patients are usually referred to the specialist brain trauma or pain clinic by their family doctor. Commonly, following an accident, people check in at hospital emergency services, where they see medical specialists and undergo tests and scans to rule out a more serious brain or neurological injury. Such medical investigations are vital, but patients are often puzzled about the conclusion that there is apparently nothing wrong with them. Some people are told that because their scans were clear or that, because they did not lose consciousness, their brains are fine. Whilst patients are certainly relieved about such news, such medical reassurance does not always eradicate their headaches. Head trauma clinics based on the psychosocial and early intervention approach offer the opportunity to explore their questions and uncertainties.

In a review of patients who found themselves waiting for a specialist headache clinic session, many reported not having dared to leave the house in the early stages following a trauma event due to the severity of the headaches they were experiencing. They impatiently awaited their appointment as they did not know how to help themselves, whilst the pressures to either return to work or to carry on with their roles in their family continued to mount.

Patients with complex mild brain trauma problems, including headaches, most benefit from the reformulation of their experience in the light of their critical life events, underlying anxiety and stresses. The clinic's success may be found in patients' decisions to take their lives into their own hands by participating in headache therapy or generic cognitive behavioural therapy.

Patients who predominantly experience headaches as their mild brain trauma symptom seem to get the most out of the one-off specialist clinic. The skilful combination of validation, reassurance and education about pacing and proactive lifestyle changes has been shown to optimise posttraumatic headache patients' coping repertoire.

According to the aforementioned research, the single clinic session can offer long-term prevention of secondary problems or prolonged unnecessary medical and therapeutic involvement.

This also means that the clinic setting must offer a close-to-ideal milieu so that patients can make the most of this opportunity. A welcoming environment is, therefore, just as important as the empathetic and attentive manner of the health professional.

The clinic for people with posttraumatic headaches follows the same structure as the full-length headache therapy introduced here.

First, attention is given to assessment and assessment outcomes.

Second, rapport building and patient engagement are the key elements to guide the person towards behaviour change.

Third, the major part of the session focuses on the reformulation and shift away from the fear about organic lesions towards an understanding of the biopsychosocial interplay of all their personal and social factors, with a particular focus on stress factors and long-term demands.

Finally, patients are encouraged to explore their emerging ideas about the changes they can make in order to reduce their headaches and their stresses and to improve their health and lifestyle.

Engagement and assessment

The first step is nevertheless symptom-focused. It is important to meet the patient at their present point in time. Patients may come prepared with their headache diaries and questionnaires, which perhaps were sent in the post along with the appointment details. They may be required to briefly reiterate what originally had happened to them and how they are affected by their headaches. In contrast to their initial visit at the doctor's, they will be guided to tell their story slightly differently this time. Active listening and careful attention to the elements related to their past history, personal and social factors, as well as to their coping attempts, shape the story in such a way that the underlying, less obvious, but still crucial predispositions and concurrent complications will surely come to light.

This is the time for rapport building; assessments of types of symptoms, their frequency and intensity; a discussion of the medical findings and an exploration of the physiological theories. The examples of Alice, Harry or Anthony come to mind here.

Psycho-medical education, reformulation and reassurance

Although everyone benefits from clarification, it does not mean that explaining everything is useful for everyone.

The psycho-medical explanations include sharing the understanding of:

- the medical investigations, tests and scan results or the lack of any findings
- the reasons why they were given a preliminary diagnosis of concussion and posttraumatic symptoms
- the psychologically relevant headache variables obtained via questionnaires and headache interview
- the way the patient's posttraumatic headaches fit with the Pain Gate, integrated neuro-behavioural, neuropsychological or other formulation models (see Chapter 1)
- the neuropsychological and information-processing disturbances and how they are triggered and set off by autonomic arousal and maintained by longer-lasting stress mechanisms and
- most importantly, the Central Sensitisation dynamics.

Appendix III includes a guide for patients with mild brain trauma who also experience headache symptoms. This useful tool enables the clinician to lead the patient through all the information explored in the session.

In a one-off clinic session it is vital to match the explanation model with the individual's assessment outcomes and a well-chosen formulation model. Explanations and reassurance are really well accepted by patients if they are close to their personal experience, lifestyle and individual concept about their circumstances.

Motivation for ongoing self- and health management

The skilled practitioner will be aware that the more a patient's details are tailored to their formulation, the easier it is for them to relate how their headaches have become part of their health and life story. Such insights will provide the most optimal grounding for thinking about and planning healthy lifestyle changes.

Resilience is a concept that can facilitate acceptance and motivation for adaptations to daily routines. The belief that the person might have been coping with a lot more prior to the head trauma is one that a lot of people struggle with. This is often related to the person's expectations of themselves and the amount of pressure they put on themselves to recover quickly. The metaphor of having "too much on your plate" can help patients visualise that, following a trauma event, their plate has "shrunk." As a result, people naturally become overwhelmed more quickly. Such visualisations of the many different contributing factors to the headache condition can help identify either which things can be taken off their plate or what can be done to make their plate bigger again.

Once a shared understanding about the factors that maintain the headaches has been established, one can explore strategies for exiting vicious cycles and life traps. Some of these are more straightforward, for example, referring the patient on to a vocational rehabilitation service if there are difficulties getting back to work, to physiotherapy if there are neck tension and posture problems or to community health centres if pacing, fatigue, diet or smoking are the key contributors.

Self-management strategies such as memory techniques, basic pacing strategies throughout their daily routines or simply acknowledging when they have "too much on their plate" can be enough for most people to achieve a gradual symptom reduction. Nevertheless, for a few, the idea of self-management can be an alien concept. At such a point one has to go back to the formulation models and focus on how "everything is connected" before motivating lifestyle changes and the use of strategies.

People understand that resting and relaxing are useful. However, the practice of focused relaxation exercises is difficult to justify for some and others might find it "hippyish." Relaxation practice can be introduced as an attention strategy in line with the information-processing headache models. The person can be encouraged to use meta-strategies and ask themselves, "Where is my focus?" This brings the attention to their present moment and raises awareness of the activated stress and pain pathways as, for example, described in the Central Sensitisation model. If people are caught up in self-critical thoughts and unhelpful patterns, then such concepts can help with the realisation of their complicated circumstances and self-help strategies aimed at directing attention to what is required at a particular moment in time.

People may actually feel exhausted after 60–90 minutes of focused participation in the headache clinic. In line with the message of the session, they will benefit from a reminder that an exacerbation of headache symptoms is possible after such a focused period. Consequently, they are encouraged to take a good quality rest after the session, perhaps even before they set off for their journey home.

Usually by the end of the headache clinic, people are grateful for the comprehensive explanations and will have planned how to apply self-management strategies, how to find support if their motivation fades and where to go if there are other difficulties that may get in the way of making the necessary readjustments. Some people with substantial pre-morbid vulnerabilities will require more than the one-off reformulation session and will no doubt benefit from participation in the health management and cognitive behavioural headache therapy modules.

Module 3: health management

This module is intended as a gentle introduction to self-management with a focus on relaxation practice. Health management can be successfully delivered to small groups of between two and six participants, as well as in one-to-one sessions.

The purpose and aims are:

- Introduction to the biopsychosocial headache programme
- Engagement with self-management of headaches
- Provision of health information and practice of coping strategies
- Relaxation practice.

The supplementary material includes a number of worksheets that are intended to guide the patients through the programme and to summarise the sessions. The contents will be meaningful for patients if they can reflect on it as part of the therapeutic explorations. Some patients require help understand certain terms, e.g., "locus of control" or "cognitive." Worksheets should not be given to patients as "homework" if the content has not been a matter of discussion during the session.

Relaxation as therapy

A core principle of the positive psychology concept is the shift towards enhancement of the quality of life in headache-free periods. Disconnecting conditioned anticipatory headache fears and worries via deep relaxation can reset the body's self-regulation processes.

Relaxation therapy aims to reduce the physiological stress that either triggers or maintains posttraumatic headaches and provides the patient with a tool to soften the pain in acute headache episodes.

Patients report an increased sense of control and reduced helplessness. Relaxation is something that they can do independently.

Relaxation therapy uses clear instructions and imagery in line with theory of learning and memory.

Relaxation therapy can:

- Reduce muscle tension
- Reduce anticipatory fear of pain
- Reduce the arousal resulting from pain and anxiety
- Increase the intensity of pain relief imagery
- Increase information-processing and attention
- Reduce distractibility
- Disconnect headache sensations from irrational fears about consequences
- Disconnect headache sensations from intrusive memories about the injury or accident
- Achieve peripheral and central desensitisation.

Practical considerations for learning and teaching relaxation

Learning relaxation means acquiring a new skill.

The following points are useful to consider in the early learning phase:

- regular practice is required, which can take some time
- begin with learning relaxation in headache-free periods
- choose an optimal place, with no distractions and enough time
- with advanced skill, practice can take place anywhere in any position
- with proficient skill, relaxation can be applied to reduce stress or head tension
- the difference between deep focused relaxation and "chilling out"
- how individual means of relaxing can be converted into intensive relaxation techniques by increasing self-awareness (e.g., mindful breathing and walking)
- how individual daily means of relaxing can be incorporated into personalised relaxation scripts (e.g., sense of comfort when stroking a cat)
- proceed with a staged approach: longer and detailed induction scripts in the early learning phase; advanced skill acquisition inductions can be chunked and therapy scripts can follow swiftly.

Relaxation is best administered:

- by the therapist in person
- a couple of times or more during therapy sessions
- by including the headache characteristics and preferences of the patient
- by matching administration tempo with the patient's breathing rhythm
- by including tailored self-instructions, patients' choice of wording, images and descriptions of positive experiences
- by modulating situational components (e.g., patient in discomfort or coughing, external distractions)
- by accommodating memory or attention difficulties in the instructions (e.g., more repetition, shorter pauses, shorter script)
- by accepting reluctant and sceptical points of view by suggesting that patients "pretend" to relax at first, e.g., follow the instructions and "pretend to slow down the breathing rhythm"
- by challenging a "keep busy" attitude to mask chronic pain with the experience that relaxation is safe and headaches are manageable
- by using positive reinforcement when patients report relief of tension and pain even if only briefly or only during relaxation exercises. This still represents progress, as they did not have such relief before they practised relaxation – they have acquired a powerful skill to modulate

their tension and pain; and they have evidence that they suffer from tension and not from a brain disorder
- by increasing flexibility: relaxation scripts are adjusted to patients' responses (e.g., breathing rhythm, time needed to enter deep relaxation phase)
- by using intense rapport and an empathetic relationship to enhance the sense of well-being and headache relief.

Purpose of patients' relaxation practice between sessions at home using recorded scripts:

- to familiarise themselves with the recording prior to practice; to be aware of length, content, sound of voice, background sounds of the audio script, etc.
- to use a pre-recorded script with their therapist's voice, if preferred.

Relaxation exercises are most effective if the scripts (Appendix II) are tailored to the specific patient's headache needs as well as to their attention ability and personal routines.

Relaxation exercises can be built by combining scripts in the following way:

- Relaxation induction
- Therapeutic component
- Ending

The focused body relaxation, progressive muscle relaxation or autogenic training methods are ideal induction scripts for achieving a deep level of physical relaxation. It is advisable to choose one of these relaxation methods and use it consistently during the course of the headache programme. The complete script needs to be administered, followed by an ending script. When patients have gained proficiency in their practice, the induction is followed by a therapy script and then by an ending. Eventually, patients should be able to enter the deep relaxation phase very quickly. At this stage, it might no longer be necessary to administer the full induction. For example, the focused body relaxation might then only need to be administered up to the point where the patient has settled into the exercise. This point is indicated in the text of the script and in the therapy manual with the following symbol: *. The selected therapy scripts can be administered immediately following this symbol.

Patients who have counter-productive self-beliefs – i.e., do not feel worthy of taking a rest, experience guilt and see relaxation as a waste of time, as well as patients with an endurance-type coping style – may feel challenged as they want to work as hard as possible to get better or may be mentally overactive, with a solution-seeking approach. These people need to address such core patterns as part of the individual cognitive therapy, perhaps including a schema-focused approach.

Meta-strategies and complementary aids

Following mild brain trauma some people can have substantial problems with planning and organising their daily routines. This initial therapy module should also include practice of "meta-strategies." These are generic strategies that can be applied across a number of activities. It is useful to design the meta-strategy with the patient and to make it very specific to their need. Importantly, just like any other CBT technique, this requires a lot of practice. Self-talk, self-instructions, mental imagery or habit changes should be rehearsed several times with patients in the session and practised again as "homework" before they are applied in the challenging, stressful or (head)painful situations.

Modern technology can be an asset in therapy. Numerous programmes and apps can help patients keep track of their lifestyle changes and headache-health management. The preparation for the use of such compensatory aids including the traditional diaries and worksheets should also be supported by the headache therapist. For instance, reminders or alarms can be set for headache monitoring or to practice stress-reduction exercises.

Self-management programmes on the internet can also complement the headache therapy promoted here. Especially towards the end of the programme, patients might be grateful for ongoing support.

Appendix IV includes examples of healthcare sites that share our biopsychosocial perspective and emphasise the importance of self-motivation and positive engagement if symptom-reduction and improvement in quality of life are envisaged.

Additionally, there are many health community services (e.g., exercise referral schemes), which can be incorporated into patients' ongoing well-being goals or plans.

Health management session I

Useful material

Abdominal breathing worksheet
Effect of stress on the body worksheets 1 & 2
Introduction to relaxation & relaxation practice worksheets
Positive self-talk worksheet
Focused body relaxation script

Welcome and objectives

It is assumed that the headache therapist has already met the individual patient or the group participants during the assessment stage. The welcome can emphasise the understanding about their headache as well as all associated components of their condition. People can be directed towards a more optimistic outlook.

What is the purpose of the health management module?

The patients might like to know that this module:

- is a preparation for the individual one-to-one therapy; this will build on the foundation strategies learnt here
- is a non-medical approach; rather, it is based on the principle that by optimising healthy behaviours the body's self-healing capacity can be encouraged
- does not aim to directly reduce headaches
- focuses on relaxation exercises, pacing and activity management and self-motivation
- is one of their resources to improve physical, emotional and social well-being creatively.

Introduction to health management is the first step in encouraging patients to reflect upon and understand the headaches as part of their whole personal experience so that they can eventually stop fighting them. The programme aims to point to alternative, structured and paced ways of accomplishing tasks and routines.

How is relaxation useful?

Use the *introduction to relaxation & relaxation practice* worksheets

The therapist needs to be mindful of the practical considerations listed above. It is important to work out which relaxation technique and routines are best suited for the patient.

Patients with brain trauma symptoms may be slower learners and require more frequent rehearsals of new information. It might take them a little longer to master this new skill. Group attendance can support their motivation to keep going.

At the beginning of the session, patients can be encouraged to explore questions such as:

- How do I normally relax?
- How do I know my relaxation works?
- How do I notice the difference between an activity and a rest?

The therapist can use the following, or similar, words:

"In relaxation, our body works differently, just as it works differently when we sleep or when we are awake. Deep relaxation practice does not replace sleep. It is a very useful state in which the body gets an optimal chance to restore its healthy balance.

"In challenging, activity-demanding circumstances, the body uses adaptive mechanisms to restore resources. Following an accident or traumatic event, it is likely that the body's self-regulation mechanisms do not work properly. The headaches are signs that the body is struggling to adapt. The body may remain vulnerable to further demands for a long time.

"The aim of acquiring the relaxation skill is initially to reduce bodily stress, muscular tension and optimise well-being during headache-free periods. Eventually, relaxation is applied as a means of coping with acute headaches. You will be able to achieve this when you have learnt to enter the deep relaxation stage quickly and at will.

"The headache therapy is designed to help your body restore a healthy balance. It is important not only to use relaxation, but also to be mindful of how activities are planned and carried out during the day. Certain activities maintain energy levels while others drain them. Most energy-draining tasks are associated with stress, high demands, and emotional pressure (e.g., responding to guilt)."

How to practise relaxation

"Relaxation can be learnt like any other skill. Your body needs to practise regularly what it feels like to be relaxed and how to get there. You can probably relate to those moments in the evening when you feel yourself just dropping off to sleep or when you are lazing on a beach, feeling comfortably warm and heavy. Indeed, feelings of warmth and heaviness are good indicators of deep muscle relaxation.

"Relaxation is best practised when you feel all right, do not have too much of a headache and have time available, without pending commitments. Starting to practise while lying down on a bed with your eyes closed is best. Make sure that you are free from interruptions by others or your mobile phone, computer, doorbell, etc. Later on, you should be able to practise whenever or wherever you want to."

Preparing for a relaxation exercise

Use the *relaxation practice* worksheet

- Rating of relaxation versus stress or tension.
  "Look at the *relaxation practice* worksheet. On the arrow, mark your level of relaxation before you start with relaxation and how you feel after the exercise."

- Muscle tension and release

  "Next, try the following exercises to get an idea of what it is like to have relaxed muscles. While sitting down, begin by making a tight fist with your right (or dominant) hand and increase the tension until you reach a maximum tension of 100. Notice the tightness in all the muscles of your hand, your fingers, and also your forearm. Then, gently release tension down to $80 - 60 - 40 - 20 - 10 - 8 - 6 - 5 - 4 - 3 - 2 - 1$. Uncurl your fingers and notice the muscle tension draining from your forearm, hand and fingers. Repeat this exercise with your left (or non-dominant) hand."

- Abdominal breathing. Use the *abdominal breathing* worksheet

  "Practise abdominal or deep breathing, sitting or lying down. Breathe normally and regularly. Become aware of your breathing and your breathing pattern. Breathing like this means that your mind is already tuning into relaxation mode. The next time you breathe out, gently extend the breathing-out phase. You can sigh or breathe out with a hum or even count quietly and see how many numbers you can say while breathing out. Then, hold your breath for a brief moment, breathe in again gently... and so forth."

- Think "Relax." Use the *positive self-talk* worksheet

  "Practise forming positive thoughts in your mind while breathing out. To begin with think the word "relax" every time you breathe out. Notice how you become more and more aware of your normal breathing pattern. Repeat this five to ten times."

- Warm up

  "Practise some gentle physical movements to loosen your neck and shoulder muscles.

  While standing up, do some of the following movements:

  Circle your arms gently. Begin with very small arm circles and increase them into bigger swings. This helps mobilise the shoulders and arms and encourages breathing.

  Lift the arms up when breathing in and lower the arms down when breathing out. This increases attention on the breathing pattern.

  Hold both arms horizontally in front of you. Notice the weight of the arms as you keep holding them for a few moments more. Drop them down with a flop and say the word, 'Relax' as you do so.

  Roll and lift up your shoulders. Hold and notice tension and heaviness in your shoulders for a moment. Say the word, 'Relax' as you let them drop down.

  Stretch your neck gently by moving the head from side to side and release unwanted tension."

- Observe your posture

  "Have you adopted an unhelpful posture or do you have difficulties with neck and shoulder tension? If this seems a serious issue, you might want to consult a physiotherapist."

Relaxation practice

Patients rate their baseline state before the relaxation practice on a scale from 0 to 100 as on the *relaxation practice* worksheet.

Administer the focused body relaxation script.

Patients rate their post-relaxation state from 0 to 100 and add personal comments.

It is a good idea to obtain qualitative feedback from each person about their relaxation experience. Detailed explanations are not necessary. Nevertheless, it is important for the therapist to know if patients experience anything unexpected. This could be related to finding it difficult to relax, muscle stiffness, pains, cramps or unpleasant thoughts or memories. Knowledge of such events helps the therapist alter the technique in order to optimise its effectiveness.

Health information: effect of stress on the body

Use the worksheets on *effect of stress on the body 1 & 2, abdominal breathing* and *introduction to relaxation*

Patients not only want to understand the dynamics of their headaches, but also the purpose of therapeutic interventions. The provision of such information optimises their learning about their physical and emotional experiences and the mechanics of coping strategies.

Therapists are advised to familiarise themselves with the earlier sections in Chapter 1 about stress models and help their patients understand their headaches from the perspective of long-term challenges rather than from the onset event only.

The worksheets on *effect of stress on the body 1 & 2, abdominal breathing* and *introduction to relaxation* can provide a foundation for explanations and discussion.

Ending the first session

The session ends by encouraging patients to practise relaxation in their own time.

Health management session 2

Useful material

Activity planner & well-being schedule
Effect of stress on the body worksheets 1 & 2
Energy roller coaster worksheets 1 & 2
Introduction to relaxation & relaxation practice worksheets

My job? Your job! worksheet
Quality of life worksheet
Real life and ideal life worksheet
Resources and demands worksheet
Focused body relaxation script

Welcome and objectives

• Relaxation practice
• Planning activities and pacing

Relaxation practice

Begin with relaxation practice immediately after the patient has settled for the session.
Obtain the pre-relaxation score
Warm-up
Administer the focused body relaxation script
Obtain feedback and the post-relaxation score
Refer to the *introduction to relaxation & relaxation practice* worksheets

Health information: what is activity management? How to pace your life?

It is important to arrange daily activities in such a way that the body continues to build up its resources. Experiencing chronic headaches after a mild brain trauma means that the body has not yet restored its balance. Therefore, patients are more vulnerable than in the past in the face of more challenging or complex situations.

Activity planning can be approached from a very practical level. Time management and pacing are the key themes.

It is not the task or the situation *per se* that causes stress. Expectation or worries about the consequences of involvement in a task can increase the emotional pressure. It is common that underlying core personality patterns (i.e., traits or schemas) generate obstacles or unrealistic presumptions that can hinder proactive tasks – and, hence, also health management.

Personal styles or maladaptive coping strategies (avoidance, over-endurance, etc.) that might be incompatible with a therapeutic recommendation can escalate tension. Such stress overlaps with the pain pathways (see the sections on Pain Gate and Neuromatrix). Pain needs to be defused from anxiety or stress so that a solution-focused approach can be simplified.

Exploration of activity management

- Meaning of stress: use the worksheets *effect of stress on the body 1 & 2*
  "The human body is well equipped to adapt to short-term stress episodes. The autonomic nervous system is rapidly activated in the case of a real or perceived threat. The arousal resettles soon after an episode is resolved, without adverse or long-term effects. The prolonged stress and secondary problems associated with a critical health and life event require the body to supply energy to deal with this beyond the autonomic arousal. This longer-term activation is provided by neuroendocrine systems and involves what is called the HPA-axis. It works by "activation hormones" interacting with the brain and the bodily organs to withstand ongoing demands. However, if demands exceed resources, then these mechanisms cease to work and a range of additional symptoms may evolve. These increase the feelings of malaise and depression and people often try in vain to do something about them."

- Body's level of energy and impact of past and short-term stress: Exploration of perception of demands and daily hassles
  Use the *energy roller coaster* worksheets 1 & 2
  "Headache episodes can cause pressure as unfinished jobs mount up and feelings of guilt about unaccomplished tasks increase. Headache-free 'boom' periods are often used to accomplish all leftover tasks and to release built-up guilt. If the number of jobs outweighs available resources, people 'go bust.' Such ups and downs feel like being on a roller coaster and can drain the energy physically and mentally."

- Pacing: use *activity planner & well-being schedule*
  "Rest periods should be spread out purposefully throughout the day. Rest needs to be taken before the person feels tired or exhausted.
  "Relaxation practice restores energy levels. This should be planned in advance. The *activity planner & well-being schedule* helps with thinking ahead and using pacing methods."

- Graded activity management:
  "Demanding activities are best begun with relaxation practice (e.g., a car drive or a day at work). Tasks should be planned and broken down into either time sections (e.g., a break after each hour) or to sub-task sections (e.g., a break after returning from shopping and again after unpacking the shopping). The sense of satisfaction is much higher if tasks can be achieved with a remaining energy reserve."

- Confidence and mood: use the *activity planner & well-being schedule*
  "Planning fewer activities with rest periods guarantees that something can be accomplished throughout the day. There should be energy left in the evening. This maintains mood and confidence. In contrast,

feeling exhausted and completely depleted of energy is linked with feeling low and disappointed. The *activity planner & well-being schedule* can help organise activities and monitor your mood."

- Short-term gains and long-term benefits:

"Due to the unpredictability of headache episodes, people might want to cram as many activities into headache-free periods as possible for short-term gains. Making an effort to use pacing strategies and to reorganise activities may have the long-term benefit of reducing headache frequency or intensity and improving overall well-being. People will become more aware of associated health behaviours such as drinking enough water, doing physical exercise or becoming aware of sleep patterns. The shift towards planning well-being for the long term will eventually become more and more natural."

- Resources and demands: use the *resources and demands* worksheet

"The body needs to balance its resources to stay healthy. Bodily stress mechanisms are activated following a challenging or traumatic event, which often comes at the cost of developing persistent symptoms. Hence it is important to optimise resources for recovery."

- Task ownership and involvement: use the *my job? your job!* worksheet

"People can feel overloaded with activities if they take on tasks and responsibilities that do not belong to them. Often, they get involved in others' problems because they worry that these could affect them as well. This might not be the case.

Ownership of tasks and appropriate levels of involvement can be explored through some of these questions:

What is the actual task?

Whose job is it actually to complete the task?

Who 'owns' the problem?

Do I need to get involved?

How can I learn that others can be trusted?"

- Values and quality of life: use the *quality of life, real life* and *ideal life* worksheets

People sometimes get distracted from activities that would offer them a better quality of life. The following questions can refocus them on activities that do add value to their life:

"What is the purpose of the activity for which I am responsible?

Is this activity taking me towards my values?

How does this activity contribute towards my quality of life?

What lifestyle changes can increase my sense of purpose?

Work: do I want to change my working hours, direction of career?

Family: do I enjoy the support of my family or do relationship problems increase my distress?

Living arrangements: am I happy with my accommodation, transport options or neighbourhood facilities?

What steps could I take to optimise my sense of purpose and the quality of my lifestyle?"

Ending

The session ends with a brief relaxation practice using the relaxation induction and deep breathing. Patients can also focus on an image or memory linked with a past situation where they managed to focus on their values or life aims. Such images coupled with the relaxation experience can be a motivator for health management in their near future.

The *activity planner & well-being schedule* can be used to plan such proactive activities between sessions.

Finally, participants are encouraged to practise relaxation in their own time.

Health management session 3

Useful material

Activity planner & well-being schedule
Headache coping strategies worksheet
Introduction to relaxation & relaxation practice worksheets
Mind-absorbing activities worksheet
Resources and demands worksheet
Relaxation induction script: focused body relaxation
Relaxation script: resources and perspectives
Therapy story: "the hare and the hedgehog"

Welcome and objectives

- Relaxation practice
- Activity and well-being planning
- Limiting beliefs
- Resources and demands
- Avoidance
- Headache coping strategies

Relaxation practice

Begin with relaxation practice immediately after the participants are settled.

Pre-relaxation score
Warm-up

Relaxation: resources and perspectives
Post-relaxation score
Refer to the *introduction to relaxation & relaxation practice* worksheets

The resources and perspectives script is an advanced relaxation script. It can be used at this point if patients have achieved a good level of relaxation ability.

This script adds imagery to the basic focused body relaxation, which builds on the previous session, incorporating suggestions on resources, achievements and purposeful activities.

Post-relaxation scores and feedback discussions will be informative here.

Activity and well-being planning

"What has been achieved so far?
How are resources found and used?
How is relaxation practice going at home?
How were the well-being activities implemented between sessions?
How were priorities and activities towards quality of life approached?"

Health management and limiting beliefs

Some people respond well to metaphors and stories as they offer a non-threatening and creative way to explore personal difficulties. *The Hare and the Hedgehog* by the Brothers Grimm is useful in the context of managing chronic conditions in association with rigid beliefs.

What is the story about? It appears to be a simple story about a race between two unequal competitors.

In particular, patients with a preference for an endurance-driven coping style tend to continue to race like the rabbit without contemplating that their strategy does not seem to fit the circumstances. They seem so stuck in their ways and so concerned about their pace that they appear unaware of a hidden truth or an illusion they are following. Instead of changing track as they notice their failure, they try harder and harder or use more and more pain medication, with the consequence that they become more unwell rather than getting closer to their goal.

Therapeutic explorations can increase flexible solution-seeking:

The hare could go slower and then realise the deceit.
The hare could stop and investigate.
The hare could change track.
The hare could admit and accept defeat and rest.
The hare could go for a walk with Mr and Mrs Hedgehog.

Patients with pre-morbid maladaptive schemas or interaction patterns may find it very difficult to experiment with alternative behaviours and attitudes. Therefore, they require additional resources and directive guidance to let go of life traps and to move towards an alternative or healthier lifestyle.

Resources and demands

Use the *resources and demands* worksheet

"Headaches are the cause and the consequence of a disequilibrium between resources and demands. The headaches themselves place a higher demand on the body's ability to regulate this balance. In order to optimise resources, it is important to remain active, engage in gentle exercises and practise relaxation, rather than withdrawing from tasks or resting and sleeping excessively."

Avoidance

Use the *activity planner & well-being schedule*

Headache patients tend to anticipate headaches at some point in the near future. Often, activities are altered or avoided in the hope of preventing severe headaches. Avoidance can lead to de-skilling as the person loses familiarity with avoided tasks, for example, those that require cognitive processing such as sorting finances or completing benefits forms. The activity might be avoided due to the fear of failure, i.e., it might go less well than in the past. Some people feel embarrassed. People avoid activities out of the fear of pain. Avoidance leads to loss of confidence and loss of roles and life may feel meaningless. People may lose the momentum for engaging in rewarding tasks.

A graded activity approach can be initiated to enable the return to meaningful activity. Participants can explore areas where they have restricted their activities and de-skilled themselves.

Headache coping strategies

Use the *mind-absorbing activities* and *headache coping strategies* worksheets

People who try to avoid stress or challenges at all costs to prevent headaches benefit from Emotional Resilience Therapy to strengthen their healing and adaptive mechanisms.

Exposure to planned, graded and paced tasks activate healthy adaptive mechanisms. Normal sensations like muscle tension during an activity can be understood as harmless. Patients can be guided to acknowledge their physical experience, even the headaches. Rather than avoiding such awareness by keeping busy and "pushing through the pain" or by withdrawing from activity, patients are encouraged to take note of the headache and the associated physical and emotional sensations. Often, they might use the image of "kindly greeting their headache," perhaps rating the intensity or using an observation chart and, following that, "explain" to the pain that another task is due, but they will "check in" with their body intermittently.

Other measures to cope with either rapid onset or longer-lasting and draining headaches can be explored using suggestions from the *headache coping strategies* worksheets.

Proactive coping is a combination of graded exposure, pacing and proactive adjustment. That way the body and brain learn that having a headache does not imply a threat, which optimises central reorganisation.

Stress-inoculation

In the case of secondary psychological dynamics, such as people avoiding a wide range of activities, cognitive and physical abilities slow down and previous coping skills may be reduced. Stress-inoculation is a traditional cognitive behavioural technique that encourages people to expose themselves to small doses of the stressor or, in this case, to the fear of anticipated headaches. The idea is that the person can eventually adjust again to small doses of stress and can improve their adaptive systems whilst still feeling in control.

Patients can explore which activity they could gradually integrate into their routines in small doses to habituate themselves to the fear and arousal associated with the headache symptoms.

Ending

The session ends by encouraging participants to practise relaxation in their own time and by suggesting the relevant worksheets.

Patients are encouraged to identify activities they have avoided in the past. The *activity planner & well-being schedule* might be used in between sessions.

Health management session 4

Useful material

Activity planner & well-being schedule
Headache coping strategies worksheet
Meta-strategy: "GO SLOW"
Mind-absorbing activities worksheet
Positive self-talk worksheet
Relaxation scripts: focused body relaxation and future pacing scripts

Welcome and objectives

- Relaxation practice
- Meta-strategies
- Maintenance of coping and health management skills
- Future pacing
- Outlook

Relaxation practice

Begin with relaxation practice immediately after the participants are settled.

Pre-relaxation score.
Warm-up.
Relaxation practice using the focused body relaxation script including future pacing statements.
Obtain feedback and post-relaxation score.

What are meta-strategies?

Use meta-strategy: "GO SLOW" and *activity planner & well-being schedule*
    Meta-strategies are mental self-instructions that can be universally adapted to a range of scenarios. They are also generic in the sense that they can be equally useful for different people.
    Meta-strategies can support mental and practical habit changes.
    The meta-strategy "GO SLOW" is an example of how an overwhelming situation can be mastered by a reorientation towards purposeful activities. Patients can be encouraged to explore if the "GO SLOW" strategy might be helpful in facing complicated or previously avoided situations or in taking a step back, grounding themselves and moving on to an alternative task.
    Pacing and graded exposure are also meta-strategies. Patients can explore how headache and activity management work in combination.
    Most activities can be broken down into parts and linked with cognitive management strategies. Meta-strategies help patients plan ahead or implement structure and pacing.
Exercise: Meta-strategy PROM
    PROM stands for Preview – Research – Organise – Monitor. This meta-strategy supports the planning of a process or the organisation of an event. It is always advisable to practice the application of such a method with patients in the session. Here is an example:
    A person experiencing posttraumatic headaches has been invited to a party and has been asked to bring desserts. They really want to go to the party but fear being overwhelmed by the social crowd and the responsibility of contributing food.

In such scenarios, it is helpful to learn to take a step back and adopt a wider perspective. However, this is easier said than done. Acronyms can again offer a mental structure.

P = Preview:

Social challenge: What/where does the event take place? How long is it? Who is invited? Who do I know?

Food challenge: What do people like? How much do I want to spend?

R = Research:

Social challenge: Is there a quiet place at the venue? How many people might there be?

Food challenge: What is the main course? Do people prefer homemade or shop-bought desserts?

O = Organise:

Social challenge: How will I organise the journey so that I won't feel exhausted when I arrive? How can I tell the hostess that I would like a break, that I prefer to rest somewhere quietly after the meal?

Food challenge: When, where and how will I prepare or buy the dessert? What help do I need?

M = Monitor:

Social challenge: Do I have everything I need to take with me? Am I comfortable?

Food challenge: Is everything going all right with my provision of desserts?

By structuring the challenges at every level and using the acronym like a mantra, patients get better at planning and are less overwhelmed by the perception of an overwhelming task.

Maintenance of coping skills

Use the *headache coping strategies, mind-absorbing activities,* and *positive self-talk* worksheets

Patients can be encouraged to explore how they can carry on beyond the facilitated intervention and practise the strategies they have learnt.

They can reflect how, with the use of strategies, they can remain involved with their daily responsibilities rather than use avoidance or endurance behaviours.

Patients observe how they are getting better with relaxation practice and step-wise, day-to-day adjustments.

Patients explore the meaning of "relapse," i.e., occasionally forgetting to use strategies or temporary lapses of motivation, which do not mean that the patients lose their awareness of their resources or their focus on getting better.

Discussion of worksheets.

Future pacing

"Future pacing" refers here to a positive self-instruction to insert a helpful image or a motivational statement into a concrete future situation. As part of the relaxation exercise patients are instructed to form a balanced or pro-active thought (e.g., "I am calm" or "I can concentrate") and link this with an image of a time in the future when they anticipate benefitting from it. This can be any time, sooner rather than later.

Future paced instructions can also encourage people to remember an experience that they have successfully achieved in the past and that they intend to accomplish again in the future.

Ending and outlook

Five-minute deepening relaxation practice focusing on abdominal breathing and the future paced statement.

Patients will benefit from information about the next step in their headache therapy. This might be the individual therapy programme or engagement with other health promoting and supporting services.

If the health management module was offered as a group intervention, then participants might want to find a personal way to say goodbye to each other.

Module 4: individual headache therapy

The key aims of the individual therapy programme are the improvement of health-functioning and the reduction of the headaches and associated symptoms, with a focus on an overall improvement of the quality of life.

Therapy setting

The health management module introduced patients to the self-help philosophy, focused on personal efficacy and aimed at teaching foundational stress-reduction strategies.

This has given patients opportunities to experience modulating their headache condition by regularly applying positive and proactive coping strategies. It is hoped that healthier behaviours and beliefs may already have been strengthened as the headaches are better understood within the context of their lives. Patients will have observed the links between activities causing and maintaining headaches, as well as those causing avoidance and loss of confidence.

Individual psychological headache therapy aims to build on those insights and offer patients wider options for overcoming their health traps. In this sense, the therapy is intended to enhance their sense of self, their social interactions and responsibilities and to lead them towards proactive life goals and values.

Such aims are inherent to most psychotherapy approaches. The individual headache therapy module implements and tailors common cognitive behavioural methods to help headache patients achieve the above stated outcomes.

It is important to set the scene for therapeutic work. The therapist must ensure that the patients' motivation to help themselves is optimised. Genuine trust and an empathetic therapeutic relationship are vital to reduce tension in the session and to promote self-healing. The therapeutic environment is crucial for headache management. This includes attention to the light in the room (e.g., neon strips, flickering blinds, etc.), the temperature, smells (e.g., carpet or cleaning fluids), sounds (inside and outside the office) and clutter (e.g., busy walls and information boards). Some services have limited influence over their environments, but there is always something each therapist can do to help their patients feel welcome, relaxed and able to concentrate.

Patients should be asked when they last had something to eat or drink and could be offered a hot drink or a glass of water. It might be useful to ascertain how much coffee, nicotine, alcohol, medication or other drugs they consumed before the session.

As mentioned in the earlier chapters, patients with post-concussion syndrome may present diffuse cognitive difficulties or might have a headache during the session. Some patients might have travelled a long distance to the clinic or attend sessions either before or after work. They might have had to cope with traffic or finding a car park, or might have waited for some time in a crowded waiting area. These events could have undermined their ability to fully participate in their therapy session.

Headache therapy follows a structured schedule that requires the patient to be engaged and attentive. If they find the sessions demanding, they could be advised to routinely practise the relaxation, as in the health management module, immediately after their return home.

The programme contains a number of exercises and practices to be carried out between sessions. The frequency of therapy sessions depends on a patient's engagement, need for encouragement and independence with the implementation of such exercises, as well as the opportunities available for practice. Patients benefit from as much practice as possible during the programme; therefore, fortnightly sessions might be very effective. Other patients require more cognitive or motivational support. Weekly sessions might be better for these people.

Therapists are encouraged to adapt the exercises to the patient's level of participation. For instance, sessions 4 and 5 contain a range of therapy activities. Some patients may benefit from intensive exploration of selected therapy tasks, whereas others may benefit from several different examples.

Progress assessment: Depending on the therapy design and time frame, it may be advisable to repeat assessment measures following the health management module and prior to individual therapy. The selection of measures needs to be consistent throughout the therapy and follow-up.

Therapy outline

Session 1: I have had mild brain trauma.
Session 2: Why do I have a headache?
Session 3: Coping with headaches.
Session 4: How can I improve the quality of my life?
Session 5: Meaning and purpose.
Session 6: Relax!
Session 7: The world around me.
Session 8: Using what I have learnt in the future.
Session 9: Nice to see you again.

Headache therapy session 1: I have had mild brain trauma

Useful material

Activity planner & well-being schedule
Effect of stress on the body worksheets 1 & 2
Headache diary
Meta-strategy PROM from health management module, session 4
Mild brain trauma worksheet
Pain Gate worksheet and pain pathways Figure 1.5.

Objectives

*   Rationale for the headache therapy
*   Understanding mild brain trauma in the context of physiological stress mechanisms
*   Impact of symptoms on functioning and well-being
*   Activity planning
*   Headache monitoring

Main therapy section

Impact of symptoms on functioning and well-being

"In today's session you have the opportunity to explore:
    How mild brain trauma is related to a chronic state of stress.
    How headaches and other mild brain trauma symptoms impact on your activities of daily living.
    How you can focus on coping skills practice and ways of moving towards a more proactive lifestyle."
    "First, you might want to ask yourself:
    'How have my headaches or other mild brain trauma symptoms impacted on my routines and activities?'

'What has changed since my assessment appointment and my participation in the health management module?'"

Understanding mild brain trauma in the context of physiological stress mechanisms

Use the *effect of stress on the body 1 & 2, mild brain trauma* and *Pain Gate* worksheets, and *pain pathways* Figure 1.5.

Notes for therapist: Using the patient's understanding and language, the therapist can proceed to explain the changes in stress regulation and information-processing in the case of headaches following brain injury.

Explanation using a common understanding as below can be helpful.

"You experienced a mild trauma to your brain. That means you sustained a sudden unforeseeable impact on your head, which was registered by your brain's alarm system as potentially seriously harming your health. Your 'thinking brain' encoded this as a failure to notice a threat and has now prepared your bodily systems in such a way to prevent any danger in the future. Therefore, the trauma event is securely encoded in your memory. Your attentional alertness and the sensitivity of your senses are permanently heightened.

"At the same time, your head sustained a physical impact, possibly causing bruises within the muscular-skeletal structures in your neck and head. This means that pain receptors keep firing and also activate your awareness.

"To some degree, your brain might have been thrown around inside your skull, causing micro-bruising of brain tissue or shearing of the axons of nerves cells. Such disturbances change the way the nerve cells and fibres function. Nerve cells communicate with each other using chemical-electrical methods. Often after a concussion, the transmission of signals slows down or does not work properly for a short while.

"Apart from difficulties with some of your brain functions (e.g., concentration) you might have sensed changes in the way your body processes stress. The sympathetic-adrenomedullary system (SAM), which is part of the autonomic nervous system, activates the body in the case of a real or imagined threat. It works like an emergency or alarm system, supplying resources quickly so that the body can cope with an extreme situation. The worksheet illustrates how the adrenal glands release adrenalin and noradrenalin, which optimise all functions, ready for a fight or flight.

"You probably notice this hyperactivation in the form of raised stress, including symptoms such as increased heart rate and breathing rhythm, muscle tension, sweating, restlessness, sleep problems, butterflies in your stomach and so on. Some people experience intolerance to noise and struggle in complex environments, for instance, when many people come together or in busy public places.

"The SAM has been activated at the time of your head trauma event and has now become hypersensitive. It is also called the 'fight or flight' response, meaning that, in the presence of danger, one either attempts to escape from it or to fight it. The SAM also supplies the emotional and physical energy to ensure we have the strength to run or fight.

"The activation of the alarm system is designed to respond to stimuli that are present in the moment. Thoughts, memories or worries about the traumatic event or about the painful experience of headache episodes are also 'in the moment.' These memories and images have linked or conditioned the trauma with the pain pathways. Therefore, the SAM can be triggered even if you are not directly exposed to a critical event.

"What is important here is that your trauma onset event was in the past. The recent situations that trigger your arousal, distress or pain do not constitute a real threat. It is merely the mental images linked with complex attention and information-processing functions that have been conditioned to the perception of danger.

"The discrepancy between the conditioned hyper-stimulation and the absence of an external threat can cause confusion. This is called 'cognitive dissonance.' This conditioned stress response indicates danger, but nothing is there to see or hear. To resolve the cognitive dissonance, your sensory systems (e.g., eyes, ears, taste, touch, muscle sensation, etc.) focus on and absorb even more stimuli to ensure nothing is missed. Hence, the former filter function of our attention systems is deactivated. All additional sensory information needs to be analysed by the respective brain regions to make sense of it.

"People feel overwhelmed by such information-overload, especially if the short-term neural information-processing functions are slowed down due to the micro-changes of neurophysiological structures.

"Cognitive dissonance also increases arousal. This feels like emotional irritability, which may lead to anger (fight response) or fear of overwhelming situations, which can raise muscle tension. Such muscle tension and postural changes may set off over-sensitive pain fibres, etc.

"There are several vicious cycles overlapping and escalating, which maintain the trauma experience and symptoms. The SAM cannot supply the resources necessary to maintain this bodily activation for very long. Therefore, a second level of stress system helps out. This is called the Hypothalamic-Pituitary-Adrenal axis (HPA-axis). It uses longer-working stress hormones, also released from the adrenal gland, in order to strengthen the body to cope with the demand. In contrast to the SAM where the physiological balance is quickly restored after a perceived threat, HPA-axis mechanisms carry on for much longer (days, weeks, months, even years) and can eventually lead to structural changes of bodily systems (e.g., heart, muscle functioning, metabolism and digestion). Whilst this is adaptive for ongoing high demand, it may lead to symptoms (e.g., chronic tension, migraines) or lasting unhealthy changes in the body (e.g., high blood pressure, stomach ulcers, inflammations) in cases when conditioned stress responses to a past event have become overreactive.

"In summary, **these symptoms are the result of a maladaptive hyperactivation and are *not* signs of brain injury**. They are uncomfortable, and cause tension and a range of symptoms including your headaches.

"Let's look at the *effect of stress on the body* and the *mild brain trauma* worksheets to summarise how your trauma event and ongoing headaches are related and affect your overall well-being."

Rationale for therapy

"One therapy aim is to reverse hypervigilance and reduce bodily stress. You get the opportunity to learn more cognitive and physical coping skills that help dampen the overactive alarm system. Your body and brain systems need to relearn that you are safe, that vigilance can be reduced and that the attention filter can be reset to normal again."

"Lots and lots of practice of active coping strategies, adjustments to your routines and pacing are important approaches to help with this. This lightens cognitive effort, reduces fatigue and improves information-processing. The threshold for stress experiences moves up."

Mild brain trauma metaphor – earthquake

The earthquake metaphor can simplify explanations about the consequences of mild brain trauma for patients who prefer such methods rather than scientific descriptions.

"A brain trauma can disrupt the organised transport of information through the brain regions, similarly to disrupted traffic in a major city affected by an earthquake. The infrastructure is no longer in place. Traffic from one end of the city can't run smoothly via motorways and streets. Travellers have to find alternative, less affected paths or have to clear the rubble first. The usual means of transport don't work. The chaos causes disorientation that may lead to wrong decision making. One might have lost the sense of direction and move around in circles. This costs time, requires an enormous effort and is emotionally challenging.

"Following a concussion, the information in your brain cannot run smoothly and quickly. There is so much more to observe and more new information to remember. Former routines or patterns are not usable. What one was able to remember in one load in the past has to be now encoded in smaller portions. However, each time a task is repeated, the new infrastructure improves and the chaos settles. It is nevertheless necessary to be economical with energy and allow a lot of time. If the process is hurried, then bodily resources become depleted.

"A person travelling through the ruins who is also worried or traumatised might become disorientated and stressed, with an additional sense of imminent danger. This person needs to learn to remain level-headed and address emotional difficulties.

"In contrast to a place ruined by an earthquake, the brain has the capacity to rebuild some of the infrastructure itself. This happens slowly by natural healing and can be encouraged by your positive and proactive health management."

Explanations like these can evolve in conversations with the patient. It may be beneficial to use therapeutic aides (graphics, written notes, repetition, etc.) to support patients' mental processing abilities. Patients' intuitive understanding and their own words are always a good place to start.

Activity Planning and Desensitisation

Use the *activity planner & well-being schedule* and meta-strategy PROM

"Let's explore how you can adapt your routines and activities to help with your headaches.

The rationale of preparing your activities is to ensure that you can achieve what you have planned. It's about the power of the first small step and encouraging your sense of accomplishment. Such task management aims to focus your attention towards organising the situation and the task itself.

First identify a task that you would like to improve. Maybe it's an activity that has caused frustration in the past."

Use the meta-strategy PROM as described in the health management module.

Use a taskmaster approach:

- "Identify the task or activity
- Chose a 'headache neutral' task, i.e., a task that is less likely to trigger symptoms
- Aim to make the task 100% achievable by breaking it down to the smallest manageable parts
- List and grade the steps that link the parts together
- Simplify the surroundings
- Slow the pace right down
- Enable calm and controlled task performance
- Schedule a time for your task in your planner
- Think about the things you need
- Carry out the task and be aware of the process
- Check that you got it right."

Example: A patient might find it difficult to remember where their car is parked. They might have got lost in the past, which has caused anxiety or resulted in headaches. Now, the thought of parking the car triggers self-doubt, apprehension, fear of stress and headaches, actual headaches or avoidance of driving. They are encouraged to schedule suitable times for practising the taskmaster approach in order to learn to remember their car parking space.

Using this example for now, a patient is encouraged, at a planned time, to drive the car a few hundred yards from their home. They are instructed to mindfully pay attention to key features of the surroundings and, if appropriate, use memory aids (take a digital photo, use a satellite navigator or write the street name down). Through practice, they learn that every time they park their car, they have strategies to find it again. As a result, the anxiety should reduce. If headaches are experienced during the activity, then the task should be even more simplified and relaxation should be part of it (either before or during a break, or afterwards). Task accomplishment is the goal of this desensitisation activity.

Ending: headache monitoring and coping strategies

"Next session, you will have the opportunity to explore your headaches in more detail. Record the headache intensity and duration on one morning and one afternoon over a period of two hours. Use your headache diary."

"Carry on with your relaxation practice each day."

Headache therapy session 2: why do I have a headache?

Useful material

Activity planner & well-being schedule
Peripheral and Central Sensitisation Figure 1.6.
Diathesis-Stress model of migraine and mild brain trauma Figure 1.7
Headache diary
Migraine and mild brain trauma worksheet
Mild brain trauma worksheet
My well-being actions worksheets 1 & 2
Pain Gate worksheet
The energy roller coaster worksheets

Objectives

*   Review of activity planning and desensitisation
*   Information about posttraumatic headaches and stress
*   The Pain Gate: acute versus chronic headaches
*   Actions that close the Pain Gate
*   Migraine and mild brain trauma

Welcome

Review of activity planning

Use the *activity planner & well-being schedule*

"Last time we explored how an injury to the brain disturbs the underlying mechanism of normal brain processing. You were encouraged to plan and carry out a graded activity. Regular experience of the fact that day-to-day activities can be performed successfully will retrain your brain to accept that most situations are safe. Your body and brain systems do not get overloaded with a graded approach. This is important in order to reduce the persistent state of 'high alert' or hypervigilance. Eventually, you should experience less stress and hopefully fewer headaches."

"How did you get on with your scheduled activity regarding:

– Grading of the activity
– Attentive awareness of the task
– Skill improvement
– Sense of accomplishment?"

Headache diary

What observations were made regarding headache episodes (intensity, lengths of headache episodes, coping with consequences, etc.)?
How was the day structured when headaches occurred?
What happened before and after the headache episodes?
How was the day structured on non-headache days?

Main therapy section

Headaches and stress

Use the *mild brain trauma* and *Pain Gate* worksheets to reflect on the interactions between headaches and stress.

Refer to Chapter 1 of this book for a theoretical recap of these topics.

"Frequent headaches are often a symptom of chronic tension due to the physiological states of stress. Most people develop headaches due to intense and longer-lasting demands on the bodily systems. This can happen in relation to a challenging life event or strenuous mental or physical activity, especially if the situation persists for some time.

"The impact of the accident made your body more vulnerable and less able to absorb the same degree of demands as before. The headache is a symptom of a chronic mild brain trauma syndrome, i.e., a reaction of your body to overwhelming demands. It is not an indicator of a dangerous brain disorder.

"How can this be understood?

"Pain is a natural physical response. It signals the body's healing functions following an acute lesion (i.e., physical injury). The initial injuries to your head and neck (e.g., bruises, muscle sprains) have now healed. Your chronic headache is no longer associated with an acute lesion. Headaches are very common in association with mild brain trauma. Persisting headaches are, in most cases, a result of ongoing hyper-arousal and the consequence of your body's depleted energy resources. Your body's ability to rebalance physical ability and environmental demand has fallen out of sync.

"Some types of headaches (e.g., allodynia) are related to disturbed processing of nerve signals. The strategies proposed in this programme can be helpful for many different types of headaches."

The Pain Gate and pain processing

Use the *Pain Gate* worksheet, Peripheral and Central Sensitisation Figure 1.6.

One way to explain the persistent pain problems is by using the Pain Gate theory.

"Acute lesions result in pain signals, which travel from the injured area to the spinal cord. Certain nerve cells interact in the spinal cord where the impulses are relayed to nerve pathways that transport them to the brain. This relay function acts like a 'gate' that opens for the signals, which then travel upwards to the brain for further processing.

"Physiological pain sensations after an injury to the head and neck mostly stem from lesions to the scalp, skull, muscles, arteries, some cranial nerves, brain membranes and other tissues, but not from the brain itself. Any of these sensations are also relayed in the spinal cord.

"Pain can only be perceived via the brain's pain-processing systems. There are many brain systems that are responsible for identifying, analysing and responding to pain signals. The perceived pain signals are converted by the brain's Action Systems and are then transferred back down through the Pain Gate. If the gate opens, then the site of the lesions receives some feedback. In this way, the body can monitor and influence the natural healing process.

"In persistent or chronic pain, the process of pain sensations, pain monitoring and feedback continues, despite completed healing of the injured area. The pain–brain circuit develops an automatic habit and the pain perception continues.

"This might be because the brain's signal transmission may be malfunctioning due to micro-changes on the chemical-electrical information-processing mechanisms. Additional processes (such as hyper-arousal, inappropriate posture, avoidance of movement, etc.) maintain pain processing and prevent them from calming down after an acute lesion has healed.

"Your body experienced a significant onset event (i.e., the accident), which caused an *acute* micro-injury to head and neck tissue. The event was encoded as a threat to your well-being or even survival. As a result, vigilance towards external stimuli and internal sensations that could potentially indicate danger was increased. This means that a high quantity of head-related sensations (not necessarily painful sensations) get through the Pain Gate, engage the Action Systems and enter the feedback loop. The brain activates networks that specialise in pain perception, processing and actions to take.

"The redundancy of this process in the form of *chronic* headaches can be described as a continuously sounding fire siren long after the fire and damage have been cleared up. It is now necessary to employ different methods to turn off the constant alarm signal and to reassure the body that the 'alarm systems' can shut down again. They will still be able to function effectively in the case of real danger.

"The constant perception and experience of pain sensations leads to an improved, but unnecessary, ability of certain brain regions to detect and analyse them. That means the brain, which enables us to feel pain, becomes more and more skilled in letting us know about the pain. This is also called Central Sensitisation.

"These processes enable us to detect and remember the pain sensations in great detail. Constant headache syndromes are like an automatic skill or a habit that the brain has become better at doing. Headache management strategies aim to undo these inappropriate habits.

"The brain can help us do many useful things. Purposeful activities can occupy brain systems and divert the focus from pain processing. Such mind-absorbing activities are also coordinated by the Action Systems, which can positively override and distract the pain mechanisms.

"The less the pain stimuli are processed in detail by pain perception systems, the higher the likelihood that, over time, conscious awareness will be diverted and focused on more helpful behaviours, which, at the same time, dampen down and distract pain processing. This results in central reorganisation."

Central Sensitisation and Central Reorganisation

Use the Peripheral and Central Sensitisation Figure 1.6 and *my well-being actions* worksheets 1 & 2

"A shift in lifestyle and the use of therapeutic techniques is required to balance the body's resources and the cognitive capacities for information-processing with the demands that they are exposed to.

"Specific methods are required to redirect brain systems to properly interpret physical sensations and to reduce the unnecessary processing of meaningless pain signals, as well as to generate more helpful habits and behaviours. In this way, the brain is learning new options of responding. "The habitual pain reaction can be dampened by alternative behaviours. These must be learnt patiently and consistently practised. Headaches are powerful signals and spontaneous pain responses are not easily overridden, as they remain vital to one's survival.

"In addition to that, you experienced an accident. As discussed previously, the automatic 'alarm systems' fire in response to a vast range of onset event-related stimuli and images, not only to physical or pain-related ones.

"Initially, it is important to become aware of the sensations associated with headaches in a passive and non-judgemental way in order to eventually reframe their meaning in our life. Coping habits need to be reshaped; for instance, habits to respond to headaches and headache-related worries immediately and with an 'all or nothing' approach, e.g., by taking medication or ignoring the pain.

"Applying modified methods of responding to headache sensations, thoughts and behaviours means that you can learn to overcome the intrusive and uncontrolled focus on the pain. This requires an enormous amount of trust that your body will still recognise and respond to real danger, should such a situation ever recur.

"The *Pain Gate* worksheet illustrates the pathway between the pain stimulus and the brain's perception of it. Some factors that open and close the Pain Gate are listed. It is useful to find out which of these would work for you.

"The *my well-being actions* worksheets summarise how important values in life, life goals, purposeful activities and coping strategies can strengthen the brain's abilities to alter responses to pain perceptions. As a result, such actions close the Pain Gate and fewer sensations can be noticed."

"What are your well-being actions?

– What do you value in life (e.g., social relationships, achievements)?
– What are your life goals (e.g., having good friends, having a good job)?
– What activities give you a sense of purpose (e.g., helping your friend fix their car, being reliable at work)?
– What activities do you enjoy that really take your mind off things?
– How do you achieve a deep sense of relaxation?"

Migraine and mild brain trauma

Use the *migraine and mild brain trauma* and *energy roller coaster* worksheets, Diathesis-Stress model of migraine and mild brain trauma Figure 1.7.

Notes for therapist: The holistic biopsychosocial principles of the proposed headache programme apply to all types of headaches and are equally beneficial for all headache sufferers.

People who experience migraines following mild brain trauma are presumed to have a predisposition to them. It is also assumed that the psychophysiological impact of the onset event caused the breach of migraine threshold. The experience of migraine attacks can lead to secondary symptoms that substantially overlap with post-concussion symptoms and stress, which may later manifest in habits or psychological responses that perpetuate the situation.

Psycho-education for migraine patients can, thus, contain the following explanations:

- migraine predisposition
- critical events and acquired vulnerability
- stress mechanism
- Pain Gate theory with a focus on Action Systems.

"The body produces symptoms of discomfort when the regulation between internal resources and external demands has become unbalanced. It seems that most people present one kind of vulnerability or another. Some may be prone to stomach ulcers, others asthma attacks or skin eczema, if their body is under certain strain that upsets its self-regulation ability.

"You experience new onset migraines or more frequent attacks than before the accident/onset event. Therefore, it is assumed that your body presents an innate or genetic vulnerability to respond to overwhelming stimuli with a migraine attack. Your body was better able to keep demanding stimuli more or less below threshold before the accident or onset event.

"Stressful events are commonly associated with migraine conditions. The impact of the accident compounded by the impact of migraine pain and the consequences of such episodes stimulates emergency reactions and stress responses. Your body attempts to protect itself from recurring, potentially life-threatening experiences by heightening your sensory as well as generic and physical responsiveness. This results in a cascade of migraine-related and stress-hormonal processes, which make a further attack highly likely.

"In order to restore a manageable balance, it is now important to organise your lifestyle in such a way that bodily activation remains below the migraine threshold. It might be difficult at first to accept that you have to do things differently yourself. Some people may fear that they might achieve less during their work or daily activities and try to push themselves, especially in migraine-free periods. However, this could have a high price, as much time and energy is lost later on when an attack has been triggered and which might consequently take you out of action.

"Initially, it is important to help the body restore its balance at a lower activity level. This means that your lifestyle requires structure, activities need to be graded and slowed down, just as in the recent homework exercise. This has the added benefit that you can have energy left at the end of your activity or at the end of the day. The feeling of energy is often linked with positive emotion, whereas feeling exhausted and worn out with headaches can be associated with disappointment or failure, even if a task has been mastered.

"The energy roller coaster provides a useful analogy. Let's have a look at this worksheet and hear how this might apply to you."

Ending

Pro-activity

"Identify two or three activities that modify your headache. You can record them on the *my well-being actions 2 worksheet.*"

Headache monitoring

"Record your headaches during two days in the coming week in the headache diary. Record headache intensity and duration."

Coping strategy

"Carry on with relaxation practice."

Headache therapy session 3: coping with headaches

Useful material

ABC of headaches worksheet
ABC of overcoming headaches worksheet
Activity planner & well-being schedule
Headaches after mild brain trauma Figure 2.5
Headache diary
My headache formulation worksheet
My well-being actions worksheets 1 & 2
Patient's assessment information: interview and questionnaire outcomes.

Objectives

- Cognitive behavioural headache formulation
- ABC of headaches
- ABC of headache management: A = adjustment anticipation, adversity and adjustment
- Emotional resilience
- Headache coping strategies

Headache monitoring

Notes for therapist: Discuss observations recorded in the headache diary. The diary analysis at this stage in therapy should be done in comparison with responses in the initial interview and questionnaires.

- What are the headaches like exactly?
- What are the consequences of the headache?

- How were the headache episodes dealt with immediately afterwards?
- Has anything changed since the initial assessments?
- If so, what has changed and what are the consequences?
- If nothing has changed (i.e., neither headache experience nor headache-related behaviours), what are the expectations (e.g., hope for natural remission) and what is missing?

Headache coping strategies: use the *activity planner & well-being schedule* and *my well-being actions* worksheets

Notes for therapist: Review relaxation routines. The patient has been in the programme for some weeks by now and should have a good foundation regarding relaxation practice.

Has the relaxation practice been scheduled during optimal times when the patient has felt all right and had "space"? It is important to explore obstacles to relaxation practice and, if required, to find ways to adjust relaxation strategies to the patient's abilities. The *activity planner & well-being schedule* might help with that.

Reflect on spontaneously applied positive strategies:

"You have learnt a lot about your headaches in relation to stress and your body's attempts to find a balance. Your participation in the sessions means that you are very motivated to help yourself and this indicates enormous progress. You have begun to take your well-being into your own hands and have already made considerable adjustments. Maybe now you could share those activities that have helped you reduce your headache perception and perhaps dampen or close your Pain Gate (or increase the headache threshold). What additional ideas or thoughts have you had during the previous week on how to optimise your sense of purpose and on activities to help you fulfil it? How can they fit into your *activity planner & well-being schedule* for next week?"

Positive strategies and well-being actions are those which:

- Divert attention from pain perception
- Prevent pain (e.g., change postural habits, limit exposure to triggers – long car journeys)
- Prevent consequences of pain (e.g., pacing and graded activity preventing energy "bust," adaptation of commitments)
- Optimise alternative and purposeful activities (e.g., alternating outdoor activity with computer work).

Main therapy section

The cognitive behavioural headache formulation

Notes for therapist: The therapist will, by now, have very detailed information about the patient's symptoms and the variables that contribute to their complexity. It is important to relate the dynamic meanings of the headache to the personalised formulation, rather than approaching the condition from a technical cognitive behavioural model only.

The patient can learn more about how the headaches, along with the critical onset event, have taken control of their lives.

The cognitive behavioural headache formulation illustrates headache components from a life history perspective, beginning at the early history through to current lifestyle. This model describes how the headaches have developed as a very individual experience and pinpoints exactly which behaviours and psychosocial variables maintain the condition. The CBT model indicates numerous exit routes out of patients' vicious cycles and opportunities for altering their lifestyle. In negotiation with the therapist, they can select the most practical adjustments and how to go about them.

ABC of headache management: A = anticipation, adversity, adjustment

Use Headaches after mild brain trauma Figure 2.5.

Have the assessment information and the headache report at hand. Guide the patient step-by-step through the Headaches after Mild Brain Trauma figure, exploring past personal and health factors, the critical event and brain trauma and the resulting symptoms and consequences.

Discuss how cognition, behaviour, emotion and social interaction are interlinked.

Use the *my headache formulation* worksheet

Encourage the patient to complete the *my headache formulation* worksheet by relating to their personal and headache history and including examples from the assessment information.

Use the *ABC of headaches* and *ABC of overcoming headaches* worksheets

"There are other ways to illustrate the dynamics of a headache pattern. Let's say, the headaches are such an *A*dversity to deal with. Due to the natural fear of pain, people use spontaneous *B*ehaviours to achieve immediate relief. The behaviours are compounded by negative *B*eliefs associated with the headaches, resulting in thinking and worrying about them. Making an effort to *A*djust, to do things differently and think appropriately, could lead to feeling all right or gaining control. *B*ehavioural *A*djustments lead to healthier *B*eliefs and to different *C*onsequences. The headache pattern can be interrupted. The Pain Gate can close a bit."

"What adjustments can you aim for?

- Behaviour: pacing, activity planning, practice of coping strategies, improvement of posture, sleep hygiene, diet, etc.
- Cognition: challenging worries and mental traps.
- Emotion: feeling safe and in control.
- Social: communicating genuinely, taking part a little and often."

Emotions and feelings

Notes for therapist: Thoughts and emotions related to headaches must be explored in combination. Emotions are verbally processed and evaluated. Socratic questioning is an effective therapeutic technique to explore such associations. A patient whose initial thought at the beginning of the headache episode may be, "Oh no I can't cope with this!" or "A headache in the morning means I am going to have a very bad day at work," can be asked the following questions:

- "What do you mean by coping and what would it be like if you knew how you could cope?
- What exactly is it that you cannot cope with?
- What would be so bad if you continue not coping?
- What is the worst that could happen?
- What would be so bad if the worst did happen?"

Explorations of this kind address core anxieties, which can become a matter of further therapeutic attention. Patients may benefit from information about core primary fears associated with anticipated pain and the traumatic event, and secondary feelings about the headache condition as a whole. Feelings are the results of emotional evaluations of the complex and chronic circumstances in which the patients find themselves. Giving patients space in the therapeutic contexts to express and process headache-related feelings can optimise their emotional resilience.

Headache coping strategies

Therapeutic language tips:

Exploration of emotional experiences and encouragements of alternative activities benefit from using the word *"how"*; e.g., "How have you modulated your headache worries?" The word "how" implies that the patient has reflected on this already. It is an encouraging phrase.

In the case of negative responses, such as, "I have not reflected on it," or "I don't think that this would work for me," the therapist can respond, "That's right, you haven't... yet. In the meantime, I want you to *pretend* that your experience has changed. Using your imagination, just pretend to change your spontaneous mental self-talk. What happens? Let's pretend changing your belief of 'I can't cope with my daily responsibilities' to 'I am aware of my head sensations now. I can direct my attention to my breathing pattern. This will help me whilst I am reading a story to my daughter for another ten minutes.'"

Alternative activities

"The No Diet Diet" metaphor:

Psychologists have researched the effect of diverting attention away from a problem. For example, a weight loss programme "The No Diet Diet" encourages people who aim to lose weight by trying different things every day. The activities are not at all related to losing weight. This is a "pattern interrupt" technique, i.e., unhealthy behaviours are replaced by neutral or healthy ones. For example, people are encouraged to buy a different newspaper than their usual one, to drink a different type of beverage, to get up earlier, use a different bus route, wear something different, etc. It was discovered that those people who changed their habits also lost weight, not as much as dieters, but they did maintain their weight loss. Importantly, the no-dieters began to make healthier and wiser choices in many other areas of their lives. It's all about behaviour change and adopting an alternative proactive approach. People find habit changes challenging. There may be obstacles to face in relation to past problems and to circumstances related to the brain trauma and headaches. People may want to wait until certain problems are sorted (children start school, they have more money, better housing, have repaired the car, etc.), but life will always be complicated and the management of daily hassles needs to be incorporated.

The "No Diet" analogy can be implemented in the headache programme to facilitate any first steps in approaching habit change. Patients are encouraged to choose one or two small activities per week and consistently focus on breaking unhelpful habits and implementing "pattern interrupts."

Desensitisation

Notes for therapist: Desensitisation is a useful classic therapeutic approach. The patient has probably experienced a challenging event and the headache might represent relived psychological trauma. Exposure to inappropriate headache-related worries or beliefs while in a safe environment and a comfortable physical state leads to desensitisation of the stress symptoms generated by such negative thoughts. The patient identifies strategies (relaxation, grounding techniques, ideal environment) that stabilise confidence.

Desensitisation Practice:

"Let's say you want to feel less stressed when you notice your intrusive headache-related worries. Most worries are irrational exaggerations of consequence that are unlikely to happen. Your thinking brain needs to realise that the body's alarm systems have malfunctioned. They need to get 'bored' of unnecessary states of alert. Here is how you can learn to get bored of distressing worries.

"Combine this exercise with relaxation and practice by using emotion-neutral thoughts initially. Get comfortable, ground yourself and settle into your usual relaxation routine. When you are fully relaxed in the way you are used to, just allow your mind to welcome all sorts of thoughts and ideas. Just let them float through your mind without interfering with them. Like a bystander, passively observe them.

"Now, imagine a big cinema screen and, using a spray can, write the thought down that enters your mind first. Spell out the letters of your thought with your spray. Notice the writing and the colour of the paint. And as you are focusing intensely on the big screen, you become aware how the letters blur and begin to dissolve. The more you look, the more they disappear and fade away. As you strain your eyes, they become dry and the words fade even more. Notice how this happens and let the words fade away completely. Notice how you can make thoughts easily disappear, just like that. Notice the blank screen and slow down breathing... Notice how your body is so very relaxed...

"Now repeat this with the next thought that comes to mind, even if it is the same one. Spray the sentence down. Notice the writing, the letters, the spelling, and read the sentence over and over again while continuing to breathe and remaining relaxed. Notice how the words begin to disappear, they just don't stick, they just fade away, they disappear from your mind, again.

... Repeat ten times...

... You are relaxed...

"And as you are repeating this exercise over and over again, you realise how boring this becomes; you can no longer hold on to the thought, your mind just wants to let go.

"Notice how easy it is to get bored with redundant thoughts, how easy it is to let them drift past your mind, passively.

"You know now that you can do this any time, whenever and wherever thoughts and worries recur, you know how they will just want to fade away..."

It is recommended to elicit examples of disturbing or distressing thoughts in the therapy session. The patient can use their worksheets to choose and list such examples. With the help of the therapist, the distressing thoughts or images can be ranked. When the patient is skilled in applying an exercise like the one above with neutral thoughts, they can progress through their list of negative and distressing ones.

Ending

"Today you have explored how the headaches with all their components have become part of your life. You have explored a number of strategies for adjusting your routines and habitual patterns. Remember to use the *activity planner & well-being schedule* or the *my well-being actions 2 worksheet* to practise your strategies and your relaxation."

Headache therapy session 4: how can I improve the quality of my life?

Useful material

Activity planner & well-being schedule
Peripheral and Central Sensitisation Figure 1.6
Headache relief imagery-healing paradigm
Headache relief imagery-hat anaesthesia
Mind-absorbing activities worksheet
My well-being actions worksheets 1 & 2
Pain Gate worksheet
Positive self-talk worksheet
Thinking about headaches worksheet

Objectives

- Cognitive behavioural headache model
- ABC of headache management: B = behaviour
- Importance of physical exercise
- Pacing and fatigue management
- Habit changing strategies

Welcome

"We are now in the middle of your headache programme. I wonder if you have already noticed how your attitude towards your headache is changing and how you have started to take your health into your own hands."

Main therapy section

ABC of headache management

Use the worksheets *Pain Gate* and *my well-being actions 1 & 2*, Peripheral and Central Sensitisation Figure 1.6

Notes for therapist: The emphasis in this part of the therapy is on behaviour and habit change. The Pain Gate and Central Sensitisation theories can be adapted to explain the importance of the Action Systems for the development of alternate, health-promoting behaviours that dampen the pain processes and distract the transmission of pain signals. The suggested worksheets can be discussed to introduce and consolidate the theme of this session.

"Today you will discover a range of techniques designed to further enrich your choice of alternative activities and to distract your pain processing systems. We will practise these together. You should continue to use them in your own time and decide which ones work best for you.

"B is for **Behaviour**. It refers to anything we do in response to the Antecedents, i.e., the anticipated and actual headaches. Our thoughts and worries also drive our behaviours. The Pain Gate illustrates the factors that enhance the Actions Systems. The more we do, think and feel the pain, the more skilled the brain mechanisms will become in fine-tuning the pain systems.

"The idea of the Action Systems can be used to build skills in optimising alternative and well-being behaviours. If you are fully engaged in such behaviours, this means that the attention and thinking processes will prioritise your purposeful alternative over headache processing. The following strategies can help consolidate this."

Physical exercise

Notes for therapist: Gentle physical exercise is vital for healthy heads. Muscle tension and bad postural habits can be reduced by engaging in physical activities such as Nordic Walking, Pilates, Tai Chi, aerobics and many more. Such physical activities should be carried out daily or as regularly as possible. Gentle physical exercise increases blood circulation, reduces inflammatory processes and has been shown also to improve concentration and information-processing disturbances in headache patients.

Patients are encouraged to plan their exercises and perform them, at least partially, even if they have (mild) headaches at the time. In the case of severe headaches or migraines, they should apply relaxation techniques and change the intensity and length of the activity. If headaches begin during a physical activity and the patient prefers to end the activity, it is important to remain aware of thoughts and mental self-statements at that moment. Patients should be encouraged to reward themselves for having mastered parts of the activity and for their mindful regulation of thought patterns. These are substantial achievements for a person who has not attempted to exercise or use alternative methods ever before.

Patients might want to re-engage with favourite physical activities that they enjoyed before the accident and may have stopped due to the headaches, e.g., walking, gardening, dancing or horse-riding. Other patients might always have wanted to start something new, such as sailing or going to the gym. In the case study example, Josh used his juggling skills as a mind-absorbing physical activity, which he enjoyed in the outdoors. As one can see below, exercise can also balance energy levels as daytime fatigue is addressed. Now might be the opportunity to utilise the structure and therapeutic support, which is integral to this approach in order to integrate physical exercise into daily routines.

Pacing and fatigue management

"Daytime fatigue is common with chronic headache. Concussion and psychological trauma upset the natural ebb and flow of our hormone system, which regulates energy levels, mood and performance each day. The disruption of routines, the anticipation of pain and the fear of negative – especially social – consequences, disturb the diurnal stress hormone (i.e., cortisol) levels. This means that at times of high demand, there is less cortisol available to keep the systems active or to regulate micro-inflammations. Lack of resources drain bodily systems and result in ongoing fatigue, "burn out" and possibly more headaches. This can be overcome by adopting a gentle graded approach during the recovery process.

"Changing what we do and how we approach our lifestyle can help synchronize our hormonal and biochemical rhythms and as a result we have less fatigue.

"Here are some suggestions for optimising your bio rhythm:

- Arrange important tasks earlier in the day
- Take breaks
- Increase natural light exposure
- Reduce screen time
- Eat regular meals and regulate your caffeine consumption
- Explore your sleep hygiene, wake up at the same time every day and get out of bed
- Be careful with hypnotic or benzodiazepine medication use."

Mind-absorbing activities and coping

There are endless opportunities for health-focused behaviour change.

Cognitive exercises as shown below can be powerful attention diversion strategies to redirect headache worries, interrupt headache monitoring and reshape avoidance behaviour. The patient needs to practise examples of coping exercises with the therapist and at home during headache-free periods to become familiar with them. The *activity planner & well-being schedule* can be a helpful planning aid.

Thought-stopping/pattern interrupting

The therapist sets the scene to mentally expose the patient to a situation when they might have headaches, or fear or worry about the headaches.

The patient is instructed to briefly pay full attention to the worry or the pain and immediately switch attention.

"I would like you to practise 'thought-stopping.' This is a very important strategy to have. You need to practise in headache-free times first and, when you have mastered it, it will be very effective.

This is what I would like you to do:

I want you to visualise a stop sign.

Now tell me what your stop sign image looks like.

What shape does your stop sign have?

Is it two dimensional or three dimensional?

What colours does your stop sign have?

What colour are the letters of the word 'stop'?

What is the font – lower case or upper case?

What size is the stop sign?

Is the stop sign fixed to a post or is it hanging down from somewhere?

How close to you is the stop sign?

Does it just read 'stop' or does it also make a noise telling you to 'stop'?

You have a very detailed image and powerful stop sign.

Now I would like you to imagine that we have this stop sign right here. I am pretending to hold it up for you. Is that right? Distance right? Good.

Next, I am going to ask you a question and as you are giving me the answer, I will shout 'STOP' and hold your imaginary stop sign out in front of you.

Now, please describe to me how you prepare your cup of coffee at home.

(Allow three to five seconds for the answer, then interrupt in the middle of the answer – this has to be done quickly, but not in a rushed manner).

STOP!

Thank you. Now tell me about a previous holiday/family outing/weekend activity.

STOP!

Thank you. Now, please describe your best friend/supportive family member to me. What are they like?

STOP!

"Now, please tell me what happened. How did the instruction to stop interfere with your narratives? Each new question interrupted your memory and thinking about the previous one and each stop interfered with your attention to your story. From now on, I would like you to remember your stop sign as one of your most powerful tools. Initially, practise thought-stopping during your normal day-to-day routines and headache-free periods. Make sure you gain proficiency in the use of the strategy. When you experience distressing worries or headaches, briefly pay full attention to them, then quickly say the word 'stop!' to yourself and visualise the stop sign in front of you. This brief moment of focused attention allows you to select another effective coping strategy that can take your mind off the headache for longer.

"Of course, it might be much easier to interrupt an emotion-neutral image (such as coffee-making or remembering a holiday) as opposed to diverting from real pain or pain-related thoughts. Therefore, your stop sign image must be convincing, strong and well-rehearsed."

The attentive reader might notice the similarity of this thought-stopping exercise with the magic spell technique "Riddikulus!" that was helpful for

Bethan, or even Holly's Viking warrior strategy. The "No Diet Diet" meta-phor is also a "pattern interrupt" strategy.

Thought-switching

The therapist sets the scene and prepares the patient for another exercise:

"Please tell me what you had for breakfast this morning!" ... Allow three to five seconds for the answer, interrupt in the middle of the answer; this has to be done quickly, but not in a rushed manner.

"What is the colour of your car?" ... Immediately move to the next question.

"Who is the current Prime Minister?" ... Immediately move to the next question; if the patient is slow in responding, move to the next question.

"What news event do you remember from the last few days?" ... Immedi-ately move on.

"When did you move into your current home?"

"Thank you. You are doing very well indeed. This means that you are able to quickly switch from one thought to another. You can do this any time. You can also do this when you notice yourself worrying about your headaches or focusing on the pain. When this happens, quickly say the word 'STOP! ,' visualise your stop sign and switch thoughts rapidly. This is a bit like mental gymnastics, but it means that you stop rehearsing your headaches and that you detach yourself from headache-related thinking and acting."

Cognitive stimulation and mind-absorbing activities

Use the *mind-absorbing activities* worksheet

"To strengthen your mental flexibility, which will help with thought-switching and mental coping strategies, it might be useful to add cognitive stimulation to your programme.

"You can count backwards in sevens, spell backwards, recite poems, re-peat foreign vocabulary, say tongue-twisters, sing songs, use mobile phone games or many other things.

"Some people have found brain-training exercises or apps to be useful. Caution must be undertaken if using screen-based activities for too long, as eye strain and poor neck postures can lead to headaches. Beneficial al-ternatives are those day-to-day tasks that you may find slightly challenging. For instance, setting your safety alarm at home, programming your mobile phone, working out the TV remote control, preparing a new dessert or as-sembling a flat-pack piece of furniture. Make a list of such tasks. Break them down into manageable parts. Use relaxation or deep breathing to re-main calm, plan each step ahead and use the cognitively stimulating tasks in the same way as the pain distraction methods."

Stress-inoculation revisited

"Stress-inoculation is an older psychological term meaning that one can learn to adjust to certain demands in a graded fashion. For instance, your mind and body can become de-skilled if you have avoided certain activities for a long time due to your headaches or residual brain trauma difficulties affecting mental and complex tasks or day-to-day responsibilities. This means that if your headaches and other symptoms were to cease right now, you might not be as skilled as in the past at a non-practised activity.

"Maybe your attempts to get back into the swing of your previous routines have been hampered by headaches or other problems and you have given up trying to get better. You may have discovered that this has not helped either, your mood got worse and you have lost your confidence almost completely. You might have tried to find out which situations trigger your headaches. You might have eliminated most scenarios and activities from your life, but still experience the headaches. Under such circumstances, your body and mind have simply forgotten how to deal with fairly normal activities.

"Stress-inoculation works a little like a flu jab. Provided you have achieved fundamental elements of well-being and relaxation, you can begin to 'inject' tiny doses of challenge into your routines. Challenges could be those activities you have avoided up to now out of fear that they might trigger or intensify your headaches. You could start engaging with small doses of planned activity, combined with relaxation practice beforehand and afterwards. This way, you build skills in dealing with the task. You learn to plan the activity into your day. You combine your activity with positive coping strategies. That way you know how to cope should this trigger a headache. If you don't know which meaningful activity to choose for your stress-inoculation, perhaps begin with doing a short physical exercise."

Positive self-talk

Use the *positive self-talk* worksheet

"It is very important to be kind to yourself. This is a matter of emotional hygiene. Positive self-talk links realistic aims with well-being and relaxation.
   Positive self-statements are characterised by:

−   Short, simple sentences
−   Positive phrases, such as, 'I am calm,' rather than, 'Don't panic!'
−   Being phrased in a way as if the goal has already been achieved, 'act if now.' Even if you have a headache and feel stressed, the statement would be 'I am relaxed.' That's what you want your mind to focus on.

"Self-statements can be very effective if integrated into your relaxation practice. By this stage in the programme you have had plenty of relaxation practice. Next time when you practise at home, at the point when you feel

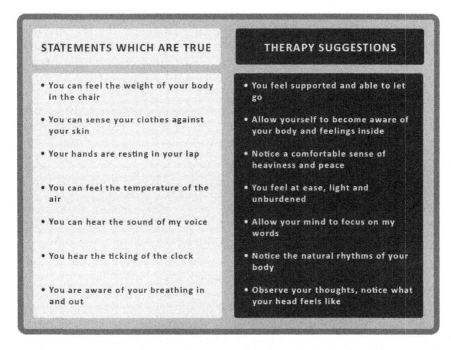

STATEMENTS WHICH ARE TRUE	THERAPY SUGGESTIONS
• You can feel the weight of your body in the chair	• You feel supported and able to let go
• You can sense your clothes against your skin	• Allow yourself to become aware of your body and feelings inside
• Your hands are resting in your lap	• Notice a comfortable sense of heaviness and peace
• You can feel the temperature of the air	• You feel at ease, light and unburdened
• You can hear the sound of my voice	• Allow your mind to focus on my words
• You hear the ticking of the clock	• Notice the natural rhythms of your body
• You are aware of your breathing in and out	• Observe your thoughts, notice what your head feels like

Figure 3.9 Therapeutic reinforcement.

the sense of deep muscle relaxation, formulate your positive self-statement and repeat it five to ten times as you are breathing out. For instance, you might say to yourself, 'I am a person who can exercise daily for 20 minutes. I am able to relax my body.'"

Therapeutic reinforcement techniques

- "Anchoring" is a psychotherapeutic term that refers to the ability to vividly memorise a positive experience and to activate its image at will. The person can link an image with a physical or sensory cue, like pressing a knuckle. Activating the cue later on should remind the person of the image.
- "Therapeutic reinforcement" involves linking statements that are true with therapeutic suggestions. Introduce the patient to a state they know is true, followed by a therapeutic suggestion. For example, "As you sit in that chair, with your feet on the ground, breathing in and out, hearing the sound of my voice, you feel grounded and can relax more deeply" (Figure 3.9). This technique can also be applied to reinforce a sense of safety: "Even if I have a headache right now, I know that my brain is fine."

- "This means" another form of therapeutic reinforcement can be achieved by linking observed patient behaviours with their future goal. For example, "Your regular attendance at the therapy programme *means* that you are making a real effort to learn positive coping strategies," or "Your practice of mind-absorbing strategies *means* that you are getting more and more skilled and can soon use them when you experience distressing worries or pain."
- "Future pacing" is a therapeutic projection of a positive event or mental self-instruction to a future situation. "I know I can use abdominal breathing each time I have to speak to a challenging customer on the phone."

Positive reinforcement exercise

"You have already participated in many sessions of the headache programme. That means you are very motivated to modify your lifestyle, thinking patterns and interactions in order to achieve improved well-being. You have, by now, begun to implement many changes into your daily routines.

"It is very useful to remain mindful of all those positive activities you have initiated and to be observant about the outcome. You are now able to achieve brief relief from your headache by the means of relaxation and coping strategies. This represents an enormous success worth celebrating. With the power of your own ability, you have been able to alter your headache experience. At all times become aware, notice and remember your increased coping abilities and success.

"Thoughts and emotions have an unbalanced relationship. Emotions may be spontaneous and, with even the best willpower, one cannot easily think them away. On the one hand, it is useful to apply emotional hygiene by not dwelling on self-pity or enhancing negative moods. On the other hand, really thrilling positive emotions can be so overwhelming that pain and unpleasant physical symptoms are hardly felt at all. The memory of a situation linked with very intense and positive emotions can be very powerful in shielding you from headache sensations. It is worth accessing images about such positively felt emotional memories.

"In your image, become intensely focused on the positive emotional experience. Pay attention to the bodily sensations associated with your pleasant emotion. During the experience of relived positive emotion, make a mental note, link this emotional image with a symbolic state, so that you can access your emotion wherever or whenever you require it. For instance, you can pinch one of your knuckles and each time you pinch this knuckle, you can retrieve this positive memory in all its facets and use it to distract you from headache-related thoughts or headache sensations."

Headache relief imagery

"Next we are going to practise the modification of pain images and pain-related thoughts.

Take a few relaxed breaths and focus on the following instructions.

For the next few moments, allow yourself to imagine a recent headache episode. First, visualise the pain itself. It doesn't matter if you think you cannot imagine your pain. For the sake of the exercise, just pretend that you can.

Think about this headache sensation now.

Let's say your headache has a shape – what shape would it be?

Would it be round, sharp, two-dimensional, three dimensional...?

Would it be solid or liquid or gaseous?

If it had a colour, what colour, what shades of colour?

If it had a texture, what texture?

If it had a smell, what would it smell like?

If it made a sound, what would it sound like?

Now imagine that the headache exists in the space around you.

What happens if you allow the headache to move around in space?

What happens if you move closer up to it or further away?

What happens if you look at it through a camera lens?

What happens if you move the pain into a faraway distance and maybe observe it from a bird's eye perspective (e.g., from a hot-air balloon or space ship)?

What happens if you could even look at the headache from such a distance through a telescope?

From the far-away distance, notice how you can alter the headache characteristics now to reduce the headache's intensity. If you are wondering how to do it, maybe imagine having a device like a computer game controller or remote control. Turn down the volume. Turn down the intensity. Surely, you can do that.

So, if your headache consists of a certain material, modify the material so that it is more bearable as headache material.

If your headache has a shape, change it into a more comfortable shape.

If your headache has a colour, change it to a more soothing colour.

If your headache has a texture and a surface, make some changes so that it feels more relaxing.

If your headache has an unpleasant smell, modify the smell into something more acceptable.

If your headache has a sound, turn down the volume, mix the sounds into more pleasant or melodic ones.

Keep the modified and more acceptable image in your mind. Build a good memory of it and give this new image a name. At any point in your daily routines you can recall the name of this new image and attend to this rather than the former headache image. This way you can switch to your chosen image anytime or anywhere you need it."

Headache relief imagery – healing paradigm

"Let's try another imagery exercise to modulate your headache experience. This is called the healing paradigm."

Read the healing paradigm script.

"Now tell me what happened."

Headache relief imagery – hat anaesthesia

"Another kind of pain modulating imagery has been used by people who have a localised pain. Let's imagine you own a magic hat that can change the headache sensations for you and can dampen your headache perception."

Read the hat anaesthesia script.

"Now tell me how that went."

Imagery incompatible with a headache experience

"Take a few relaxing breaths and settle down for the next exercise. You can visualise pleasant experiences, places or scenery that allow you to feel very comfortable. Such scenarios are incompatible with headache perceptions.

"For instance, lots of people enjoy imagining relaxing and pleasant beach scenes. The air is fresh and the temperature is comfortable. You have time and, if you don't want to be alone, you can have your favourite companion alongside you. As you are lying down on this beautiful soft sandy beach, you notice a wonderful deep sense of relaxation travelling through your body. All tension is draining away from your muscles and your head feels fresh and wonderfully relieved of all demands. As you are holding this image in your mind, you are beginning to notice how your face and head muscles are becoming wonderfully relaxed. As you imagine the sunshine on your face, you begin to notice the warmth on your skin, which means the muscles relax even further. Just allow this sense of warmth and relaxation to move over your face, over your forehead, over your head, relaxing your scalp, down the back of your head and back down your neck and shoulders. Notice your head sinking a little deeper into the soft warm sand and, as you do so, notice how you feel wonderfully free and at ease... good."

Modifying headache context

"You can surely remember stories or anecdotes where people have coped with severe events and have not noticed pain. The experience of Aron Ralston comes to mind, the mountaineer who amputated his own arm in order to escape to safety, an ordeal that took him 127 hours. Mostly, these are examples of extreme situations that threatened people's survival. Can you imagine that you can use the power of your mind to increase the importance of very useful activities and allow yourself to be so fully immersed, giving your absolute attention to the task as if your life depended on it? Imagine that for a brief moment you can focus on such a scene or event."

Setting expectations

"Some people expect that their headaches will be completely gone by the end of therapy. Often, they hope for permanent headache relief, or at least a headache-free spell lasting several days. When such a time comes, they think that then they can up the game, return to their past levels of activity or approach big projects in one go. However, things might not happen that way. It is advisable to set goals and expectations regarding valuable tasks and activities in such a way that gradual progress can be maintained. Some people, for instance, might want to landscape their garden, sort out the garage, or learn a language.

It is very advisable to find out how such activities can be broken down into smaller chunks and how and when these subtasks can be approached. Each accomplished sub-task ought to be celebrated, whether or not this achievement had been reached before.

"It is useful to have a way of quantifying your task. Set a time limit for how long you want to be involved with it – for example, 'weeding the garden for twenty minutes' – or limit the task elements – for example, 'cutting just two bushes.' Setting very precise task aims helps you accomplish them, even if a headache develops halfway through. Clear expectations tell you exactly how much further there is to go. This helps you carry on with the task, even if some headaches develop."

Ending

"We discussed many coping and positive distraction strategies today. Over the next week, continue to practise relaxation, physical exercise and attention diversion strategies at those times when you have no headaches or very mild headaches only. You can set a time for them using your *activity planner & well-being schedule*. As you know, it is important to gain proficiency in the use of strategies before applying them to really painful headache episodes or other challenging situations. You can experiment a little to find quick and efficient strategies that work for you.

"Next session, we'll explore how the strategies can be applied during headache episodes. Please monitor headache-related thoughts during three headache episodes and note them on the worksheet entitled *thinking about headaches*. Record the day and the activity linked with your headache episode. Note your immediate thoughts and any attempts to divert your attention away from them. How did you carry on with your day? You'll benefit from having concrete examples to bring along to the next session. Also, remember to discuss what you have discovered about yourself or anything unusual happening."

Headache therapy session 5: meaning and purpose

Useful material

Balancing headache thoughts worksheet
Dealing with worrying thoughts worksheets 1 & 2
Headache coping strategies worksheet
Headache diary
My well-being actions worksheets 1 & 2
Possibility dimensions worksheet
Possibility goal hotspot worksheet
Real life and ideal life worksheet
Steps to my possibility goal worksheet
Thinking about headaches worksheet
Quality of life worksheet

Objectives

- ABC of headache management: C = cognitive patterns and cognitive strategies
- Reflection on the meaning of headache
- Exploration of quality of life aims
- Coping strategies for acute headache episodes

Welcome

"One of the things you are really going to love about today's session is that some elements might be quite unusual. As you have been actively participating in therapy, you may have become used to creative methods of dealing with your headache. As you know, it is important to strengthen your Action Systems, to develop robust coping styles and to look into the things you really want to do in life."

Main therapy section

ABC of headache management: C = Cognitive pattern and cognitive strategies

Thinking about headaches & cognitive habits

Use the worksheets thinking about headaches (completed as per homework), balancing headache thoughts, and/or dealing with worrying thoughts 1 & 2.

"Let's have a look at your worksheet *thinking about headaches*. It is useful to investigate episodes when your headaches or headache-related worries have challenged your efforts to deal with them since our last session.

"The worksheets *balancing headache thoughts* and *dealing with worrying thoughts* give examples of how to reframe negative thoughts. Let's explore some of them."

Meaning of headaches

"In preparation for the next exercise using imagery, think about an example of a recent intense headache episode.

"Take a few relaxed breaths and allow your mind to settle.

"Now we have investigated and talked a great deal about your recent headache experiences and thinking patterns. It doesn't sound as if the headaches are useful for you at all. They hinder you from getting on with things you really want and need to do. They burden your relationships. They drain your energy and they worry you a great deal. All in all, they seem to be really powerful things, those headaches, as they can do all that, even though they are no use for you at all. If all that power and energy generated by the headaches has no use or purpose for you, could they be useful or purposeful for something else, for someone completely different? Think of the recent headache episode, the pressure it created, the force it had. If someone needed a force like that, one that can influence so much, what could it be used for?

"You may notice how your mind aims to free this energy. You have probably begun to wonder what will happen when the painful force is released. As you are now allowing yourself to let go of it, of this powerful force, you need to find a way to get it out of your head.

"Using your imagination, you can pretend to release the headache from your body and find a useful purpose for it somewhere else. Some people have imagined that their terrible headache could be useful for frightening unwanted intruders away and have placed it inside their home's alarm system. Other people have extracted the pain out of their ears and placed the headache mass on their front lawn as fuel for friendly aliens. What could your headache be used for?"

Headache message

"Let's continue with another imagery exercise. Take a few relaxed breaths and get settled. Allow your mind to wander. You have time and space right now. This means you can invite some pleasant memories into your mind. Memories about a beautiful place where you know you can be at peace. You can feel safe and relaxed. Notice the sensations in your body. If you sense any pain, just allow yourself to observe it, passively.

"Now, imagine that this pain has left your body and you can look at it, its shape, its colours, its texture – all its features. If they are particularly unpleasant, move away from them a little bit. Keep a comfortable distance and continue to observe this distant pain, because it seems that it wants to tell you something. It seems that it has a message for you. Notice how it conveys its message. It may change its features or release some sounds. It may simply show you where it wants to be in order to fulfil its purpose. Now, let yourself decide what you want to do with the pain. Just accept the message. Let it fulfil its purpose and let it go."

Purpose and life aims

"We'll now continue with another imagery exercise. It's called the "miracle question." Take a few relaxed breaths and allow your mind to settle.

Now, just imagine a fairy that could make a miracle come true for you. One day, without your knowledge, this fairy intends to release all the necessary resources and opportunities for you to achieve the dream of your life.

How would you know that your dream had come true?

What would you have? What would you no longer have?

How would the miracle affect others around you?

What can you do now that you couldn't do before?

With another spell, the fairy can swish your headaches away completely. Just like the first time, you won't know when she casts the spell, but one day, sooner rather than later, you will realise that you no longer suffer headaches.

What will this enable you to do?

How do others react?

What will no longer happen?

What will you gain?"

(See case examples: Terry, Connor, Henrietta, Tracey and Katie.)

Real life versus ideal life

Use the *real life and ideal life* and *quality of life* worksheets

"Now, have a think about the amount of time you spend on activities that offer you a better quality of life. What fraction of time during a day or week do you have for quality experiences? On the worksheet *real life and ideal life*, indicate on the top pie chart how much of your time you allocate at present to activities that are meaningful and give you pleasure. The pie chart at the bottom represents your ideal share of time and resources between quality of life and headache activities. How do the proportions work out in your case? What is the difference between reality and your ideal distribution of your time and resources?"

Depending on the patient's response, e.g.:

"It looks as if only a little time is allocated, realistically, to the activities that you value the most. On the other hand, ideally, you would like to have much more time for them. What is it you must do, to make the most of those times that fill you with purpose and give you a sense of accomplishment?"

Possibility goals

Use the *possibility goal hotspot* and *possibility dimensions* worksheets

"We want to look at a different chart now. Let's call the aim you really would like to work towards in life your 'possibility goal.' We call it that because life is full of possibilities.

What exactly is your possibility goal? How can you describe or name it?

Sometimes we get closer to our life aim or possibility goal and sometimes we move further away. On your goal dimension from 0% to 100%, how close have you come towards your possibility goal already?

How much of your possibility goal would you like to achieve in… days or weeks?

How much would you like to achieve in…months or years?"

Depending on the patient's response, e.g.:

"You seem to have made some progress already; what resources do you have available to achieve more of your goal?

What else do you need to move towards your goal in… years… months… weeks?

How can you make the best use of your current resources in future?

What other resources, skills or support can you use to gradually accomplish your goal?"

Additional explorations:

"Let's think about possibility goals other people might have.

Let's imagine your… spouse, parent, teacher, neighbour… has a possibility goal just like you.

How close are they to their aim? Take a guess.

How much do you imagine they would like to accomplish in… years… months… weeks?

In comparing your possibility goal with that of others, what insights and ideas can you gain?"

Feedback and normalisation:

"Even though others might not have headaches, it is unlikely that they are perfect and have fully achieved all their aims."

Reflecting on a possibility goal

Use the *possibility goal hotspot* worksheet

"Now, having discussed your life aims and the possibilities for moving towards them, it seems a good idea to allow you more time to reflect on those things. I am going to ask you a few questions about your possibility goal. This time you don't have to answer them aloud. Just listen and observe the answers your mind comes up with.

Take a few relaxed breaths and sit back."

Note for therapist: Therapist reads the questions on the *possibility goal hotspot* worksheet, slowly, one by one. Patients are simply encouraged to consider and contemplate their personal answers.

Some patients may insist that they have no ideas about developing life goals, no resources or may report a low achievement level. Whilst it may be true that some are more fortunate than others and some may have a more complex trauma or headache conditions than others, most people have the opportunity to make a few positive changes at least. Reluctance and presentation of obstacles can be an indication of a mismatch in expectations or of poor engagement. Such issues require different therapeutic skills, for instance a motivational interviewing style or a deeper exploration of the meaning of the obstacles.

Possibility goal hierarchies

Use the *steps to my possibility goal* worksheet
"You are exploring the steps towards your possibility goals and life aims. List activities you possibly want to accomplish in your life. What is it you really value?

"Alternatively, you could imagine yourself at an age of about 75 or older, reflecting on your life and your achievements. What would you say was really valuable to you in your past life?

"What strategies and resources do you have now in order to get there?

"What are the things that need to happen next?"

Purpose and accomplishment during headache-free periods

Use the worksheets *headache coping strategies* and *my well-being actions 1 & 2*
"Now let's review the activities you have accomplished during headache-free periods.

–   Physical exercise
–   Coping strategies and mind-absorbing activities
–   Positive emotional and thoughtful attitudes.

What has worked best?
What was the best time for your activities?
What have you changed in order to improve your well-being?"

Coping during headache episodes

Use the *mind-absorbing activities* worksheet
"You have gained practice and skill in the application of different coping strategies. You can now have them ready and apply them when you have headache episodes. You can still revert to taking medication or using your usual pain relief if necessary.

"At the onset of a headache episode, immediately use the pattern interrupt method 'STOP!' followed by your most effective coping strategy. Your aim at this point is to divert your attention from thinking about and monitoring the pain, not directly to stop the pain. In order to carry on with your routines, you have to adjust your pace in combination with brief and effective relaxation. You can combine your task or job with abdominal breathing and your positive self-statement (e.g., 'I can cope. I am all right'). Think ahead about switching your strategies. If you have used relaxation for a few minutes, then go for a walk next or aim for a change of environment.

Later on, when you notice that you are coping better or your headache is easing off, practise deep relaxation once more and combine it with pain relief imagery to consolidate the experience that you can influence your Action Systems."

Notes for therapist: The therapist has, by now, a good understanding of the task management needs, and the memory and cognitive support that is required to set up a coping strategy plan for use during headache episodes. The patient might benefit from guidance regarding the selection and timing of the coping strategies for application during and after headache periods. Relaxation should still be part of the daily schedule.

Ending

Use the *headache diary, mind-absorbing activities* and *possibility dimensions* worksheets

"Use the headache diary and record your coping strategies as you apply them during headache episodes. Continue to keep track of your purposeful activities and possibility goals."

Headache therapy session 6: relax!

Useful material

Introduction to relaxation & relaxation practice worksheets
Headache message (see therapy session 5)
Meaning of headache (see therapy session 5)
Modifying headache context (see therapy session 4)
Relaxation induction script:
    Focused body relaxation
    Release-only relaxation (or equivalent)
Relaxation therapy scripts:
    Deepening breathing
    Deepening relaxation
    Headache relief imagery – healing paradigm
    Headache relief imagery – hat anaesthesia
    Headache relief imagery – happy moments
    Headache relief imagery – water and bubbles

Headache relief imagery – time travel
Reducing stress and tension
Resources and perspectives

Relaxation practice worksheet
Steps to my possibility goal worksheet

Objective

- Focused relaxation practice
- Application of pain relief imagery within relaxation
- Deepening of individual relaxation experience

Welcome

"By now you have realised the importance of deep relaxation practice for helping your body restore its balance in response to your headaches and many other demands. You have begun to make adjustments to improve your lifestyle. You have already noticed how such changes can gradually move you towards the things you really want in your life.

"Today, we are going to practise relaxation in the session. Rather than using a general relaxation script as in the health management group, we are going to use pain relief images that you have used in the previous sessions."

Main therapy section

Notes for therapist: relaxation induction, deepening and therapy scripts can be combined and varied according to the recorded headache descriptions and according to what works best for the patient.

Pre- and post-relaxation scores can be obtained as in the health management module.

It is advisable to practise relaxation a number of times during the session. This is important to increase the patient's self-confidence and their ability to memorise as much as possible from each exercise. Each relaxation module can be practised separately.

Relaxation: practice modifying the headache perception

Relaxation induction scripts:
Focused body relaxation
Release-only relaxation (or equivalent)

Relaxation therapy scripts:
    Deepening breathing
    Deepening relaxation or
    Reducing stress and tension
    Headache relief imagery – healing paradigm
    Headache relief imagery – hat anaesthesia

Anchor and future pace
Ending the relaxation practice

Relaxation: practice modifying the context and use imagery incompatible with headache

Induction, deepening and ending scripts as above.
Relaxation therapy scripts:
    Modifying headache context
    Headache relief imagery – happy moments
    Headache relief imagery – water and bubbles

Anchor and future pace
Ending the relaxation practice

Relaxation: practice modifying the meaning of headache

Induction, deepening and ending scripts as above.
Relaxation therapy scripts:
    Meaning of headache
    Message of headache
    Headache relief imagery – time travel
    Relaxation: resources and perspectives

Anchor and future pacing (see headache therapy session 4)
Ending the relaxation practice

Relaxation practice: possibility goals

Induction, deepening and ending scripts as above.
Relaxation therapy script:
    Steps to my possibility goal worksheet

Anchor and future pacing (see headache therapy session 4)
Ending the relaxation practice

Ending

Use the *introduction to relaxation & relaxation practice* worksheets

"You can include the one relaxation exercise that works best for you into your daily routine. Be mindful about what you have started to notice during your relaxation practice. Observe your progress using the *relaxation practice* worksheet.

"The *introduction to relaxation* worksheet reminds you of the key points."

Headache therapy session 7: the world around me

Useful material

Meaning of messages worksheet
My headache formulation worksheet
Possibility dimensions worksheet
Possibility goal hotspot worksheet
Steps to my possibility goal worksheet
Selection of buttons or pebbles

Objectives

Explorations of

- the impact of headaches on social situations and interactions
- social possibility goals and social values
- communication styles
- the sense of belonging within social networks

Welcome

"Today we want to explore how other people respond to your headache experience. I want you to imagine that you are now a health coach for your family, friends, colleagues and acquaintances. Imagine what it would be like for them to benefit from all the insights you have gained. How can people within your social group support your efforts to achieve your possibility goals, regardless of your headaches?"

Main therapy section

Social interactions

Use the *my headache formulation* worksheet
"First, let's have a look at your worksheet *my headache formulation*.
What has changed regarding your social interaction and contacts over recent weeks?

How have you noticed others responding to your condition?

What has helped you engage more socially and perhaps experience the benefit of social support and understanding by others?

What changes have you made to feel more involved, to feel more connected?

What strategies and pacing methods have helped in your interactions with people?"

Social possibility goals and social values

Use the *possibility dimensions, steps to my possibility goal* and *possibility goal hotspot* worksheets

"The fact that you have already practised your possibility goal means that you can now apply this to your social goals.

How are social activities important for you?

What would you say are your social roles? Could you rate them on the worksheet?

What is the one goal you can potentially achieve in most areas of your social life?

How can you pace your routines in order to enjoy a healthy social life?

How can you communicate assertively and interact positively to gain and maintain pleasant relationships?

Use the possibility goal-related worksheets as guidance to reflect in more detail about your social needs and goals."

How do other people respond to your headaches now?

"The people in your life may have also been affected by your accident and your persistent health problems. Immediately after the injury, they tried to help you recover as quickly as possible. Relatives and others often feel deeply affected if someone close to them has experienced a significant health event. They may attempt to do anything in their control to gain relief from their worries and to restore the situation to normality as soon as possible. One way of achieving this is to be as actively involved in your care and headache relief as possible. Surely, you have noticed sympathetic responses from others. They might have taken over tasks and responsibilities from you in the hope that easing the burden for you will speed up your recovery. However, after a while and when symptoms persist, such an approach can become counter-productive. Perhaps, you might have felt excluded from your usual activities and responsibilities, but have lost the confidence to take them back. Others may have become frustrated as they did not expect to carry out extra tasks and commitments for prolonged periods.

"In therapy, you have made gradual changes to your routines, graded and paced your tasks, used coping strategies and relaxation to improve your energy levels. The people around you may now benefit from acknowledging your progress so that you can take back some of your former roles and responsibilities.

How can you regain your former level of responsibility and independence without offending others?

You might have come across responses like these:

'Oh, you don't look very well. Would you like to lie down; have a cup of tea/glass of water/an aspirin; let me do this for you.'

Other responses may indicate some frustration about your headache condition:

'Have you got a headache again? This means I have to do this... for you; I have to do the shopping on my own/you won't come out with me tonight.'

What would it be like if you confidently inform your family or friends that even if you have a (mild) headache, you have now learnt to pace yourself, that you can carry out some of your jobs or that you only have to modify your approach and this will allow you to do a great deal more than in the past?

You can now ask others to encourage you and perhaps even join you in using strategies and adapted routines."

Meaning of messages

Conversations can often lead to misunderstandings as a result of different interpretations by the speaker and the listener.

On the other hand, talking with others who share similar experiences can be very powerful in reducing the subjective experience of distress caused by acute and chronic pain.

People who are better integrated socially complain about less pain disability and pain-related anxiety. Also pain patients who live close to their family or have a bigger social circle show more potential for adequate pain management. Most people would agree that better social integration and mutual social support seems to have a long-term improving effect on the functional impairment that chronic pain can cause.

Consequently, it is favourable to communicate and interact with others in such a way that closer bonds can be established. Authentic connections with others can happen when the content of a conversation and its inherent meaning is aligned with the listener.

Use the *meaning of messages* worksheet

"As you know, messages can convey direct or indirect – i.e., subtle – meanings.

At times, meanings are not understood on the same level as intended by the sender. This is how misunderstandings are created.

This diagram on the worksheet describes four options of sending and interpreting messages.

Which one is direct and which ones are more indirect?

How would you like to be understood?

How can you make sure your message contains the intended meaning?"

I-messages

One way to communicate more clearly is to use "I-messages." This means, the speaker's intentions are stated from a first-person perspective and include the following three components.

- State the situation: "I have a headache."
- State the intention: "I want to continue preparing the vegetables for ten minutes. Then I am going to practise my relaxation. I would like you to let me carry on with my task and make sure I am not disturbed during my relaxation practice later."
- State the consequence of the intention: "Doing it this way helps me get something done while also coping better with the headaches."

Direct communication provides an opportunity to clean up conversations and prevent unnecessary assumptions, obscure meanings and misunderstandings.

"Applying a direct and authentic communication style may take a while to get used to. Tell your significant other that you wish to talk about your headaches differently. Rather than commenting on headaches and well-being, you may wish to talk about your tasks, how you plan your day, how you are pacing yourself to move towards your possibility goals and how you can achieve a sense of purpose."

Social networks

Notes for therapist: Interactions with people within social networks can illustrate the helpfulness or dilemmas of relationships. Systemic or family therapy methods can be very useful in this section of the programme. It is beyond the scope of this manual to go into detail with regards to systemic therapy techniques. Nevertheless, one simple and interactive method can be implemented to illustrate the different roles and dynamics in social groups.

Sociogram

The therapist can supply a selection of different buttons or pebbles.

For the purpose of this exercise, each button represents a person within the family or social network. Patients then lay out representations of their own networks. The features of each button (size, material, shape) symbolise the characteristics of the person it represents. The strength of relationship can be indicated by the distance between buttons. By using the buttons, patients can reflect on the communication and interactions they have with the people in their social network. They can explore how relationships have changed over the course of their headaches therapy and perhaps what would need to happen to optimise their network.

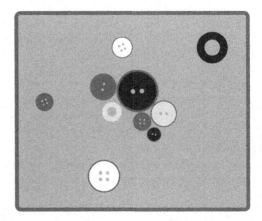

Figure 3.10 Sociogram. The big button represents the client who is surrounded by the family and friends.

Ending

"Think ahead about how you can implement examples of clear communication styles with people in your social network. Try to practise them once a day over the next week. Tell me what happened."

Headache therapy session 8: using what I have learnt in the future

Useful material

Possibility goal hotspot worksheet
Quality of life worksheet
Real life and ideal life worksheet
Steps to my possibility goal worksheet

Therapy outcome measures I

Headache disability inventory
Headache needs assessment
Hospital anxiety and depression scale
SF-36 or Nottingham health profile
Headache intensity scale
Headache frequency scale
Headache diary

Objectives

- Revision of possibility goals, life aims and values
- Administration of therapy outcome measures

Welcome

"Today is your last therapy session. I am curious to hear how communicating more directly or how phrasing your needs using 'I-messages' has been received within your social relationships.

As you know, the ultimate way of overcoming adversities and headache problems is to focus on the things you really value in your life. Processes like pain monitoring and scanning for possible danger can move backstage again, where they can do their work without interfering with your main intentions.

"Today, we'll revisit your life goals and values. The exercises are meant to motivate you to proactively use the self-management approach beyond this programme."

Main therapy section

Quality of life

Use selected *possibility goal* and *quality of life* worksheets

"You identified your possibility goals in previous sessions. Let's have another look at them. Should new ones be added or some dropped? What values do they represent? How do they fit with quality-of-life activities, i.e., are your possibility goals important for you and not urgent?

With these values and possibility goals in mind, what now gives you a feeling of a better quality of life:

- Each day?
- Each week or in the medium term?
- Each month or in the longer term?"

Use the *possibility goal hotspot* worksheet:

"Now, it seems a good idea to allow you once again to mindfully reflect on your possibility goals. I am going to read the questions about your possibility goal hotspot. You just listen and observe which answers come to mind."

Read the questions from the *possibility goal hotspot* worksheet.

Following that, discuss:

"How are your values demonstrated in your daily activities and routines towards your possibility goals?

How can you increase activities that can move you towards your goals?

What resources are you using now in order to gradually achieve your goals or outcomes?

You have explored, practised and applied headache management strategies. You have noticed the benefits of your efforts.

What headache coping strategies and coping resources have you preferred? How useful can they be in the near future?

How can you now use your new insights and learning to progress with your goals and optimise your health management?"

Therapeutic Reinforcement Techniques

Circle of accomplishment

"You have thought about your top life goal many times. I want you now to pretend in your imagination that you have already accomplished this top goal.

We have a large circle here on the floor in the office. Let's imagine that as you enter the circle, you enter the scene when you have fully accomplished your life goal. In a moment, you are going to step into this circle and vividly imagine what it is like to have achieved your goal.

Now, take a few breaths, let the air out slowly and allow your mind to settle into the exercise. Do this a couple of times and then step into the circle.

Now allow your mind to get used to the new situation you find yourself in.

You are experiencing the mastery of your life goal. You have done it!

Without talking about it out loud, just reflecting on it in your mind, notice *how* you know that you have achieved your goal.

What in your body tells you that you have it?

What is the sensation like?

Notice whether the sensation in your body remains stable or whether it changes.

Watch the scenario around you, seeing it through your own eyes.

What is it that you see, hear, feel that resembles the accomplishment of your goal?

Notice the characteristics of the scene in which you have achieved your goal. Notice every detail.

Move around in the scene and take everything in.

Are you alone or with others?

How do others respond to your achievement? How does their response to your top achievement affect you?

Absorbing all these experiences into your mind, build a good memory of everything and of what it is like to have accomplished your goal. Do this right now. Anchor your achievement.

Build a good memory of all the sensations and images so that you can retrieve this experience whenever and wherever you like. Make it as strong as you can.

Step out of the circle now. Well done."
This exercise should be repeated in the session.

Imagery: movie about your success story

"Now I want you to focus on your achievement and success again. I want you to pay attention to my instructions and just notice your thoughts and images.

Take a deep breath and relax. Do this a few times. Allow your mind to settle into the exercise.

I want you to imagine that you have created a movie about your journey, beginning at the moment when you set your aim until the actual moment of achieving it.

You are the main character acting out your story.

Let's get the movie going. Become aware of the scene, the other characters and the time frame.

Maybe, the movie starts with a distant memory, long before you had much awareness about the direction of your life. In a moment, right now, you find the beginning of your chosen episode – the point when you began to consciously reflect on your life and decided to make gradual changes. Step inside the movie now.

You are the main character enacting your vision towards your goal. Immerse yourself in the feeling of moving towards your goal and coming closer and closer to the points when you can accomplish it.

Take all the time it needs. Revisit the stages on your journey.

Notice what happens and how you feel.

You have now reached your goal. What is that like, exactly?

Now replay the movie again. Take in every detail of the experience, your gradual progress, your step-by-step success. Relax.

Now replay the movie again. Notice what you didn't notice before. Use all your senses. Take your time. This is important. Relax.

Now replay the movie once more. Totally experience yourself working towards your goal and achieving it. Relax.

Anchor the experience so that you remember it today or tomorrow or anytime you need it."

As the therapist has detailed knowledge about the patient's goals and values, these can be mentioned specifically instead of the generic words "goals" or "values."

Real life and ideal life

Use the *real life and ideal life* worksheet

"You are coming to the end of your therapy. You have made great progress in applying proactive headache management strategies. You eventually focused on improving the quality of your life, rather than just focusing on overcoming the headaches. You have formulated your values and the purposeful activities that can move you towards them.

How have you managed to accomplish this?

How have your diaries, scores and charts reflected any changes over time?

What needs to happen next?

What was hindering your activities and what is helpful?"

Ending

Therapy outcome measures I

"Today you have focused on your ways of achieving your possibility goals. You have made very good progress in optimising your activities and coping with residual headaches. Be mindful every day of your resources and your steps towards them.

Before you go, it seems a good idea to record the changes in your headache experience using the questionnaires."

Therapist administers therapy outcome measures I, as listed above.

Headache therapy session 9: nice to see you again

Depending on the patient's independence and whether therapy was run weekly or fortnightly, the follow-up can take place any time after the headache programme, but with a suggested time interval of at least four weeks and an optimal follow-up interval about five months after the end of the programme.

Useful material

Energy roller coaster worksheets 1 & 2
Headache coping strategies worksheet
My headache formulation worksheet
Any other worksheet that is meaningful for the review

Therapy outcome measures II

Headache disability inventory
Headache needs assessment
Hospital anxiety and depression scale
Sf-36 or nottingham health profile
Headache intensity scale
Headache frequency scale

Objectives

* Summary of coping strategies and evaluation of progress
* Relapse prevention: what to do when the patient has stopped using coping strategies

- Self-motivation (cognitive, emotional, behavioural, social)
- Administration of follow-up measures

Welcome

Notes for therapist: The previous outcomes from therapy measures can be used to illustrate progress for the patient. The patient can be encouraged to identify how their strategies can be implemented to continue improving in areas that may still seem difficult.

"You have learnt a lot about managing your health, optimising your quality of life and coping better with headache episodes. Today you can reflect on the progress you have made in the meantime and on your own. You can also explore ways of helping you continue in the future."

Main therapy section

Summary of coping strategies: use the *headache coping strategies* worksheet

"The *headache coping strategies* worksheet summarises the main strategies you have practised throughout therapy.

How have you been able to implement them?

What has been your experience?

What else do you need to do to improve your outcome?

How are you going about it?

What resources and coping strategies can be most helpful for you?"

Relapses: use the *energy roller coaster* worksheet

"Relapse, in our understanding, would be regression to a situation where you lost the routine of practising and applying your coping strategies.

"How could this happen? It could happen at times of additional or unexpected demands. Some people change their jobs, move house, experience bereavement or any additional adverse events. These things do happen. Life rarely runs smoothly. You have managed to implement healthy and proactive life changes and this means that you can improve your routines at any time again.

"It is useful to understand that diversions from your health management strategies are part of the normal experience. Maybe you have not used deep relaxation for a while and a difficult life scenario might remind you about the usefulness of recharging your batteries regularly. Sometimes, people misunderstand their progress. Feeling more active and healthier does not mean that your body should be overloaded with unreasonable demands. Avoid the energy roller coaster. You are much stronger and more resilient now and your body still requires the resources to remain that way.

"Keep your worksheets within reach, so that you can refresh your motivation to keep moving towards your life goals and values. Reduce any inappropriate focus on your headaches."

Self-motivation

Use the *my headache formulation* worksheet

- Setting:
  "How can you improve your current environment and your current situation, so that you can independently carry on with a healthy activity schedule?"
- Cognition:
  "What strategies can be useful in the near future for challenging headache-related thoughts and beliefs?"
- Emotions:
  "How can you process unpleasant emotions? What helps you remain resilient?"
- Behaviour:
  "What can you do in the near future to improve your physical strength? How can you carry on with forming new habits? What are your next steps in facing the challenges in your life?"
- Social:
  "How can you enjoy social participation the most?"
  "How can you use 'I-messages' and unambiguous forms of communication with everyone you know?"
  "How can you show others how much you benefit from your coping strategies and how much they enable you to re-engage in your roles and responsibilities?"

Ending

Therapy outcome measures II

Administer questionnaires as listed above. "Please complete the following questionnaires again. They indicate your progress in coping with your headaches and your level of improvement."

With kindness, thank the patient for their engagement with and participation in the programme.

Bibliography

Cheshire, H., & Shanker, S. (2018). *Patient perspectives on treatment and services for mild traumatic brain injury.* Unpublished dissertation. Faculty of Science and Technology, Bournemouth University, Poole, UK.

Cramer, J. A., Silberstein, S. D., & Winner, P. (2001). Development and validation of the Headache Needs Assessment (HANA) Survey. *Headache, 41*: 402–409.

Del Pozo, J. (2019). Being Awake Better. Having energy and cognitive reserve during the day to function at our best. *Psychology Today,* Sussex Publishers, LLC.

Fletcher, B. C., Penman, D., & Pine, K. (2005). *The No Diet Diet. Do Something Different.* London: Orion.

Foster, R., & Kreitzman, L. (2017). *Circadian Rhythms: A Very Short Introduction.* New York: Oxford University Press.

Foxhall, M., Marks, E., & Tooze, A. (2018). Improving the treatment approach to mild TBI through the lens of lived experience (Doctoral dissertation). University of Bath, Bath, UK.

Foxhall, M., Tooze, A., & Marks, E. (2019). Improving guideline concordance for the treatment of mild TBI. *The Neuropsychologist*, 7: 36–46.

Gordon, T., & Edwards, W. S. (1995). *Making the Patient Your Partner: Communication Skills for Doctors and Other Caregivers.* Westport, CT: Greenwood.

Gurr, B., & Coetzer, B.R. (2005). The effectiveness of cognitive-behavioural therapy for post-traumatic headaches. *Brain Injury*, *19*(7): 481–491.

Gurr, B., & Wickes, S. (2006). The usefulness of a relaxation programme for brain-injured patients. *Clinical Psychology Forum*, *166*: 14–18.

Hunt, S. M., McEwen, J., & McKenna, S. P. (1985). Measuring health status: A new tool for clinicians and epidemiologists. *Journal of the Royal College of General Practitioners*, *35*: 185–188.

Jacobson, G. P., Ramadan, N. M., Aggarwal, M. D., & Newman, C. W. (1994). The Henry Ford Headache Disability Inventory (HDI). *Neurology*, *44*: 837–842.

Miller, L.J., Mittenberg, W. (1998). Brief cognitive behavioural interventions in mild traumatic brain injury. *Applied Neuropsychology, 5*: 172–83.

Mittenberg, W., Canyock, E. M., Condit, D., & Patton, C. (2001). Treatment of post-concussion syndrome following mild head injury. *Journal of Clinical and Experimental Neuropsychology*, *23*: 829–836.

Packard, R. C. (1979). What does the headache patient want? *Headache, 19*: 370–374.

Packard, R. C., & Ham, L. P. (1993). Impairment rating for post-traumatic headache. *Headache*, *33*(7): 359–364.

Potter, S.D., Brown, R.G., Fleminger, S. (2016). Randomised, waiting list controlled trial of cognitive-behavioural therapy for persistent postconcussional symptoms after predominantly mild-moderate traumatic brain injury. *Journal of Neurology, Neurosurgery, and Psychiatry*, *87*: 1075–1083.

Ralston, A. (2004). *127 Hours: Between a Rock and a Hard Place.* New York: Atria Books.

Schulz von Thun, F. (1994). *Miteinander reden 1. Störungen und Klärungen. Allgemeine Psychologie der Kommunikation.* Hamburg: RoRoRo Sachbuch.

Silverberg, N. D. (2019). Behavioral treatment for post-traumatic headache after mild traumatic brain injury: Rational and case series. *NeuroRehabiliation, 44*(4): 523–530.

Silverberg, N. D., Hallam, B. J., Rose, A., et al. (2013). Cognitive-behavioural prevention of postconcussion syndrome in at-risk patients: A pilot randomized controlled trial. *Journal of Head Trauma Rehabilitation, 28*: 313–22.

Young, J. E., Klosko, J. S., Weishaar, M. E. (2003). *Schema Therapy: A Practitioner's Guide.* New York: Guilford Press.

Zigmond, A. S., & Snaith, R. P. (1983). The Hospital Anxiety and Depression Scale. *Acta Psychiatrica Scandinavia*, *67*: 361–370.

Therapy worksheets

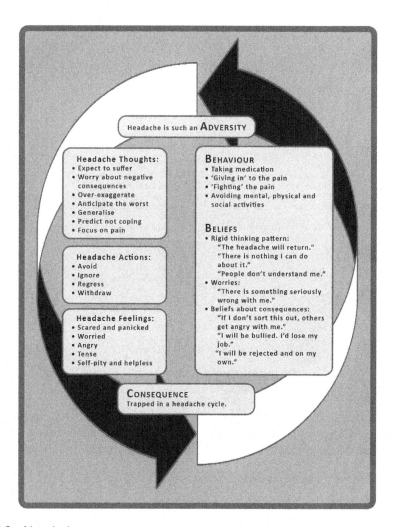

ABC of headaches.

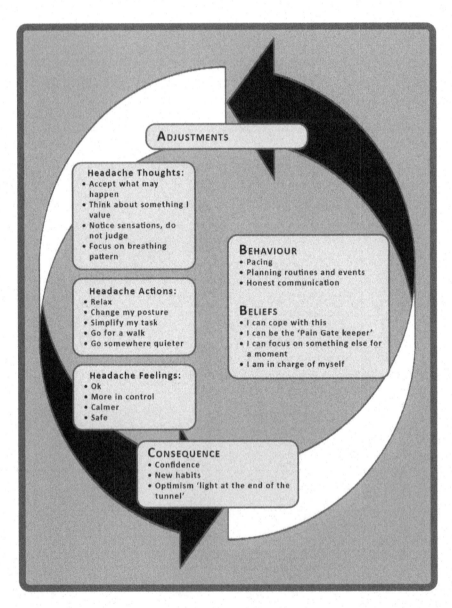

ABC of overcoming headaches.

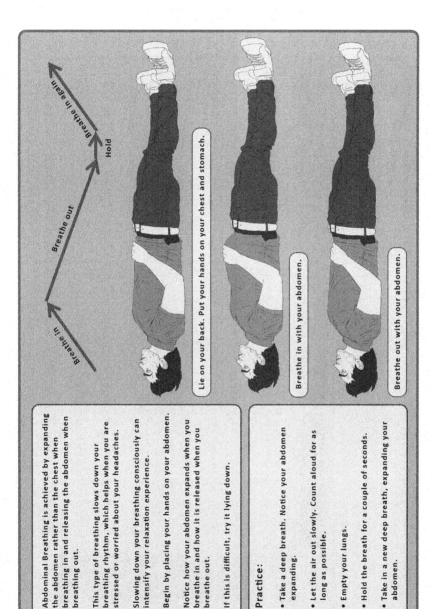

Abdominal breathing.

ACTIVITY PLANNER & WELL-BEING SCHEDULE

Plan your chosen activity using the Meta-Strategy PROM.
PREVIEW - Think of your activity beforehand.
RESEARCH - Think about things you need including time, place and space.
ORGANISE - Get organised and start.
MONITOR/MEASURE - Monitor your process and measure achievements.

	Monday	Tuesday	Wednesday	Thursday	Friday	Saturday	Sunday
08-10							
10-12							
12-14							
14-16							
16-18							
18-20							
20-22							
22-24							
24-08							

Activity planner and well-being schedule.

HEADACHE THOUGHTS	BALANCED THOUGHTS

• **Oversimplified:**
Thinking in 'black and white'. Example:
   This will give me a headache.
   Feeling either sick or well.
	• **Life is full of variation:**
	Extreme headaches are rare.
	Headaches vary.

• **Over-generalisation:**
Always generalising from one
experience to all situations. Example:
   Last time I got a headache from this.
   I will always get a headache doing this.
	• **Keeping things in proportion:**
	Today, things are different,
	because...

• **Exaggeration:**
Losing perspective. Example:
   If I have a headache when going out, it
   will ruin everything.
	• **Perspective:**
	What else is happening?
	I can use my coping skills.

• **Expectations:**
Making unreasonable demands upon
yourself. Example:
   I ought to be over this.
   I should not complain.
	• **Acceptance:**
	I am at ease with my body.
	I am mindful of my abilities and can
	pace my tasks.

• **Self-blame:**
Example:
   It's my fault entirely.
   I am always letting people down.
	• **Appropriate responsibility:**
	I can consider other aspects of my
	situation.
	I am doing the best I can.

• **Emotional reasoning:**
Feeling the emotion means that there is
something wrong. Example:
   I feel really ill, I must have a serious
   disease.
	• **Defuse thoughts from emotions:**
	I can use relaxation and passively
	observe my feelings.
	Gradually, the fear will fade away.

• **Mind reading:**
Predicting what others think. Example:
   They think I'm making excuses.
   They think I am lazy.
	• **Remain in the present:**
	I am taking comments for what they are
	and responding with clear information.
	That way I can contribute and participate.

• **Demands on others:**
Transferring high expectations to others.
Example:
   They ought to do this properly and on
   time.
	• **Accepting others:**
	I can accept that others have to take
	responsibility for their own actions.

• **Hopelessness:**
Feeling that nothing can change your
headaches. Example:
   Whatever I do, it won't help.
   There is no point.
	• **Assertiveness:**
	I can make small changes.
	Modifying pain pathways takes time.
	I can motivate myself to carry on.

Balancing headache thoughts.

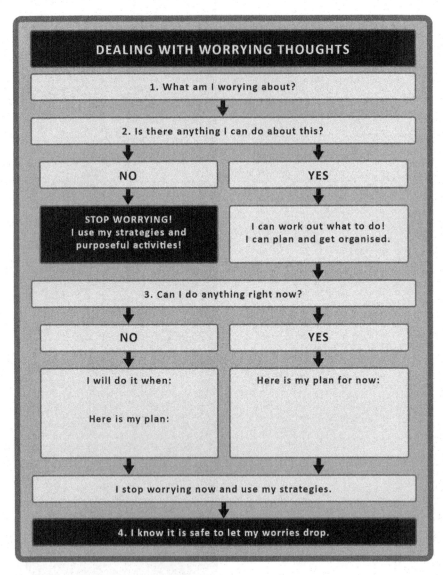

Dealing with worrying thoughts I.

DEALING WITH WORRYING THOUGHTS

WHAT IS THE EVIDENCE?

What evidence do I have to support my thoughts?

What evidence do I have against them?

WHAT ALTERNATIVE VIEWS ARE THERE?

How would someone else view the situation?

How would I have viewed the situation in the past?

WHAT IS THE EFFECT OF THINKING THE WAY I DO?

Does it help me or hinder me from getting what I want? How?

What thinking error am I making?

WHAT ACTION CAN I TAKE?

What can I do to change my situation?

Am I overlooking solutions based on the assumption that they don't work?

WHAT IS THE WORST POSSIBLE OUTCOME?

What is the worst thing that can happen? How bad would that really be?

Dealing with worrying thoughts 2.

EFFECT OF STRESS ON THE BODY

Stress responses in humans are generated by two bodily systems.

1. The Sympathetic-Adrenomedullary System (SAM):

The SAM is part of the autonomic nervous system. It is responsible for short-term activation in case of an acute threat. It works like an emergency or alarm system supplying resources quickly so that the body can cope with an extreme situation. At the same time, bodily functions associated with growth or reproduction are dampened and several internal functions like heart rate are reduced. The adrenal glands release stress hormones like Adrenalin and Noradrenalin which signal and regulate such processes.

2. The Neuroendocrine System:

The neuroendocrine system consists of interlinked glands and cells which communicate via cortisol hormones which are released into the blood stream. These also fulfil an important signalling function, especially in case of long-term challenges. Hormones produced by the endocrine glands influence metabolism, growth and development, immune function, sleep, mood, cognition and regulate bio-behavioural stress systems. These mechanisms interact slowly within the body to achieve an adaptation to long-term and complex demands.
Frequent and persistent over-activation of the bodily stress mechanisms can lead to a range of health problems such as asthma, stomach ulcers, heart disease, high blood pressure, arteriosclerosis and also headaches. Long-term imbalance of stress hormones can lead to many negative consequences including immune system dysfunctions, low mood, poor memory and many more.

Effect of stress on the body I.

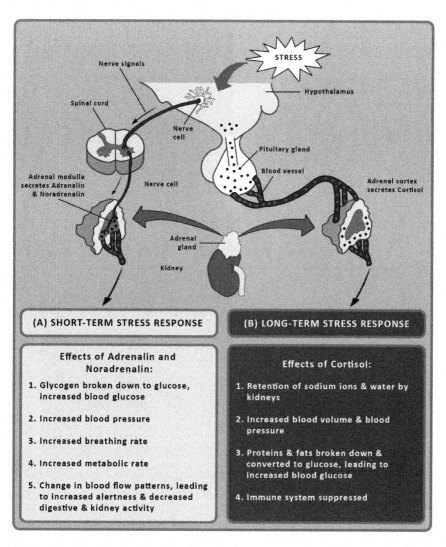

Effect of stress on the body 2.

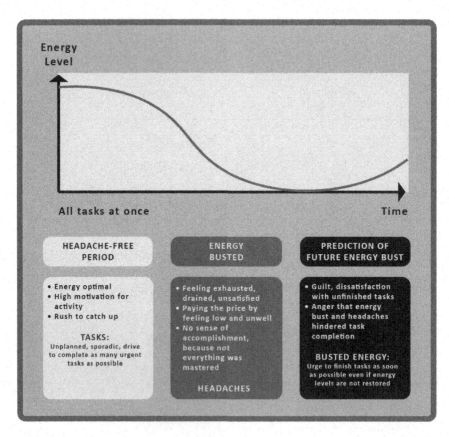

Energy roller coaster I.

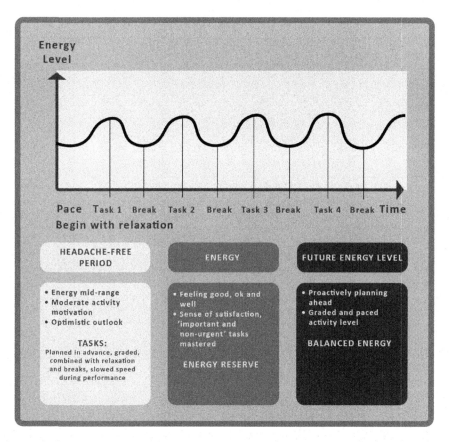

Energy roller coaster 2.

HEADACHE COPING STRATEGIES

- Relaxation
- Abdominal breathing
- Thought stopping and attention diversion
- Cognitive stimulation
- Physical exercise
- Practical and meaningful activities
- Hobbies and mind-absorbing tasks

MODIFICATION OF HEADACHE EXPERIENCE

- Re-framing the meaning of the headache
- Headache relief imagery:
    Modification of environment = incompatible with pain
    Modification of headache characteristics = more bearable
- Stress-inoculation = graded and paced activities
- Desensitisation to headache worries
- Defusion and re-framing of headache worry and headache anxiety

EMBEDDED RELAXATION DURING DAILY ROUTINES

- Important and non-urgent activities = quality of Life
- Paced activity management
- Planning breaks and building resources
- Well-being schedule
- Positive self-awareness = focus on coping
- Positive self-talk
- Life values and possibility goals
- Clear and direct communication
- Healthy social interaction

Headache coping strategies.

HEADACHE DIARY

Monitor your headaches as advised by your therapist.
Record activity before, during and after a headache episode (A).
Record your coping method (C).
Score headache intensity (I: 1 - mild, 2 - moderate, 3 - severe)
and duration (D: length of headache episode in hours).

	Example	Monday	Tuesday	Wednesday	Thursday	Friday	Saturday	Sunday
08-10								
10-12	A: Shopping. C: Sat in car quietly afterwards I: 2, D: 1							
12-14								
14-16								
16-18								
18-20	A: Dinner. C: Washed my face with cold water I: 2, D: 1.5							
20-22	A: Audiobook, C: husband massaged my back I: 1, D: 1							
22-24	Went to bed							
24-08								

Headache diary.

INTRODUCTION TO RELAXATION

Why is relaxation useful?

Stress causes the muscles in the body to tense up. Over time this can result in uncomfortable bodily sensations such as headache, backache, tight chest and so on.

Aches and pains add to mental worry which can increase the tension. Constant tension is linked to low energy and fatigue. A person who is deeply relaxed cannot be tense at the same time.

Deep relaxation is a comfortable, enjoyable feeling, which is incompatible with tension and worry. Deep and focused relaxation helps to restore the body's systems which regulate resources and demands.

RELAXATION IS A SKILL

One can learn to relax fully by regular practice. Eventually a deep state of relaxation can be achieved easily and quickly. The ability to relax does not always come naturally at first. It is a skill which has to be learnt and regularly practised like playing the piano.

Relaxation exercises are designed to help you learn this skill. You may use a relaxation app or MP3 to carry out the routine.

When you are able to relax more easily and have memorised your relaxation instructions you can begin to apply the relaxation strategies to situations which are stressful or when you have a mild headache.

- Decide in advance when you are going to practise. This way you can develop a routine. Make relaxation practice an 'important and non-urgent' priority for you. Schedule other activities around it.
- Choose somewhere quiet to exercise. Make sure you practise undisturbed (turn off mobile phone).
- Check that your room (temperature, light) and your surface are comfortable. Wear loose clothes. Take off your shoes or glasses.
- Adopt a passive attitude and just observe what happens.
- Start by breathing through your nose, using your abdominal muscles. Breathe slowly and regularly. Place your hands on your stomach and feel the movement when breathing in and out. Try this before your exercise so that it feels natural.

EMBEDDED RELAXATION DURING DAILY ROUTINES

- Do your activities calmly.
- Give yourself short breaks - relax, stretch, go for a walk. Plan these in advance.
- Adopt a relaxed posture. Deliberately relax your muscles if you notice yourself tensing up. Drop your shoulders, sit back in your chair, unclench your fists and release your jaw.
- Notice positive moments and intentionally inject pleasure into your daily routine.

Introduction to relaxation.

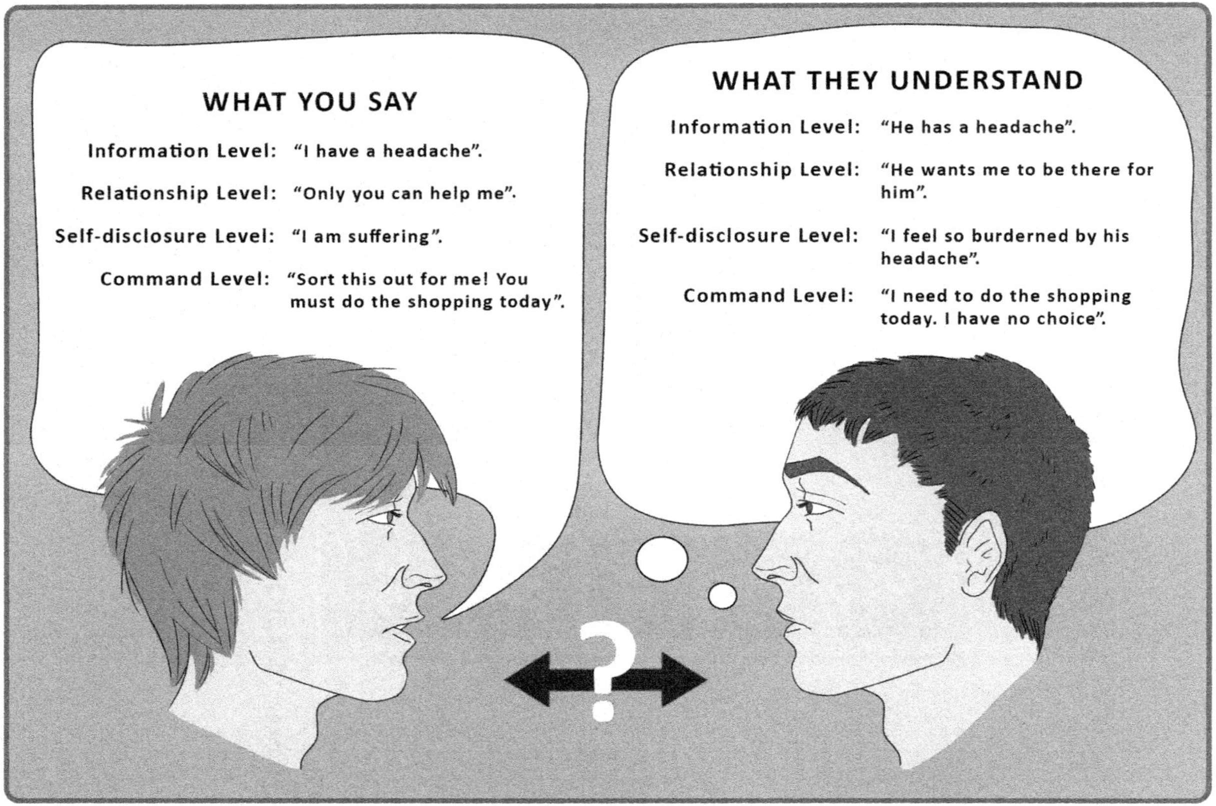

Meaning of messages.

Meta-strategy: "GO SLOW."

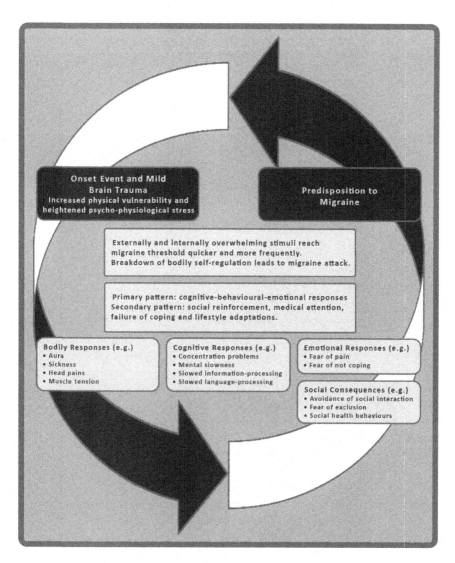

Migraine and mild brain trauma.

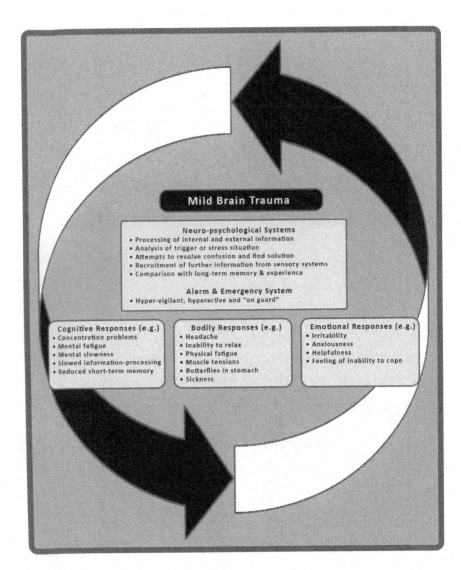

Mild brain trauma.

MIND-ABSORBING ACTIVITIES

These tips help to divert attention from unpleasant symptoms and headache-related negative thoughts.
These are short-term coping strategies.

Thought stopping

Shout out loud "STOP!" and visualise a stop sign and the letters of the whole word in bright colours, large fonts, etc. This is to interrupt the pattern of headache monitoring and to mark the start of alternative coping strategies.

Games

Absorbing exercises, tongue twisters, reciting poems or singing songs are all positive distraction techniques. Others include counting back from 1000 in 7s, thinking of animals beginning with each letter of the alphabet in turn, backwards spelling or remembering a favourite walk in detail - indeed, any focused mental activity.

Mobile apps

Games on mobile phones can divert attention from headaches. Select short games which are fun. Choose the right level of difficulty. Notice your posture and eye strain. Use relaxation or mindfulness apps.

Environmental focus

Concentration on a specific detail of the world around you, for example, making words out of the number plates of cars or guessing what people do for a living.

Using an object

This might be a photograph or a special brooch or a souvenir from a happy time. Focus your attention on the object and describe it in as much detail as possible. Cue questions include: What exactly is it? How big is it? What colour is it? How does it feel? What is it made of? Exactly how many of them are there? What is it for?

Physical activity

Giving yourself a task, for example, hanging the washing out, cleaning the car or gardening, takes your mind off focusing on your pain. Gentle exercise and sport like table tennis, cycling or juggling requires mental focus and physical flexibility. Making something is equally mind-absorbing and physically stimulating. Physical activity reduces bodily tension, which, in turn, can reduce head pain.

Positive self-statements

Focus your mind upon your self-statements linked with your possibility goals in an effortless, relaxed way. Be kind to yourself. Focus on helpful thoughts and motivate yourself towards your goals.

Mind-absorbing activities.

MY HEADACHE FORMULATION

Predisposing factors (early vulnerability):
My personal, social and medical history

Headache onset (acquired vulnerability):
Critical event and mild brain trauma

Setting:
Circumstances at the time of critical event and headache onset

Stress and headache triggers:

Lifestyle Consequences

COGNITION

• Headache thoughts:

• Headache beliefs:

• Mental coping:

• Monitoring of pain:

• Locus of control:

BEHAVIOUR

• Avoidence of activities:

• Habits:

• Medication:

• Posture:

SOCIAL INTERACTION

• Withdrawal:

• Gaining care:

• Communicating pain:

• Stigmatisation:

EMOTION

• Fear of pain:

• Fear of brain illness:

• Fear of not coping:

• Fear of being left behind:

• Fear of not coping:

My headache formulation.

MY JOB? YOUR JOB!

What is the job/responsibility?

Who owns the job/responsibility?

What is the problem?

Who owns the problem?

What are the alternatives?

My job/My responsibility & My problem:

Your job/Your responsibility & Your problem:

My job? Your job!

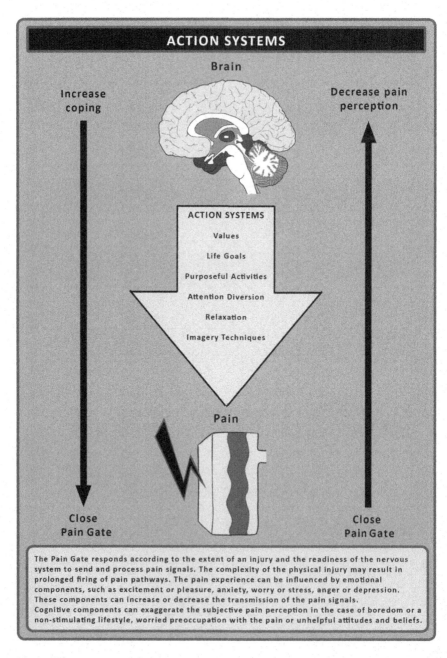

My well-being actions 1.

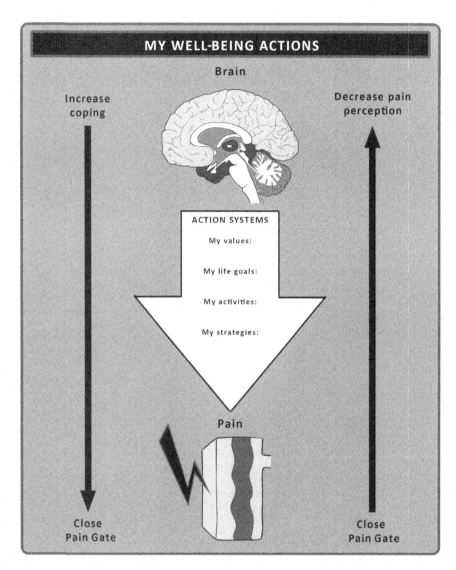

My well-being actions 2.

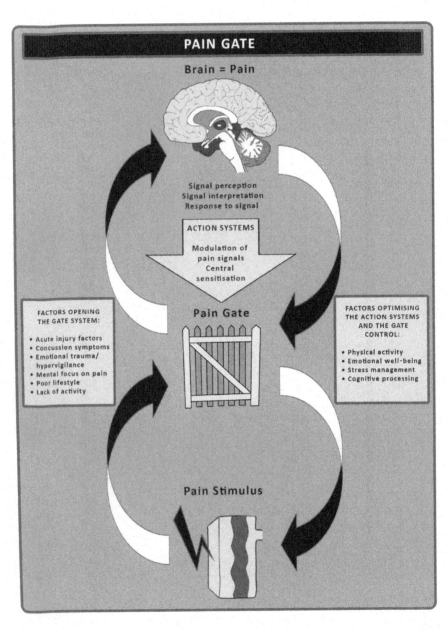

Pain Gate.

POSITIVE SELF-TALK

Worrying and angry thoughts (i.e. about the headaches) can make you feel physically tense and increase the headache perception. Worries can quickly trigger unpleasant emotions and can be very intrusive.

Naturally, you want to brush those thoughts out of your mind immediately to prevent tension, negative emotions and potentially recurring headaches.

Sometimes you are aware of your thoughts and often you are not. They may take the form of fleeting images or half-formed pictures in your mind.

By being kind to yourself you can change the vicious cycle in which negative thoughts increase your tension and symptoms.

OBSERVE WHAT YOU ARE THINKING

Just allow your mind to observe those thoughts or worries as they come and go without judgement. Passively notice what they are about without changing anything.

Take a note of the worries and thoughts. Make an agreement with yourself to re-visit them at a more suitable time. Set a time like making an 'appointment' when you plan to 'meet' with your worry.

At the arranged time, start by practising your relaxation or deep breathing. Passively observe what is happening for a while. Allow your worries to enter your mind. Notice, as you are relaxed, how those annoying thoughts can come and go and eventually fade away.

EXPLORE HOW APPROPRIATE THE THOUGHTS ARE

When people are under stress or in pain, their thinking can often get distorted.

Gently question your thoughts. Am I exaggerating? Am I thinking in 'all-or-nothing' terms? Am I ignoring alternatives? How helpful is my thinking?

Identify some of your disturbing thoughts and examine their relevance. Write them down.

REFRAME YOUR THOUGHTS

Positive means realistic, balanced and achievable. Re-frame or rewrite your thoughts using kind language. Switch your thinking to your practical life aims. What is it you really want? Use short, simple sentences and positive phrases such as "I am calm" (rather than "don't panic"). State your balanced thoughts as if your goal has been achieved i.e. "as if now".

Even if you have a headache or feel stressed, the statement would be, "I am relaxed. I can cope by working slowly and using deep breathing". That's what you want your mind to focus on. Use your positive statements as part of your relaxation practice.

Positive self-talk.

POSSIBILITY DIMENSIONS

My possibility goal is...

Percentage of my possibility goal achieved so far:

0%   100%

Percentage of my possibility goal which I want to achieve in ... days, in ... weeks:

0%   100%

Percentage of my possibility goal which I want to achieve in ... months, in ... years

0%   100%

In comparison, how would my ... (other person) achieve this possibility goal in ...

0%   100%

In comparison, how would my ... (another person) achieve this possibility goal in ...

0%   100%

Possibility dimensions.

POSSIBILITY GOAL HOTSPOT

Stated in the positive

What specifically do I want?

My outcome

What will I see, hear, feel, etc. when I have it?
I can imagine it right now.
I can imagine it working out when... (concrete event in future).

My evidence

How will I know when I have it?
How is it possible that I don't have my goal now?

Is it my real desire?

What will I get from this outcome?
What will it allow me to do?

Is it my initiative?

Is it only for me?

Is it part of my circumstances?

Where, when, how and with whom do I want it?

What resources do I have and what else is needed?

What do I have now, and what do I need to achieve what I want? Have I ever had or done this before? Do I know anyone who has? I act now as if I have it already.

Is it meaningful?

For what purpose do I want this? What will I gain or lose if I have it? What will happen if I get it? What won't happen if I get it?

Possibility goal hotspot.

QUALITY OF LIFE

What is the purpose of the activity for which I am responsible?

Is this activity taking me towards my values?

How does this activity promote my quality of life?

Important and Not Urgent = Quality of Life
Activity:

(Example: Spending time with partner or friend. Planning purposeful and valuable activities.)

Urgent and Not Important
Activity:

(Example: Administrative deadlines.)

Important and Urgent
Activity:

(Example: Repairing a water leak.)

Not Urgent and Not Important = Time Wasters
Activity:

(Example: TV 'channel-hopping'.)

Quality of life.

REAL LIFE AND IDEAL LIFE

This pie chart reflects your current situation, your real life.
Which proportion is occupied by purposeful and planned activities?
Which proportion is occupied by headaches and headache behaviours?

This pie chart reflects your ideal situation, your ideal life.
Ideally, how do you want to spend your time?
Which proportion do you allow for residual, occasional headaches?

How can you gradually move closer towards your ideal?
How can you adjust your ideal to make it more realistic?

Real life and ideal life.

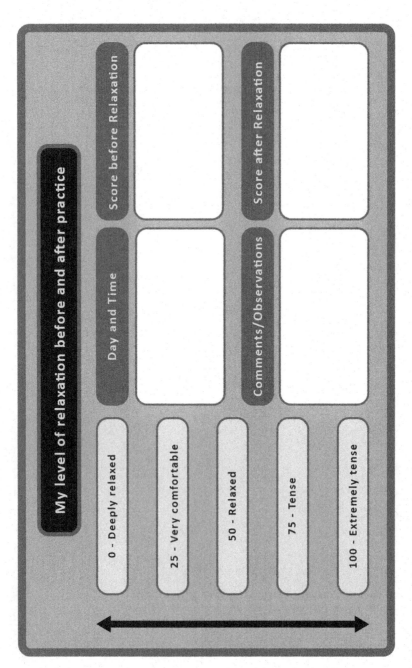

My level of relaxation before and after practice

Score before Relaxation	Day and Time

Score after Relaxation	Comments/Observations

0 - Deeply relaxed

25 - Very comfortable

50 - Relaxed

75 - Tense

100 - Extremely tense

Relaxation practice.

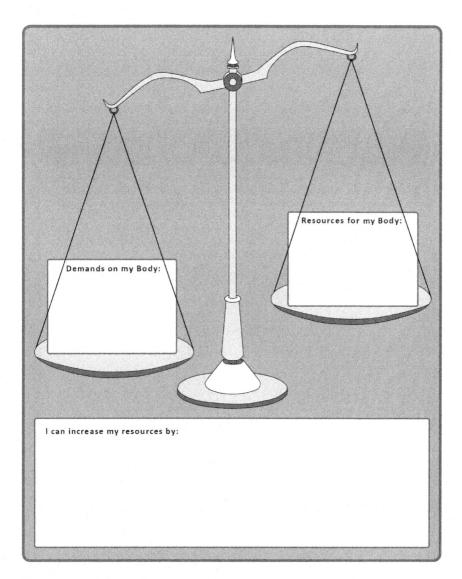

Resources and demands.

STEPS TO MY POSSIBILITY GOAL

I want to describe my goal in as much detail as possible. I am specific.
I think of steps or smaller goals which help me to achieve my 'top goal'.
I can sort my goals with the most important one on top.
I start with the easiest goal/situation and practise it.
If something is too hard, I can look at ways of breaking it down into
intermediate stages. I acknowledge my achievements.

My Possibility Life Goals:

1. ...
2. ...
3. ...
4. ...
5. ...
6. ...
7. ...
8. ...
9. ...
10. ...

Steps to my possibility goal.

THINKING ABOUT HEADACHES

Activity Day Time	Headache Intensity: 1 = mild 2 = moderate 3 = severe	Immediate Thoughts or Worries	Balanced Thoughts or Coping Strategies	What Happened Next?

Thinking about headaches.

Relaxation scripts

Focused body relaxation

Just make yourself as comfortable as possible in your chair.
Notice what it feels like, having just arrived here.
What it feels like sitting here, in this chair.
And as you notice yourself sitting here,
you can allow yourself to sink deeper into the chair,
and feel supported by the back of your chair.
That's right. Good.
Now, most people enjoy doing this relaxation with their eyes closed,
and if it is all right with you,
then just allow your eyes to close right now;
and if it's not all right, that's fine as well,
then just let your eyes rest on a spot on the carpet or the wall;
and at any time, sooner or later or right now,
when they feel heavy, so very, very heavy,
just let them close.

Now, I would like you to listen to the noises outside the room.
And now listen to the noises inside the room.
These noises will probably come and go throughout this session,
and just like the thoughts which might be passing through your mind,
you can choose to let them pass through your mind,
and choose to ignore them if you so wish.
You will probably notice how these noises and the sound of my voice
will become softer and louder and softer again during this session.
This is quite normal and means that you are in a state of relaxation.
Let your whole body relax much deeper. (* = *end of induction*)

Now, keeping your eyelids closed and without moving your head,
I would like you to look upwards.
Keep your eyes closed, just look upwards. Good.
Notice the feeling of tiredness, sleepiness

and relaxation,
in your eye muscles.
And when your eyes feel tired, so very, very, tired,
just let your eyes drop back down. Good.
Notice the feeling of tiredness, sleepiness and relaxation deepen in
your eyes.
Notice how your eyelids feel droopy and heavy. So very, very, heavy.
Let this feeling of heaviness and relaxation travel down your face,
down your cheeks,
down to your jaw.
Now just relax your jaw.
If your teeth are clenched, then unclench them.
Swallow to release any tension in your throat.
Just let your tongue relax at the bottom of your mouth.
That's good.
Notice the heavy warm feeling of relaxation spreading across your
whole face.
You are beginning to enter a much deeper phase of relaxation.
You are already much more relaxed than a few moments ago, are you
not?
Notice the relaxation of all your face muscles.
Notice the warmth of your skin.
As you are becoming more aware of your skin –
maybe your cheeks are a bit warmer than your nose,
maybe your cheeks are much warmer than your forehead.
Let the feeling of warmth and relaxation slowly travel up over your
face to your forehead.
Notice the release of tension on your forehead and temples
as the feeling of relaxation is travelling up your head, to the top of
your head,
to the back of your head,
then slowly down through the neck muscles,
releasing all tension in your neck,
spreading a wonderful warm sense of relaxation through your neck.
Spreading a wonderful warm sense of relaxation through your
shoulders and shoulder blades.
Now concentrate on relaxing your shoulders, just let them drop down.
Good.
Now let that feeling of relaxation in your shoulders slowly travel
down through your arms,
down through the muscles,
down through your elbows,
down through your wrists,
down to your hands,

right down to the tips of your fingers.
Just notice the feeling of warmth and relaxation spreading along your arms,
down to your hands and fingers.
Your hands and fingers feel warm and heavy.
Very, very, heavy.
Indeed they feel so heavy right now,
that you are very glad that you don't have to move them, right now.
Just let them rest,
right there in your lap. Good.
Allow your mind to notice this deep sense of relaxation and warmth,
spreading across your shoulders once more.
And let that feeling of relaxation in your shoulders,
slowly travel down your chest,
right down to your stomach.
Notice that every time you breathe out, you feel more and more relaxed.
Notice how your breathing has slowed right down,
as you are relaxing more and more deeply.
Let that feeling of relaxation and tiredness
travel down from your shoulders once more,
down your back, right down all your back muscles.
Notice that you are becoming so very relaxed right now, deeply relaxed,
that you are allowing your body to sink deep down into your chair.
Good.
Now let that warm feeling of relaxation travel to the lower parts of your body,
down through your bottom,
down through your thighs,
down through the muscles,
down through your knees,
down though your calves,
down through your ankles,
down into your feet,
right down to all your toes.
That's good.
I'll give you a few moments now,
to allow your mind to wander through your body once more
and enjoy those wonderful feelings of relaxation
spreading through your body right now.
And if you would like, and I am sure you would,
concentrate on any part of your body that you would like to relax even further.

*(This is followed either by one of the therapy scripts or
an ending script.)*

Ending and future pacing scripts

In a few moments time, but not quite yet,
I am going to count to three, and when I do,
you will open your eyes and wake up, and feel relaxed and refreshed.
You will be able to remember, or forget, whatever you want to of this
relaxation.

Future pacing

And you can use this memory to allow yourself to relax whenever or
wherever you want to.
You can now,
use this wonderful feeling of relaxation at any time or place you wish.

You are now aware of many more resources,
you have experienced, are you not?
You can make all those helpful changes,
which can make you feel more in control,
and less tense.
I want you now to think once more about your image,
so that you can build a good memory
of your resources and your coping skills,
which you can now
use any time, any place, whenever or wherever, you need them.
Just remember how good it is to have those resources, in the future,
now.

(Note: Future pacing is related to an image of resources or meaningful adaptations, which must be established prior to relaxation, so that it can be referred back to there in. See health management sessions 4 and 6.)

Ending

In one moment now, you will wake up,
and you will be in full control of your body and mind,
and without becoming tense,
wake up today on *(insert here the day, time and location)*.
As I count to three, you will wake up,
(therapist speaks a little bit louder with each subsequent number).
One ...,
Two ...,
Three ....
Open your eyes in your own time.

Therapy script: reducing stress and tension

Day by day, week by week, month by month,
as you become more relaxed,
and far less tense,
gradually, the tension in your shoulders,
and in your neck, and in your head will fade.
And you will stand and sit and move in a very relaxed manner,
and as you do, you will feel so comfortable that any tension,
and stress will become a distant memory.
If you concentrate now on your face,
and on your neck, notice how, as you relax further,
gradually your head and face are starting to feel comfortably
warm (or *comfortably cool, if more appropriate for certain headache
patients*),
and as this feeling of warmth increases,
you are starting to feel even more relaxed than you did a few minutes
ago,
and day by day,
as you feel less tense, in your body, head and mind,
this state of relaxation will help to prevent stress occurring.
Day by day,
as you become more relaxed and less tense,
the stress will diminish, more and more.
and if you ever feel the stress returning,
you will be able to sit down, relax your shoulders,
relax your neck muscles,
relax your face and head,
and the stress will just drift away.
That's good. Well done.

Therapy script: deepening breathing

I want you now to concentrate on your breathing.
Notice how every time you breathe out,
you feel more and more relaxed.
With each breath you take, you feel so relaxed, so very, very, relaxed.
Breathing like that means you can relax very deeply.
That's right.
Breathe in slowly through your nose and slowly out through your
mouth.
With each breath you take,
every time you take a new breath of air,
you are becoming more and more relaxed.

Gradually you are drifting much deeper as you are relaxing. Now.
Good.
On every breath you are becoming more and more sleepy,
more and more deeply relaxed.
Notice how, as you relax, you are breathing more and more slowly,
and more, and more, steadily, as you become more and more,
deeply, very deeply, relaxed.
You are drifting down into a state of deep relaxation.
Your whole body is becoming more and more relaxed,
every time you breathe in
and
every time you breathe out.
Deeply relaxed.
Good.

Therapy script: deepening relaxation

I'm slowly going to count to five,
and as I do, you will feel even more relaxed than you do now.

One.
Now you are feeling more and more relaxed than you did a few minutes
ago. More and more relaxed than you did a few seconds ago.

Two.
Notice how you are feeling so relaxed that you are finding it so difficult
to concentrate on my voice all the time.
Deeply relaxed.
Very deeply. Good.
By the count of three you allow your mind to double the level of relaxation you have right now.

Three.
Good.
Going deeper still.

Four.
Enjoy this deep sense of relaxation as I count ...

Five.
...
Just let go.

Progressive muscle relaxation

This stepwise relaxation approach can be fitted into the four-session
health management module.

Session 1

Progressive relaxation is the progressive tensing and relaxing of muscle groups: hands, arms, face, neck, shoulders, back, chest, stomach, bottom, legs and feet.

1 Induction: focused body relaxation up to the mark (*).
2 Abdominal breathing.
3 Progressive relaxation. Continue as follows:
  Focus your attention on your hands, first clench your fists,
  hold, notice the tension, ...
  now release, completely relax your hands and
  notice the feeling of warmth and heaviness spreading through your hands.

(Carry on with all parts of the body as above.)
4 Ending script.

Session 2

1 Induction as in session 1.
2 Release-only relaxation script (see below).
3 Ending as in session 1.

Session 3

Cue-facilitated relaxation, that is, a combination of abdominal breathing with positive self-statements.

1 Induction as in session 1.
2 The patient is instructed to breathe out and to think the word "relax." Repeated up to ten times.
3 Ending as in session 1.

Session 4

1 Application training *in sensu*, i.e., practice of relaxation strategies "as if" in headache-related or stressful situations.
2 Application training *in vivo*, i.e., use of relaxation strategies in actual headache-related or stressful situations.

Therapy script: release-only relaxation

Induction: focused body relaxation up to (*)

Lie on your back,
and let the air out slowly.
Continue breathing without interfering with its rate or depth.
Become aware of the space between your hairline and your
eyebrows.
Imagine it becoming wider. Just relax your forehead.
Allow that feeling of relaxation from your forehead to move down over
your eyes.
Let your eyeballs rest quietly in their sockets.
Notice the tiredness and heaviness of your eyelids.
Become aware of the skin over your face.
Let it soften and loosen.
Relax your lips.
Slacken your jaw.
Let your tongue rest at the bottom of your mouth.
Swallow to release any tension from your throat.
Become aware of the relaxation spreading over your whole face.
Become aware of the skin over your whole scalp.
Relax your neck muscles.
Move your awareness to your shoulder muscles and joints.
Loosen your shoulders and let go.
Drop your shoulders down where they feel more comfortable.
Move your attention to your arms.
Relax your upper arms, elbows, forearms.
Release any tension.
Notice how your hands and fingers feel.
Become aware of the warmth and heaviness as they relax.
Shift your awareness to your body, your trunk.
Allow your breath to move your chest
and abdomen whilst relaxing your muscles.
Relax your back and let your body sink into your mattress.
Imagine your spine lengthening and your back widening.
Let your buttocks and hips relax.
Allow your legs to rest on the mattress.
Become aware of the warmth and heaviness spreading through your
legs as they relax even further.
Listen to the sound of your breathing.
Use its sound to focus your attention.

Ending script: as in focused body relaxation

Headache relief imagery – healing paradigm

Induction: focused body relaxation

Your body is fully relaxed now,
which means that the things going through your mind,
are more easily accepted.
In this way you can allow yourself to pay attention to your head.
If your head hurts,
then just allow yourself to notice what the pain sensations are like at
the moment.
Try not to change anything yet,
just be a passive observer of the sensations you notice,
affecting your head.
As you continue to notice any pain sensations,
become more aware of their characteristics.
What does the pain feel like? What are the sensations like?

Now I would like you to imagine the pain in the form of a shape,
and if that is difficult right now,
just pretend for a moment that your pain can have a shape.
What shape is it and does it remain in the same shape or does it
change?

Pay attention to other characteristics
such as its colour, texture, smell, temperature.
Does it make a noise?
Does it float?
Does it sit somewhere?
Notice the details.
Good.
This shape, right now, would like to move around in your body.
Notice how it is moving, shifting position.
Where does it want to go first, I wonder?
Maybe from your head down your neck and down into your shoulders.
I wonder which shoulder wants to welcome your pain first.
And from that shoulder,
notice it moving down through your arm,
down to your elbow,
down to your wrists,
right down through your hands and out of your fingertips.
That's right.

It seems that your pain is moving and flowing down through all those parts of your upper body.
You are doing very well.
And just before you let go of the pain now,
ask it what its message is.
The message is very important,
because as your pain leaves your body now, out of your fingertips,
it has a purpose in the outside world.
As you become aware of its message,
you can make sure that the pain fulfils its purpose in the outside world.
Make sure that the pain fulfils its purpose in the outside world.
That's good.

Repeat this script about three times or more
  Note: See Headache Therapy Session 5 for an example of the 'headache message' metaphor or case example Harry.)

Ending script: as in focused body relaxation.

Headache relief imagery – hat anaesthesia

Induction: focused body relaxation

Now let your mind focus on your head again.
Pay attention to the bones of your head, to your scalp, your hair, your ears and your forehead.
Notice the base of your head and feel your head supported by your neck.
Now, being mindful of all those parts of your head,
I would like you now to imagine that you are wearing a hat.
Maybe it is a comfortable hat that you have worn before,
or a kind of hat you would like to have.
Imagine the hat covering your head.
And as you are thinking of it,
you begin to notice the material against your hair and skin.
You begin to notice the weight of the hat and the warmth.
What else do you notice has changed since you began paying attention to the hat?
While you are keeping those sensations in mind,
I want you now to become aware of your head pain.
Where in your head do you feel the headache?

Is it only in one place or is it moving around?
What is its intensity?
What does your pain feel like? Pulsating? ... Stinging? ... Throbbing?

Be observant of your headache sensation and, at the same time,
notice how the pain is moving about through the parts of your head
and,
as it does, it gently gets absorbed through your skull,
through the pores of your skin and soaked up by your hat like a
sponge.
Notice your hat soaking up all pain sensations, notice how they slowly
go away ...
all gone.
Now, imagine you take off your hat.
It feels rather different now as the hat has soaked up your pain.
Place your hat somewhere, in a meaningful place.
Somewhere you know you can find it, should you need it.
It's useful to know that your hat can guard your pain and you can
leave it behind.
What a wonderful feeling. Notice what that's like for a moment
longer.

(Repeat this about two to three times or more.)

Ending script: as in focused body relaxation.

Headache relief imagery – time travel

Induction: focused body relaxation

Now, feeling deeply relaxed as you are, become intensely aware of your
body, the sensations within it, your breathing, and just observe yourself in this moment. Don't try to change anything yet, just watch and
observe yourself. Increase your self-awareness so that you can imagine
what you look like in the position that you are in.

Now, allowing your mind to leave your body, step outside your body;
you are now watching your body sitting or lying there completely relaxed and comfortable. That's good.

Your mind is now free, roaming about, exploring your immediate
surroundings. Let the images come and go, floating through your mind.

Your body is fully relaxed now, which means the things going through
your mind are more easily accepted.

Allow your mind to imagine your past, all the memories and experiences you have made at some time during your life.

If you were to imagine a direction in the space around you, which direction do you think your past memories would come from?

If you were to imagine a direction in the space around you, where do you think your ideas and plans for the future would take you to?

Allow your mind to connect your past memories with your future plans.

Create a line or a path of your life with all your experiences, past and future, placed upon it.
Have you got it? Good. Well done.

Now, still being aware of your relaxed body and your calm breathing as you are sitting/lying down here,
allow your mind to float up above your life path, above your own timeline.
Rise up above this moment in time,
leaving your body relaxed and comfortable down below.
If you like, you can use a softly floating vehicle like a hot-air balloon,
to take you even further above your timeline.
That way you can see over many years of your past.
Float just above your timeline, floating back a few years,
back to a time when you felt well and comfortable,
maybe back to a time long before you experienced any headaches.
Keep hovering above your timeline until you have found a very pleasant, comfortable or very happy memory.

Notice in your mind what it means to revisit this memory.
Maybe allow your balloon to travel a little closer
so that you can take everything in,
every detail of the situation,
just absorb with all your senses what you can experience
in this pleasurable memory.
What can you see, hear and feel?
What are the things like, around you?
Are you on your own or with company?
How does it feel being on your own, or with someone else,

feeling so good and so well?
What have you accomplished in this memory?
And now, being a visitor to this memory, what do you learn?
Explore the resources you find there, solutions, practical things,
company, strength, creativity, confidence … all those things that are
helpful.
All those things you know you once had.
Now you can revisit them and best of all, take them away with you.

Make a good mental note of all the insights and opportunities that you
can take along with you.
Take them on board your balloon and, floating higher up above your
timeline, take your insights and opportunities
as you are floating forwards past your present life,
forward even further into the future.

Find a place in time, when you would like to realise your Possibility
Goal and float closer into that situation.
Establish what you would like this situation to be and release all your
resources and opportunities into this time, in the not so far away
future, because you will be back there soon.
Notice how you can use those pleasant experiences
and your resources to accomplish your goal.
Moreover, as you are experiencing your progress,
notice what this feels like,
notice the excitement and the sense of well-being
and anything that you feel is beneficial.
Build a good memory of your ability to use your resources well.
Build a good memory of accomplishing your Possibility Goal
sometime in the near future,
maybe in the next few weeks, or days,
you certainly can have a specific time in mind right now.
When you have got all that and that is a lot, indeed,
let your hot-air balloon float back into the present.

Take all the time necessary to move all the way back down
towards that place where you began, very slowly,
regaining focus of your relaxed body,
regaining awareness of your breathing, and the feelings within your
body.

Notice how good this feels, being fully relaxed
and bringing all your resources with you.
Have a good think about what insights and wisdom you brought back
with you and realise that you can take action in relation to that,
at a specific time in your life which you choose.

Ending script: as in focused body relaxation.

Headache relief imagery – happy moments

Induction: focused body relaxation

Now, feeling deeply relaxed as you are, become intensively aware of
your body, the sensations within it, your breathing, and just observe
yourself in this moment, don't try to change anything yet, and if there
is any pain, just observe this pain as well. Your awareness will soon
enough drift to other things.

You must be more aware now,
of the things coming and going through your mind.
And as you continue to breathe in and out gently,
I want you to ask yourself where you imagine all your past memories
coming from.

Allow your mind to explore in space which direction you might like to
go in order to find your past.
And if there is a direction or a place where you can locate your past,
I'd like you to keep this in mind as you are now thinking about your
future.
And when you have thoughts or ideas that take you to your future,
just ask yourself which place or direction that is.
You might be wondering where this is going,
but in a minute or so you will surely realise
that you can connect your future with your past.

In your mind, link up the two directions or the two places representing
your future and your past
and as you link them up you have created your own timeline.
This is the path that your life is taking you along. Well done.

This is more or less the right time now to explore some events in your past.
You might like to find a way to raise yourself up above your timeline.

Most people like to use a hot-air balloon and get on it and ever so gently rise up,
way up high in the air, hovering above the timeline.
As you look down carefully from your balloon, you can see your whole life path down there in front of you and you can even see a little into the future, can't you?

Now, allow yourself to float back and forth a little over your timeline and find those times in your life when you were particularly happy.
Think about such moments in your 40s, or 30s or even when you were very little.
You probably know much better than I do
how easy it is to find some happy times.
They stand out indeed.
They are like landmarks on your timeline.

Having found and chosen one of those happy moments now,
I want you to lower your balloon,
so that you can clearly see
what happened during that very joyful episode in your life.
Come as close as you can.
You could even land and enter this episode.
Become once more the person of that moment,
celebrating your enjoyment and feeling very, very, happy.
Notice what that is like.
Notice in your body and where exactly in your body,
you can feel this happiness.
Find a way to describe the feeling and all the sensations going with it.
And notice what is going on around you.
If there are people in your company, who are those people?
How are they sharing your happiness with you?
What is the place like, exactly?
What can you see and hear?
What makes you feel that happiness so intensely?
Take in everything you can.
In fact, take in everything.
Absorb those feelings of happiness once again.
Fully absorb them into your breathing and into your heart.
And carrying them with you,
all these lovely feelings and the vivid memories that you can be happy and
have good times, you now step back into your balloon carriage
and travel back high above your timeline.

You know, you could settle down now anywhere on your timeline and
feel happy and excited as you are carrying those happy feelings and
memories along with you.

You could settle down in your present and
you could also insert some happy memories into your future.
Knowing that you can have them anytime, anywhere,
you come down now,
into your presence on this day and wake up feeling excited and full of
energy.
On the count of three, you wake up.
One,
Two,
Three.
Open your eyes and notice how wonderful you feel.

Headache relief imagery – water and bubbles

Induction: focused body relaxation

Now, feeling deeply relaxed as you are, become intensively aware
of your body, the sensations within it, your breathing, your bodily
rhythms,
and just observe yourself in this moment, don't try to change anything
yet,
and if there is any pain, just observe this pain as well.
You'll soon notice this pain draining away more and more.
Isn't it strange how some things slowly drain away from our
awareness?

For the next few moments, imagine that you are about to take a
shower.
Visualise your own shower
or any shower that you have, in the past, enjoyed a lot.
Your calm breathing right now means that you are ready to step into
the image.
And in your mind you turn the shower on and
adjust the temperature so that it feels so comfortable.
You can now notice, precisely,
the water drops trickling and flowing down your body.
Notice the water pouring down your face,
down your head,

down your shoulders and back,
and all the way down your body.
You notice the tingling of the water drops,
running down along your head and face and neck,
and those parts of your body that you want to relax most.

You may not know this yet –
in a minute, you'll discover that this is indeed a magic shower.
Enjoy the comfort and the warmth of your shower just one moment
longer,
and now I want you to move the shower head and adjust the spray
setting.
You can change the setting to whatever you like,
have the water coming out more intensely or spraying away more
broadly.
See what is right for you.
And as you are adjusting this, you'll notice now that the water coming
out of the shower has magic powers.

As it runs down over your head and down over your face and down
over your neck,
it washes away your headache.
Notice that, little by little, as you are standing under the shower,
your pain gets gradually washed away.
Every little drop takes a little pain along with it and takes it down and
flushes it away.
Every drop is taking a bit of pain and it gets flushed away.
Every time the water drops come in contact with your skin they take a
bit more pain away.
So, bit by bit, and little by little, the longer you are standing under the
shower,
the more the pain is washed away.
It's drained and flushed away.
Notice that the longer you are enjoying your shower,
the more refreshed and lighter and happier you feel.
The pain is nearly washed away completely.

I bet you are now ready to use your magic shower lotion, which you've
only discovered right now.
Amazing.
Squeeze a little lotion into your hand.

As you are beginning to rub it onto your chest and your hips and your thighs,
you are beginning to notice how the bubbles form on your skin.
The lotion continues to bubble and bubble.
And I can tell you,
these bubbles can be filled with happiness or strength or whatever you like and need right now.
Wouldn't it be nice to fill all those bubbles with all the happiness you deserve?

Imagine that you can inject your happiest moment into each of these bubbles,
which are slowly washing down your body.
Think of your very happy moment and the very happy images entering your mind.
Visualise everything involved in this happy image and inject your bubbles with it.
Try some more.
And some more.
Each time you spread the shower gel onto your body you are also spreading happiness across your chest and your stomach and all over your body.
You know the feeling.
The shower is washing all those happy bubbles all over you,
so that now you are feeling refreshed and energetic and so happy.
Very bubbly indeed.
That feels so good. Wonderful.

And each time from now,
every time you are getting into the shower,
you know you can feel very bubbly and happy.
With that image in mind,
I want you to come out of this exercise.

Ending script: as in focused body relaxation.

Resources and perspectives

Induction: focused body relaxation

Now, feeling deeply relaxed as you are, become intensively aware of your body, the sensations within it, your breathing, and just observe yourself in this moment, don't try to change anything yet, just watch

and observe yourself, increase your self-awareness so that you can imagine what you look like in that position that you are in.

Now, allow your mind to leave your body and step outside your body,
you are now watching your body sitting or
lying there completely relaxed and comfortable.
That's good.

Your mind is now free; allow it to roam about,
explore your immediate surroundings,
let the images come and go,
floating through your mind.

Now, allow your mind to float much higher, to float up, high above
your body,
which is staying down there completely relaxed.
Maybe your mind wants to use the aid of a hot-air balloon to
gently rise even further up and up.

Notice, as you are looking down at your body, how it gets smaller and
smaller.
This allows you to observe the environment around your body and
the context of your life more fully.
Maybe you would like to rise a bit further up still to take everything in
and change your position so that you can see more clearly.

Watch and observe what your life is like right now.
Become aware of all the resources you have used to help you to move
on.
Become aware of all the activities you have been able to get involved
in.
Notice what it feels like, being aware, deeply aware of your progress.

From your bird's eye perspective, do take everything in.
Spend all the time necessary to do this step in an enjoyable way.
Notice the different perspectives as you move further away from that
point where your body remains.
Take in all sensory experiences, all you can see, all you can hear,
all you can feel, and what that is like, for you, right now and up here.

Become aware about how you are gaining insight, wisdom and perspective.

You can start to think about things you wish to achieve.
You can start to contemplate the importance of issues.
You can start to consider what is holding you back from moving towards your values, towards your Possibility Goal and
just enjoy the bird's eye perspective and freedom thinking, way up here.
Use this space and time away from distraction to ponder, question, think truthfully and consolidate your insights.
Think about actions you can take, steps that will lead you forward and things you can do to make positive and progressive changes in your life.

Now, when you have spent all the time you feel is necessary to do this, build a good memory of all of your resources and opportunities.
Feel how useful they are and then anchor them in your awareness.

Equipped with your insight and perspective,
start descending down and return to your starting place.
Take all the time necessary to move all the way back down
towards that place where you began.

Very slowly, regain focus of your relaxed body,
regain awareness of your breathing, and the feelings within your body.
Notice how good this feels,
being fully relaxed and bringing all your resources with you.
Have a good think about what insights and wisdom you brought back with you and choose to take some action in relation to that.
Picture yourself right now, take action, and initiate the next step towards it.
You surely can take this action at the very specific time in your life that you choose.
Well done.

(Note: The "anchor" metaphor is explained in Headache Therapy Sessions 4 and 6.)

Ending script: as in focused body relaxation

Autogenic training

Each session consists of one to two relaxation exercises.

The general suggestion, "I am at peace with myself and fully relaxed," is practised throughout the first session and is, in all later sessions, repeated following the consecutive instructions. The new instructions in each session are added to the previous ones. Eventually, the final script contains the whole set of instructions.

Each statement is repeated five times, before moving on to the next one.

Induction: focused body relaxation up to the mark (*)

Therapeutic instructions:

General suggestions "I am at peace with myself and fully relaxed."

Session 1	"My right arm is heavy. I am at peace." "My left arm is heavy. I am at peace."
Session 2	"My right leg is heavy. I am at peace." "My left leg is heavy. I am at peace."
Session 3	"My neck and shoulders are heavy. I am at peace."
Session 4	"My right arm is warm. I am at peace." "My left arm is warm. I am at peace."
Session 5	"My right leg is warm. I am at peace." "My left leg is warm. I am at peace."
Session 6	"My neck and shoulders are warm. I am at peace."
Session 7	"My breathing is calm and regular. I am at peace."
Session 8	"My heartbeat is calm and regular. I am at peace."
Session 9	"My abdomen feels warm. I am at peace."
Session 10	"My forehead is cool. I am at peace."

Ending statement "I am alert, refreshed and fully relaxed. I am at peace."

Therapy story

"The Hare and the Hedgehog" by the Brothers Grimm

This story seems to be false, but it really is true, for my grandfather, from whom I have it, used to always, when relating it, say complacently, "It must be true, my son, or else no one could tell it to you."

The story is as follows. One Sunday morning about harvest time, just as the buckwheat was in bloom, the sun was shining brightly in heaven, the east wind was blowing warmly over the stubble-fields, the larks were singing in the air, the bees were buzzing among the buckwheat, the people were all going in their Sunday clothes to church and all creatures were happy. The hedgehog, however, was standing by his door with his arms akimbo, enjoying the morning breeze and slowly trilling a little song to himself, which was neither better nor worse than the songs that hedgehogs are in the habit of singing on a blessed Sunday morning.

While he was thus singing half aloud to himself, it suddenly occurred to him that, while his wife was washing and drying the children, he might very well take a walk into the field and see how his turnips were going on. The turnips were, in fact, close beside his house, and he and his family were accustomed to eating them, for which reason he looked upon them as his own.

No sooner said than done. The hedgehog shut the house-door behind him, and took the path to the field. He had not gone very far from home, and was just turning round the sloe-bush that stands there outside the field, to go up into the turnip field, when he observed the hare, who had gone out on business of the same kind, namely, to visit his cabbages. When the hedgehog caught sight of the hare, he bade him a friendly good morning. But the hare, who was in his own way a distinguished gentleman and frightfully haughty, did not return the hedgehog's greeting, but said to him, assuming at the same time a very contemptuous manner, "How do you happen to be running about here in the field so early in the morning?"

"I am taking a walk," said the hedgehog.

"A walk!" said the hare, with a smile. "It seems to me that you might use your legs for a better purpose."

This answer made the hedgehog furiously angry, for he could bear anything but an attack on his legs, just because they are crooked by nature. So now the hedgehog said to the hare, "You seem to imagine that you can do more with your legs than I with mine."

"That is just what I do think," said the hare.

"That can be put to the test," said the hedgehog. "I wager that if we run a race, I will outstrip you."

"That is ridiculous! You with your short legs!" said the hare, "But for my part I am willing, if you have such a monstrous fancy for it. What shall we wager?"

"A golden louis-d'or and a bottle of brandy," said the hedgehog.

"Done," said the hare. "Shake hands on it, and then we may as well come off at once."

"Nay," said the hedgehog, "there is no such great hurry! I am still fasting, I will go home first and have a little breakfast. In half-an-hour I will be back again at this place."

Hereupon, the hedgehog departed, for the hare was quite satisfied with this. On his way the hedgehog thought to himself, "The hare relies on his long legs, but I will contrive to get the better of him. He may be a great man, but he is a very silly fellow and he shall pay for what he has said." So when the hedgehog reached home, he said to his wife, "Wife, dress yourself quickly. You must go out to the field with me."

"What is going on, then?" said his wife.

"I have made a wager with the hare, for a gold louis-d'or and a bottle of brandy. I am to run a race with him, and you must be present."

"Good heavens, husband," the wife now cried, "are you not right in your mind, have you completely lost your wits? What can make you want to run a race with the hare?"

"Hold your tongue, woman," said the hedgehog, "that is my affair. Don't begin to discuss things that are matters for men. Be off, dress yourself and come with me."

What could the hedgehog's wife do? She was forced to obey him, whether she liked it or not. So when they had set out on their way together, the hedgehog said to his wife, "Now pay attention to what I am going to say. Look you, I will make the long field our race-course.

The hare shall run in one furrow and I in another, and we will begin to run from the top. Now all that you have to do is to place yourself here below in the furrow, and when the hare arrives at the end of the furrow, on the other side of you, you must cry out to him, 'I am here already!'"

Then they reached the field, and the hedgehog showed his wife her place and then walked up the field. When he reached the top, the hare was already there. "Shall we start?" said the hare.

"Certainly," said the hedgehog.

"Then both at once," added the hare.

So saying, each placed himself in his own furrow. The hare counted, "Once, twice, thrice and away!" and went off like a whirlwind down the field. The hedgehog, however, only ran about three paces and then he stooped down in the furrow, and stayed quietly where he was.

When the hare, therefore, arrived at full speed at the lower end of the field, the hedgehog's wife met him with the cry, "I am here already!" The hare was shocked and wondered not a little. He thought nothing other than that it was the hedgehog himself who was calling to him, for the hedgehog's wife looked just like her husband.

The hare, however, thought to himself, "That has not been done fairly," and cried, "It must be run again, let us have it again." And once more he went off like the wind in a storm, so that he seemed to fly. But the hedgehog's wife stayed quietly in her place.

So when the hare reached the top of the field, the hedgehog himself cried out to him, "I am here already."

The hare, however, quite beside himself with anger, cried, "It must be run again, we must have it again."

"All right," answered the hedgehog, "for my part we'll run as often as you choose."

So the hare ran seventy-three times more, and the hedgehog always held out against him, and every time the hare reached either the top or the bottom, either the hedgehog or his wife said, "I am here already."

At the seventy-fourth time, however, the hare could no longer reach the end. In the middle of the field he fell to the ground, blood streamed out of his mouth and he lay dead on the spot. But the hedgehog took the louis-d'or he had won and the bottle of brandy, called his wife out of the furrow and both went home together in great delight, and if they are not dead, they are living there still.

This is how it happened that the hedgehog made the hare run races with him on the Buxtehuder heath till he died, and since that time no hare has ever had any fancy for running races with a Buxtehuder hedgehog.

The moral of this story, however, is, firstly, that no one, however great he may be, should permit himself to jest at anyone beneath him, even if he be only a hedgehog. And, secondly, it teaches that when a man marries, he should take a wife in his own position, who looks just as he himself looks. So, whosoever is a hedgehog let him see to it that his wife is a hedgehog also, and so forth.

Recovering from mild head trauma – a guide for patients

Who is this guide for?

This guide is for people who experience persistent difficulties following a mild head trauma.

Information in this brochure includes a description of mild head trauma symptoms, why they may persist and how vicious cycles between unhelpful thought patterns and actions can develop. Furthermore, tips about overcoming some of these symptoms and additional support are provided.

People can sustain mild head traumas as a result of road traffic accidents, falls, assaults or other injuries involving a blow to the head.

This guide aims to cover a range of difficulties that may be relevant to some people and not to others.

Mild head trauma symptoms

Mild head trauma can occur following a blow to the head. This may cause short-term confusion, disorientation or dizziness. Loss of consciousness may happen for a few seconds or minutes. Many people who suffer such mild injuries may choose not to go to hospital or seek medical care as the injury may not affect them in a substantial way.

Sometimes, following mild head trauma, people develop a number of symptoms. These include:

- *Physical* difficulties such as headaches, dizziness and fatigue
- *Emotional* difficulties such as irritability, anxiety and depression
- *Cognitive* difficulties such as problems with concentrating and remembering things.

The experience of a *potentially* highly dangerous event alerts the body's stress or arousal system. This may lead to a range of difficulties that become associated with fear of having damaged the head or brain. Permanent damage to the brain under these circumstances is very rare.

It is important to be aware that mild head trauma symptoms are relatively common. A lot of people get headaches or forget things from time to time. However, the combination of prior experiences of headaches or forgetfulness with the stress of having had a sudden unexpected life event, like an accident, may aggravate the situation, resulting in mild head trauma symptoms.

Following a sudden, unexpected life event, the body tends to absorb information from the environment so as to make sure that any signs of danger are not missed again. This can activate our fight/flight or threat system, placing our brain on "high alert."

This is an understandable and normal reaction and will usually go away with time. *It is important that you remind yourself of this fact.*

What if some symptoms persist?

Some people experience symptoms for longer. This can be because these symptoms interact with each other, which can make them more troublesome. For example, after just a few days, if someone experiences a headache that won't go away (*physical*), they may feel more irritable (*emotional*), have less patience and begin to worry that something might be seriously wrong with their brain (*cognitive/thinking skills*). Eventually, they may have problems concentrating on anything else, find it hard to pay attention and to remember information (*cognitive/thinking skills*). Thus, a vicious cycle may develop where physical symptoms (e.g., head pain or dizziness) trigger intense fears (that there might be something seriously wrong with the head/brain) leading to constant worries (which distract the attention and ability to focus, leading to the impression of forgetfulness).

A vicious cycle of mild brain trauma symptoms:

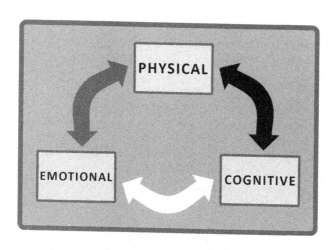

Another example is that worries about changes to your lifestyle may substantially exacerbate the situation. For instance, if someone is unable to return to work straight away because of an injury (*physical*), they may begin to worry (*emotional*) about financial issues, job security or meeting their social and family responsibilities. The intensity of such unhelpful thoughts (*cognitive/thinking skills*) may lead to increased muscle tension, which is often experienced in the neck, shoulder and back area, resulting in tension-type headaches (*physical*). Additionally, sleep problems (*physical*) are a common consequence of distress and worry, which then further increase difficulties with concentration and thought processing (*cognitive/thinking skills*).

Many of the described symptoms and difficulties are common in everyday life for everybody (we all get tired, stressed and forget things from time to time). However, people may notice these difficulties and worry about them more when they are feeling stressed. After mild head trauma, it can be easy to forget that memory and concentration lapses, feelings of fatigue or even exhaustion used to happen even *before* the accident.

As mentioned earlier, different head trauma symptoms interact and complex patterns or vicious cycles may develop, which may be harder to resolve. In such cases, it is vital to find proactive coping strategies to disrupt these unhelpful patterns and to improve well-being.

Emotional difficulties

It is common to experience a variety of emotional difficulties following mild head trauma. Apart from simply not feeling well physically and being in pain, you may often experience additional worries such as the following:

- feeling unsafe or vulnerable in the world
- believing the world is unpredictable
- fear of unexpected harm
- anxiety and/or nervousness
- fear of severe health problems
- frustration and irritability
- guilt
- low mood
- uncertainty about the future, e.g., work, family
- loss of control

These symptoms are a natural response to the sudden, unexpected traumatic event, and can fade completely with time. They are also the *common consequence of many different types of stressful experiences* or critical life events.

WHAT CAN I DO?

Talk about and reflect on your thoughts and feelings with someone.
This is the best way to overcome low mood.

The following questions may shift the perspective you hold:

• How do these thoughts make me feel?
• What are the advantages and disadvantages of thinking this way?
• Am I thinking in a particularly negative way, such as jumping to
  conclusions or seeing things just in black-and-white?
• What is the evidence for thinking or believing this?
• What possible alternative views are there? Is there evidence to
  support these alternative views instead?
• Can I test any of these thoughts in real-life?
• What would I say to a friend who was in a similar situation?

Worrying about your health and your ongoing symptoms can be very
stressful. Persisting symptoms after an accident can raise more
questions about underlying missed injuries or whether you can even
get better.

It is important to become aware of how you can manage stress and
tension by maintaining a positive outlook about the recovery.
Feelings of vulnerability and loss of personal safety can be extremely
disturbing and can lead to the vicious cycles outlined above.

Fears and anxiety

The emotional impact of mild head trauma may be experienced as fear or
increased anxiety about certain situations, e.g., being around people or returning to driving, particularly if these are related to the accident. When
people feel more stressed, worried or anxious, they often become "better" at
noticing the things that might go wrong (this is called *hypervigilance*).

Avoidance of anxiety triggers

Avoiding situations that make you feel anxious can in fact keep your symptoms or anxiety going. A good example of this is travel anxiety, where people
avoid using the kind of transport associated with their accident. The stress

and anxiety, which might be triggered by travelling, results in a "prediction" that this type of transport will cause another accident.

People may also avoid reminders of events around their injury, or avoid talking about it with friends or relatives. While this is an effective way of reducing anxiety and distress in the short term, it can cause substantial disruption over the medium and long term. For example, if a person no longer drives as a result of an accident, they may find their life becoming increasingly restricted and less pleasant.

WHAT CAN I DO?

Tackling avoidance is an important component in overcoming your symptoms. One helpful strategy is called exposure. Exposure means 'facing your fears' and is the opposite of avoidance. When we avoid something we fear, the fear gets stronger. If we acknowledge our fears and learn we can cope then we can manage similar situations in the future. Exposure can be done in real situations or in imaginary ones. The key to success is starting with something not too scary and gradually strengthening your coping skills.

Generate some positive statements. Practise them when you're feeling okay. Have them 'ready at hand' in situations which may make you feel anxious. For example:

- "I may feel anxious now, but it will become easier and easier over time".
- "Anxiety is not dangerous - it's just uncomfortable".
- "I am going to take some nice, slow breaths and keep going".
- "Gradually, I am getting better".

Remain focused on your activity.
Practise relaxation. Slow down the breathing rate during the exposure. This will reduce the arousal.

Depression and low mood

People sometimes become depressed when unpleasant things happen to them. Traumatic accidents or prolonged periods of negative health symptoms are associated with the release of stress hormones, which cause depressive symptoms (amongst other disturbances). These symptoms and difficulties can create concern, upset and worry. Individuals may wonder if they will ever improve. In addition, there may be a number of ways in which a person's life has changed (e.g., people may go from working to not working, from financial security to financial uncertainty). Often, the effects of these changes can result in losing or restricting opportunities to do enjoyable, rewarding things. This can contribute to someone becoming, and staying, depressed.

When people are low in mood, they tend to have negative thoughts about themselves. These thoughts may not be helpful or an accurate picture of the situation. They maintain the negative feelings about oneself or feelings about being stuck. Sitting around doing very little can maintain low moods and provide extra opportunity to worry and ruminate about problems and concerns.

WHAT CAN I DO?

- Focus on manageable, meaningful activity on a regular basis.
- Have specific plans about what and when things can be done.
- Adapt activities on a 'bad day'. Stick to the main task.
- Shift unhelpful thoughts:
  Become aware of what you are thinking and how it is making you feel.
  Balance your thinking. Explore alternatives.
  Look at situations from different points of view.
  You might say to yourself:
    'What other ways are there to view the situation?'
    'What would I say to a friend if they were thinking that?'
- Balanced thoughts can enhance your mood.

Irritability

Irritability is another sign of heightened arousal originating from a traumatic incident. Following an incident, the body becomes more receptive to surrounding signals in order to check for unexpected danger. This leads to an information overload, resulting in a range of posttraumatic symptoms, including irritability.

This is not just an unpleasant experience; it also interferes with one's ability to get along with others. Many people who are affected in this way comment that they used to be very laid-back and feel as if their personality has changed. This sometimes triggers the fear that other people might reject them or that they might be aggressive with others without meaning to be.

WHAT CAN I DO?

The helpful hints and tips also apply to overcoming irritability.
It is important to adopt a healthy lifestyle:
  Sleep
  Involvement in purposeful activities
  Exercise
  Daily relaxation practice
This can reduce over-arousal and reduce the stress experience.

* Be open and communicate to others if you are feeling on edge.
* Become aware of the situation and make adaptations:
  Wear ear plugs
  Talk calmly
  Expose yourself for a limited time only
* Plan ahead. Think about solutions.
* Avoid negative thinking traps e.g. taking comments too personally, jumping to conclusions or overreacting.

Physical symptoms

Headaches

Headaches that develop some time after the accident and persist are most commonly tension-type headaches or posttraumatic migraines.

WHAT CAN I DO?

It is important to adopt a helpful routine including rests and relaxation.
When headaches are occurring:
* Reduce or change your activity.
* Try a short relaxation or mindfulness exercise.
* Go for a walk.
* Promote relaxation in your neck and shoulder muscles
* Use warmth like a wheat pack or hot water bottle.
* Mobilise your head and neck or roll your shoulders to relieve tension.
* Prevent stiffness and tightness.
* Avoid pain killers as a preventative measure.

Sensitivity to noise and light

Increased sensitivity to bright lights or loud noises can be a sign of an over-active nervous system. Following an accident, the nervous system is likely to absorb more sensory stimuli to make sure that potentially dangerous signals are not missed again. This means that the sensory systems are highly sensitised, which can also increase tension or the likelihood of headaches.

WHAT CAN I DO?

- Think ahead about the places you intend to visit: can you prepare yourself or can you make reasonable adjustments?
- Reduce the time you spend in places with bright lights or loud noises.
- Use tinted glasses or ear plugs.
- Plan only one challenging activity per day.
- Use relaxation and slow breathing techniques before, during and after exposure to over-stimulating situations.
- Divert your attention to alternative and purposeful activities.
- Perform tasks that require mindful awareness as these help to take your mind away from uncomfortable sensations.

Dizziness and vertigo

Dizziness and vertigo are also very common head trauma symptoms. They are associated with micro-changes to our vestibular system. This system is responsible for helping us balance; information is sent to the brain from our visual processes, our inner ear and proprioceptors in our joints. Our brain then has to make sense of all this information and make adjustments to keep us balanced. If any part of this system is disturbed, we sometimes experience feelings of dizziness, loss of balance or vertigo.

You may be referred to a specialist in Vestibular Rehabilitation, who can carry out an assessment of your dizziness and balance. They will select relevant exercises to help you manage your symptoms. You will probably be advised to do these exercises several times a day. You are likely to experience some dizziness as you perform these exercises. Remember that you are in control of your symptoms – if the dizziness becomes too much, then stop and allow it to settle. You may need to do the exercises a little more slowly at first but do not skip them – regular practice will optimise the recovery of your balance system. Think of a ballet dancer – most people feel dizzy when they spin around; however, with practise, a ballet dancer can perform multiple spins at speed without becoming dizzy, as their brains have learnt to adapt. This is similar to the training you are doing to your vestibular system whilst performing these exercises.

Before you start any exercises prescribed by your therapist, set aside a few minutes to practise relaxation. Start by making sure you are breathing slowly. Keep your shoulders down and your chest still, and breathe by just letting your stomach go in and out. After you have been breathing slowly for a few minutes, follow each of your exercises and, once you can do this, practise staying relaxed while carrying out the vestibular exercises.

WHAT CAN I DO?

Dizziness and vertigo after head trauma are often experienced as having 'sea legs'. Such sensations resolve eventually if you carry on with your normal activities and move around naturally. Specific vestibular exercises can improve your recovery.

- Ask your head trauma specialist or physiotherapist for guidance regarding such exercises.
- Combine vestibular exercises with relaxation practice to optimise the desensitisation and reduce potential distress.

Sleep problems

Difficulty falling asleep and/or disrupted sleep throughout the night can have a profound effect on our ability to function during the day. People with sleep disturbances often report problems with memory and concentration. They might feel irritable and stressed and may have low energy levels. Some people might experience nightmares or disturbing dreams about feeling out of control, being chased or being in danger. Sleep problems are most likely to be related to worry, stress, anxiety and low moods. Discomfort or pain may aggravate the situation.

Here is an example of a vicious cycle of sleep difficulties:

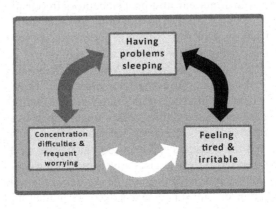

WHAT CAN I DO?

It is important to create the right conditions for effective sleep. This is called 'Sleep Hygiene'.

• Review your sleep environment:
  Dark bedroom
  Comfortable mattress and pillows
  Right temperature
  Remove screens
• Have a regular sleep routine. Go to bed and get up at the same time every day.
• Have a laid-back approach. Do not try to will yourself to sleep.
• Have a relaxing bedtime routine:
  Use relaxation exercises
  Take a bath
  Read
• Avoid:
  Heavy meals
  Alcohol
  Excessive exercise
  Over-stimulating material before bedtime e.g. TV, computer games and mobile phones
• Discuss sleep medication with your GP if necessary.
• Find a way to problem-solve your worries and concerns during the day:
  Talk them over with someone
  Write them down

Fatigue and reduced energy levels during the day: "The Boom and Bust Trap"

Some people who experience frequent mild head trauma symptoms can be disappointed or feel guilty that they cannot perform their daily activities or fulfil their responsibilities to the standard they were once used to. Instead of slowing down or letting go of those expectations, they try to squeeze as many tasks into symptom-free periods as they can, or try to catch up with unfinished activities. Later, they find that their fatigue has become so severe that they have to rest for longer periods.

This is called the "Boom and Bust Cycle." This can interfere with people making changes in their life.

A vicious cycle of over-activity and prolonged rest:

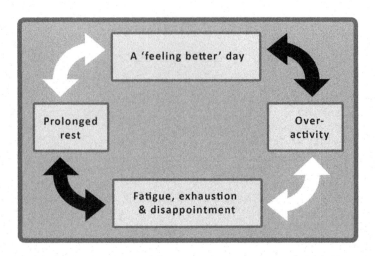

A 'feeling better' day

Prolonged rest

Over-activity

Fatigue, exhaustion & disappointment

WHAT CAN I DO?

The body needs to balance its resources to stay healthy. Persisting mild trauma problems indicate that the body is short on resources. It is vital to increase resources and energy before one can gradually engage in more demanding activities.

Some people set themselves high standards or expect a much quicker recovery. Replace unhelpful thoughts like:
    'I used to do so much more'
    'I should be doing more'
    'If I push myself harder, I will recover quicker'
with kind and balanced thoughts like:
    'I can take a step at a time'
    'If I look after myself well, I can recover'.

* Monitor energy levels and keep a steady pace regarding daily activities.
* Keep activities at a sustainable level of energy. This may mean:
    Saying 'no' to extra jobs or responsibilities
    Turning over some responsibilities to other people
    Getting enough rest
    Limiting the number of working hours.
* Schedule rest periods before getting tired in order to recharge your batteries. Rest requires being mentally and physically still and quiet i.e. not watching television.
* Allow yourself to slow down, rather than being 'on the go' all the time.
* Stick to the plans and resist the temptation of pushing harder on the 'good' days, or not doing anything at all on the 'bad' days. Remember, the goal is to build up a sustainable level of energy.
* Set realistic standards. This is how balanced thoughts can be formed which can enhance one's mood.

Cognitive difficulties

Cognitive, or thinking, difficulties include problems with short-term memory, attention and concentration, reduced thinking speed or diminished ability to problem solve.

There are a number of reasons why you may experience cognitive difficulties after a mild head injury. It is important to remember that your cognitive, emotional and physical systems are all linked. The stress of the accident, the resulting symptoms and life changes often cause people to forget that lapses of memory and attention are very common for everyone.

Short-term memory problems are usually related to problems with attention; if you find it difficult to attend to information, it will be difficult for you to remember it later. After a sudden, unexpected injury, the brain can go into a "high alert" or "danger" mode, which means the attention systems are set to focus on and look out for danger. This can then interfere with your brain's ability to attend to usual, everyday information and, in turn, may lead to forgetfulness.

In other words, when your brain is trying to take in all the information in your environment to check for potential danger, it can struggle to focus on the information you would like it to. For example, you might find yourself becoming distracted easily, it might be difficult to focus in busy environments and you may not be able to recall information that you would usually remember.

Other mild head trauma symptoms can also interfere with thinking. For example, pain, anxiety and fatigue can all impact your ability to process information. The brain only has the capacity to focus on so much at one time. Therefore, if it is telling you that you are in pain or if you are focusing on worries (e.g., about the symptoms you are experiencing) then it will not be working as effectively on processing other information or problem solving.

You may have extra responsibilities following a head trauma in addition to your usual activities, for example, visiting health clinics, having meetings with employers or seeking help from solicitors. These sorts of additional responsibilities can also add to the load on your cognitive systems and lead to you feeling overwhelmed.

WHAT CAN I DO?

- Simplify your life and your environment in order to reduce distractions.
- Ask yourself 'Where is my focus?'
- Practise relaxation.
- Allow time to process information.
- Use breaks and rests efficiently.
- Repeat and rehearse important information and tasks.
- Have a structured schedule for appointments and commitments. Use a compensatory aid e.g. a diary or a phone.
- Remember memory lapses are common. Try not to dwell on them when they happen.
- Remind yourself that gradually you will be getting better. Be mindful of your improvements and of situations in which you can be attentive and remember well.

Appendix IV

Supplementary material

Headache needs assessment (HANA)

HEADACHE NEEDS ASSESSMENT (HANA)		
We are interested in knowing how you feel about having headaches and the problems caused by your headaches in usual daily activities. This information will help us to understand the problems you face related to having frequent and severe headaches. Please answer questions A and B for each problem listed (1-7) describing how headaches affected your life in the past 4 weeks.		
In the past month...	A. How often has this occurred? 1 - never 2 - rarely 3 - sometimes 4 - often 5 - all the time	B. How often has this problem bothered you? 1 - never 2 - rarely 3 - sometimes 4 - often 5 - all the time
1. I have felt anxious or worried (tense, wound-up, frightened) about having another severe headache.		
2. I have felt depressed, discouraged about my headaches.		
3. I have felt that I am not in control of myself because of my headaches.		
4. I have less energy; I am more tired than I should have been because of my headaches.		
5. I functioned and worked (attention, concentration, etc.) at a lower level than I should have because of my headaches.		
6. I have felt that my family and my social activities were limited because of my headaches.		
7. I have felt that my life centred or revolved around my headaches.		

Scoring instructions: The sections A and B are multiplied for each item. This is the items score. It gives a range of 1x1=1 to 5x5=25 for each of the seven items. Item scores are added. Range of summative item scores 7-175.

Self-help resources

Examples of healthcare websites that share our biopsychosocial perspective and emphasise the importance of self-motivation and positive engagement:

www.change-pain.com

www.talkinghealth.org

www.selfmanagementuk.org

www.livinglifetothefull.com

https://www.getselfhelp.co.uk/

Examples of websites and apps to assist with relaxation:

Progressive muscle relaxation: https://www.youtube.com/watch?v=1nZEdqcGVzo

Smiling mind: https://www.smilingmind.com.au/smiling-mind-app/

Headspace: https://www.headspace.com/headspace-meditation-app

CALM: https://www.calm.com/

Index